Review of Medical Physiology

Questions with Answers

Review of Medical Physiology

Questions with Answers

Edward G. Schneider, Ph.D.
Professor of Physiology and Biophysics
Department of Physiology and Biophysics
University of Tennessee, Memphis
Memphis, Tennessee

Steven L. Bealer, Ph.D.
Professor of Physiology and Biophysics
Department of Physiology and Biophysics
University of Tennessee, Memphis
Memphis, Tennessee

Lippincott - Raven
P U B L I S H E R S
Philadelphia • New York

Acquistions Editor: Richard Winters
Developmental Editor: Brian Brown
Manufacturing Manager: Dennis Teston
Production Manager: Larry Bernstein
Production Editor: Pamela Blamey
Cover Designer: Karen Quigley
Indexer: Dr. Leon Kremzner
Compositor: Maryland Composition
Printer: Victor Graphics

Printed in the United States of America

9 8 7 6 5 4 3 2 1

Library of Congress Cataloging-in-Publication Data

Scnheider, Edward G.
    Review of medical physiology / by Edward G. Schneider, Steven L. Bealer.
        p.   cm.
    Includes bibliographical references and index.
    ISBN 0-397-58403-2
    1. Human physiology—Examinations, questions, etc.   2. Physiology, Pathological—Examinations, questions, etc.   I. Bealer, Steven L.
II. Title.
    [DNLM: 1. Physiology.   QT 104 S3588r   1997]
QP40.S36   1997
612′.0076—dc21
DNLM/DLC
for Library of Congress   97-18245
                                                                    CIP

Care has been taken to confirm the accuracy of the information presented and to describe generally accepted practices. However, the authors, editors, and publisher are not responsible for errors or omissions or for any consequences from application of the information in this book and make no warranty, express or implied, with respect to the contents of the publication.

The authors, editors, and publisher have exerted every effort to ensure that drug selection and dosage set forth in this text are in accordance with current recommendations and practice at the time of publication. However, in view of ongoing research, changes in government regulations, and the constant flow of information relating to drug therapy and drug reactions, the reader is urged to check the package insert for each drug for any change in indications and dosage and for added warnings and precautions. This is particularly important when the recommended agent is a new or infrequently employed drug.

Some drugs and medical devices presented in this publication have Food and Drug Administration (FDA) clearance for limited use in restricted research settings. It is the responsibility of the health care provider to ascertain the FDA status of each drug or device planned for use in their clinical practice.

To our wives, Sally and Jan, and to our children and grandchildren,
Kendra, Cynthia, Edward, Jr., Katherine, Lauren, Kevin, and Tracy.
You make it worth the effort.

Contents

Preface

As *Essential Medical Physiology* by L. R. Johnson was being revised and expanded into a comprehensive medical physiology text, we were asked to generate a textbook of questions that could be used in conjunction with it. As we began this project, it became obvious that the usefulness of these questions was not limited to students reading *Essential Medical Physiology 2nd edition*. We found, for instance, that test questions asked by faculty at other institutions were similar to and emphasized the same physiological principles as the ones presented here. This point, in retrospect, is not surprising, but the widespread recognition of these questions' applicability may be reassuring to the readers of both this book and Dr. Johnson's textbook: we do indeed seem to be getting at the essentials of medical physiology as understood in most universities in this country.

This book, then, is for medical students and other health science students to determine if they are prepared to take a major examination at their university or to sit for a national examination requiring the use of the principles covered in medical, graduate, and/or health science physiology courses. Although this book will help students master the major physiological principles, it is not designed to be used as a primary textbook. To obtain the maximum benefit from this book, students should first rely on their primary physiology textbooks and then test their level of understanding by answering the corresponding questions presented in this book.

This book is comprised of two parts. In the first, approximately 900 questions are presented under seven major topics. Students will find that these questions involve a broad understanding of human physiology which will help them review and prepare for national examinations. In the second part of the text, the answer for each question is given, along with an explanation as to why each choice is correct or incorrect. Many students have been frustrated when using examination review books by the constant need to flip back and forth between the question section and answer section, and so each answer and explanation in this book is preceded by the relevant question. This feature also lets students answer a long series of questions and then review the answers without referring to the question section.

Furthermore, to aid students in determining whether they have mastered the physiological concepts contained within the major areas of physiology, the questions within each section are arranged in random order. Hence, students can test their level of preparedness by answering half the questions and then using the last half as a check after they have completed their review. We have presented the major topical divisions of the questions in the same order as used in *Essential Medical Physiology, 2nd edition*.

The questions in this book have all been used by the authors or their colleagues, either at the Medical/Dental Schools of the University of Tennessee, Memphis, or at similar health science universities. A multiple-choice format is used, similar to that seen in national examinations, in which the student chooses the single best answer. Most questions have a stem that may include a figure or data set. Importantly, both the correct and incorrect choices are explained in many of the answers. This technique results in the reader viewing a point of physiology from several different angles, which facilitates a deeper, more comprehensive understanding of that point, and it also answers the oft-repeated and perfectly justified student lament: ''I see why that answer is right, but why is mine wrong?'' Some questions ask the student to identify the EXCEPTION, and the commentary to these questions begins with a reminder of that fact. Both the exception (*not A, e.g.*) and the correct choices (choice B, *e.g.*) are identified; and, again, explanations are given as to why the choices correctly describe a physiological principle or are exceptions to it.

Part of the fun and excitement of learning any new subject rests in the ability to solve problems by integrating ideas. Many of these questions will serve such a function. It is also our hope that students and teachers will find this book helpful as they prepare to either take or develop a comprehensive examination.

Acknowledgments

The authors are particularly thankful to the publishers for their encouragement and foresight in letting the scope of this project expand into its final form. We are particularly indebted to Mr. Brian Brown of Lippincott-Raven, who suggested that we reprint the questions in the answer section. This feature has definitely helped make this a user-friendly book. The authors are thankful to Jin Emerson-Cobb, who diligently reviewed each question and answer and helped us generate the style that became the standard used throughout this book. The artwork was produced by Laura Malinick with assistance from her colleague, Danny Morse.

We are indebted to our many faculty colleagues in the Department of Physiology and Biophysics and the Department of Anatomy and Neurobiology at The University of Tennessee, Memphis. Their willingness to review these questions and the accompanying answers was greatly appreciated. We are also grateful to those colleagues at other institutions who were kind enough to make the questions used in their physiology courses available to us.

Review of Medical Physiology

Questions with Answers

SECTION I: QUESTIONS

GENERAL PHYSIOLOGY

The following measurements were made in an adult human. (Note: some or all of these data will be used for the next three questions).

total body water	42 liters
plasma volume	3 liters
hematocrit	0.40
extracellular fluid volume	14 liters
plasma osmolarity	300 mOsm/l

1. The interstitial fluid volume in liters is:
   A. 10.0
   B. 10.4
   C. 11.0
   D. 14.0
   E. 28.0

2. The cell volume in liters is:
   A. 10.0
   B. 10.4
   C. 11.0
   D. 14.0
   E. 28.0

3. The blood volume in liters is:
   A. 3.0
   B. 4.0
   C. 5.0
   D. 7.5
   E. 12.0

4. The subject above ingests 3 liters of water. Assuming no water loss from the body, the plasma osmolarity in mOsm/liter after steady state has been attained will be:
   A. 260
   B. 265
   C. 270
   D. 275
   E. 280

5. Which of the following substance(s) would you need to inject into a patient to obtain a measure of intracellular volume?
   A. deuterium oxide (D_2O) and ^{131}I-albumin
   B. tritiated H_2O and inulin
   C. inulin
   D. inulin and ^{131}I-albumin
   E. deuterium oxide (D_2O)

6. Which of the following infusions would cause the greatest increase in extracellular fluid volume? (Assume that these infusions have equilibrated, but have not been excreted.)
   A. 1 liter of H_2O
   B. 1 liter of isotonic saline
   C. 1 liter of plasma
   D. 1 liter of iso-osmotic urea
   E. 1 liter of hypertonic sodium chloride

7. The following data were obtained in a normal human subject:
   Inulin: 3 g injected intravenously; extrapolated zero-time plasma concentration = 0.2 mg/ml.
   Evan's blue dye: 50 mg injected intravenously; extrapolated zero-time plasma concentration = 0.01 mg/ml.

   The measured plasma volume in liters is:
   A. 42
   B. 15
   C. 10
   D. 5
   E. 2

8. Approximately how much Na would you have to give to a 70-kg patient to increase plasma Na concentration from 140 to 160 mMol?
   A. 60 mMol of Na
   B. 280 mMol of Na
   C. 420 mMol of Na
   D. 560 mMol of Na
   E. 840 mMol of Na

9. When a red blood cell is placed in a hypertonic environment, initially its volume will (X) because of the movement of (Y).

	X	Y
A.	increase	water into the cell
B.	increase	electrolytes into the cell
C.	decrease	water out of the cell
D.	decrease	electrolytes out of the cell
E.	decrease	water and electrolytes out of the cell

The next two questions (10 and 11) are based on Fig. 1-1:

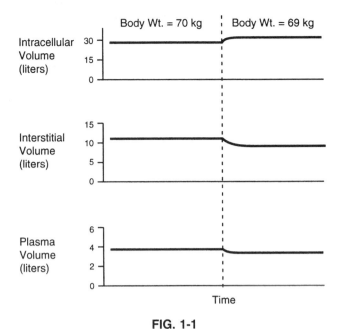

FIG. 1-1

10. **What happened to plasma osmolarity (tonicity) in this individual?**
    A. increased
    B. no change
    C. decreased

11. **Which of the following situations could account for the above results?**
    A. a loss of hypertonic urine
    B. a loss of isotonic urine
    C. an infusion of hypertonic saline
    D. an infusion of hypotonic saline
    E. an infusion of hyperoncotic albumin

Questions 12–14. The diagrams in solid lines represent the volumes and osmolarities of the extracellular (EC) and intracellular (IC) fluid compartments of a normal adult. For each situation, select the diagram with a dotted line that best reflects the change that will occur.

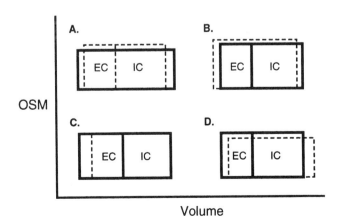

FIG. 1-2

12. **Loss of isotonic salt (NaCl) solution**

13. **Water deprivation**

14. **Intravenous infusion of hypertonic saline**

15. **Over a short period of time, a patient loses 3 liters of isotonic fluid (NaCl/HCO$_3$) due to diarrhea and then ingests 3 liters of water. All of the following are true EXCEPT:**
    A. body weight decreases
    B. extracellular fluid volume decreases
    C. plasma volume decreases
    D. plasma osmolarity decreases
    E. intracellular volume increases

16. **Approximately 30 min following the infusion of 1 liter of isotonic saline (0.9% NaCl) or 1 liter of isotonic glucose (5% dextrose) in an anephric adult, you would expect these infusions to cause:**
    A. similar decreases in plasma osmolality
    B. similar increases in extracellular volume
    C. no change in cell volume in either group following either infusion
    D. a similar increase in total body water
    E. no change in plasma osmolality following either infusion

17. **When the concentration of extracellular alanine increases and the flux of alanine into a cell increases, the flux of leucine into the cell is found to decrease. How might this be explained?**
    A. increased activity of the Na/K ATPase
    B. diffusion
    C. restricted diffusion
    D. decreased activity of the Na/Ca exchanger
    E. competition for a carrier protein

18. **Following a feast of wild mushrooms, an individual arrives in the emergency room. The mushrooms were of the species *Inocybe*, which has a very high muscarine content. One probable symptom is:**
    A. an overresponsive, or exaggerated, patellar tendon reflex
    B. increased blood glucose levels
    C. fast heart rate
    D. muscle contractions or spasms
    E. constricted pupils

19. **What is the approximate osmolarity of a solution containing only 10 mM NaCl, 120 mM KCl, and 1 mM CaCl$_2$?**
    A. 120 mOsm/liter
    B. 131 mOsm/liter
    C. 243 mOsm/liter
    D. 263 mOsm/liter
    E. 295 mOsm/liter

20. **For a neuron, which of the following could account for a decrease in temporal summation?**
    A. an increase in the duration of EPSPs occurring post-synaptically
    B. a decrease in the postsynaptic space constant
    C. a decrease in the duration of IPSPs occurring post-synaptically
    D. an increase in spatial summation of EPSPs
    E. a decrease in the interval between presynaptic action potentials

21. **A lipophilic substance is likely to:**
    A. have a low permeability coefficient
    B. be a charged particle
    C. have a high partition coefficient
    D. be more concentrated in the extracellular fluid than in the cell membrane
    E. be a substrate for the Na^+/K^+ pump

22. **The receptor potential created due to an environmental stimulus:**
    A. sums spatially, not temporally
    B. decays as a function of the space constant
    C. is self-propagating
    D. is not caused by changes in membrane permeability to ions
    E. is fixed in amplitude regardless of stimulus intensity

23. **The antagonistic nature of sympathetic and parasympathetic innervation leads to:**
    A. finer autonomic control of organs
    B. tonic activation of the autonomic nervous system
    C. increased activity of organs
    D. decreased activity of organs
    E. activation of both α- and β-adrenergic receptors

24. **As the threshold for the generation of a nerve action potential is reached:**
    A. Na^+ influx exceeds K^+ efflux
    B. Na^+ efflux and K^+ influx are equal
    C. Na^+ channels are time-inactivated
    D. Na^+ efflux begins
    E. K^+ efflux begins

25. **Typically, normal nerves at rest have a net electrochemical driving force on K^+, causing a continual leakage of K^+ out of the cell. Because of this, we can say that:**
    A. K^+ is not in a steady state
    B. K^+ is not passively distributed
    C. K^+ is continually pumped out of the cell
    D. there is a net passive influx of K^+
    E. intracellular $[K^+]$ continually decreases

26. **Drug X has a molecular weight of 500 g/M, while Drug Y has a molecular weight of 50 g/M. The net flux of Drug X across the lipid bilayer will be:**
    A. greater than the net flux of Drug Y if both drugs are lipophilic
    B. inversely proportional to the concentration gradient of Drug X
    C. independent of Drug X's partition coefficient
    D. directly related to Drug X's permeability coefficient
    E. independent of the thickness of the lipid bilayer

27. **The net electrochemical driving force on a permeable ion:**
    A. is independent of the concentration gradient of the ion
    B. is dependent on the ion's equilibrium potential and independent of the cell membrane potential
    C. can lead to a violation of the law of electroneutrality
    D. will determine the direction of net flux of an ion
    E. is independent of the ion's net charge

28. **Plasma membrane proteins:**
    A. are present in equimolar concentrations with phospholipids
    B. are found exclusively on the outer or inner surface of the membrane
    C. determine the transmembrane movement of hydrophobic substances
    D. may span the membrane and move laterally within the membrane
    E. are all ion channels

29. **The "all or none" principle for nerve conduction means that under a given set of conditions:**
    A. the number of nerves excited by a stimulus is independent of the stimulus intensity
    B. the electrical potential above threshold can be transmitted long distances
    C. all nerves are refractory for the same duration of time after a stimulus
    D. all EPSPs and IPSPs will summate
    E. all nerves conduct action potentials at the same velocity

30. **Immediately after a bullet transects (cuts) the spinal cord, all sensation and voluntary movement of the legs are lost. Weeks later, the legs become spastic (involuntary contractions), and the drug baclofen is prescribed. One way in which baclofen may decrease leg spasms is to:**
    A. decrease the number of IPSPs on the motor efferent
    B. decrease the magnitude of IPSPs on the motor efferent
    C. decrease the action potential threshold of the motor efferent from -50 mV to -55 mV
    D. decrease the relative refractory period of the motor efferent
    E. increase presynaptic inhibition on the afferent nerve

31. The duration of the after-hyperpolarization of a nerve action potential:
    A. determines the absolute refractory period
    B. can be influenced by a decrease in K^+ permeability
    C. is not significantly influenced by TEA
    D. is the period immediately after an IPSP
    E. would increase if Na^+ channels were open

32. Neurotransmitter X opens Channel Y on the postsynaptic membrane. The reversal potential for ions flowing through Channel Y is equal to $+102$ mV. Which ion is probably flowing through Channel Y? (Assume extracellular ions: $Na^+ = 140$ mM, $K^+ = 4$ mM, $Ca^{2+} = 2.5$ mM, $Cl^- = 110$ mM, $HCO3- \leqq 2 0$ mM and intracellular ions: $Na^+ = 14$ mM, $K^+ = 120$ mM, $Ca^{2+} = 0.001$ mM, $Cl^- = 11$ mM, $HCO3- = 10$ mM.)
    A. Na^+
    B. K^+
    C. Ca^{2+}
    D. Cl^-
    E. HCO_3^-

33. Tricyclic antidepressants are used to treat major depression. This class of drugs acts at synapses by blocking the reuptake of biogenic amines into the nerve terminals. Tricyclic antidepressants act as a:
    A. GABA antagonist
    B. facilitator of GABA
    C. neurotransmitter
    D. neuromodulator
    E. neuroactive peptide

For questions 34–36, refer to Fig. 1-3.

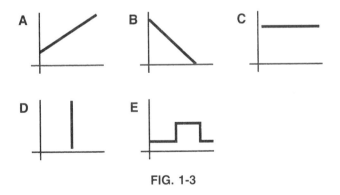

FIG. 1-3

34. Which figure best illustrates the relationship of acetylcholine concentration in the synaptic cleft (Y-axis) as a function of extracellular $[Ca^{2+}]$ (X-axis)?

35. Which figure best illustrates the relationship of the amplitude of a muscle action potential (Y-axis) as a function of acetylcholine concentration in the synaptic cleft (X-axis)?

36. Which figure best illustrates the relationship of frequency of action potentials along an autonomic nerve (Y-axis) as a function of potassium channel relative permeability (X-axis)?

37. In cell membranes:
    A. hydrophobic phospholipid heads associate to form a bilayer
    B. solutes with a low partition coefficient move more readily across the lipid bilayer than solutes with a high partition coefficient
    C. membrane proteins have no known function but are necessary for life
    D. membrane proteins can increase the speed of solute transport
    E. when a lipid-soluble solute is in equilibrium across the membrane, there is a net flux of that solute from an area of high concentration to one of low concentration

38. During an action potential, the direction of net flux of K^+ during repolarization and of Na^+ during depolarization are (respectively):
    A. inward, inward
    B. outward, outward
    C. inward, outward
    D. outward, inward
    E. no net flux, outward

39. Typically, postganglionic neurons of the parasympathetic system release:
    A. acetylcholine, which binds to muscarinic receptors
    B. acetylcholine, which binds to nicotinic receptors
    C. norepinephrine, which binds to α-adrenergic receptors
    D. epinephrine, which binds to beta-adrenergic receptors
    E. norepinephrine, which binds to β-adrenergic receptors

40. At the neuromuscular junction, the influx of sodium ions that partially determines the endplate potential is due to:
    A. hyperpolarization of the postsynaptic membrane
    B. a net outward driving force for sodium
    C. potassium efflux
    D. high intracellular Na concentrations in the endplate region
    E. a ligand-activated process

41. Sympathetic stimulation of the adrenal medulla:
    A. decreases dopamine concentration in the blood
    B. increases acetylcholine concentration in the blood
    C. increases epinephrine concentration in the blood
    D. would occur through stimulation of somatic nerves
    E. would occur through stimulation of cell bodies in the sacral segment of the spinal cord

42. **For a cell with 120 mM K$^+$ protein$^-$ inside and 4 mM K$^+$ protein$^-$ outside, with proteins$^-$ impermeable and K$^+$ permeable to the membrane, which of the following statements is true *at equilibrium?*
   A. The chemical potential driving K inward is equal in magnitude to the electrical potential driving potassium outward.
   B. Bulk movement of K out of the cell occurs due to the impermeable proteins$^-$.
   C. The net flux of potassium equals zero.
   D. There will be 62 mM K protein inside and 62 mM K protein outside the cell.
   E. The inside of this cell will be electrically positive with respect to the outside.

43. **Electrical synapses:**
   A. deliver the electrical signal to multicellular preparations more quickly than chemical synapses
   B. conduct an action potential in only one direction
   C. have a direct susceptibility to receptor antagonist drugs
   D. have longer synaptic delays than chemical synapses
   E. do not lead to the generation of an action potential in the postsynaptic neuron

44. **If an uncharged solute crosses the cell membrane by diffusion, then the flux of that solute will be:**
   A. inversely proportional to the concentration gradient of the solute across the cell membrane
   B. inversely proportional to the molecular weight of the solute
   C. directly proportional to the radius of the solute
   D. directly proportional to the thickness of the membrane
   E. inversely proportional to the partition coefficient of the solute

45. **What would the approximate resting membrane potential be for a cell with intracellular concentrations of K = 120 mM and Na = 14 mM, extracellular concentrations of K = 4 mM and Na = 140 mM, and the following ion permeabilities: P_{Na} = 0.09, P_K = 0.91 (permeability for all other ions is zero)?**
   A. -50 mV
   B. -60 mV
   C. $+60$ mV
   D. 0 mV
   E. -30 mV

46. **A hypothetical cell contains 10 mM Na$^+$ and 10 mM proteins$^-$ and is immersed in a 10-mM NaCl solution. The cell membrane is permeable to water, Na$^+$, and Cl$^-$, but impermeable to proteins$^-$. Which of the following will occur?**
   A. Osmolarity inside the cell will be less than osmolarity outside the cell.
   B. The [Na] inside the cell will be less than the [Na] outside the cell.
   C. Millimoles of Na outside the cell will not equal millimoles of Cl outside the cell.
   D. The impermeable proteins will cause an asymmetric distribution of ions.
   E. [Cl] inside the cell will be greater than [Cl] outside the cell.

47. **Which of the following statements is true regarding normal propagation of an action potential?**
   A. When extracellular [Na] decreases, the peak of the action potential decreases.
   B. It requires opening of voltage-gated channels: first to potassium, then to sodium.
   C. The peak amplitude of the action potential decreases as the distance from the stimulus increases.
   D. Action potential propagation is typically bidirectional in nerves.
   E. Action potentials can summate spatially.

48. **Which of the following statements is true regarding an uncharged solute X that enters a cell through facilitated diffusion?**
   A. Inhibition of the carrier proteins that transport solute X would increase the net flux of solute X.
   B. For all increases in extracellular [X], a decrease in net flux would result.
   C. Oxygen would be a good example of solute X.
   D. Solute X would be transported from an area of low concentration to one of high concentration.
   E. When solute X is in equilibrium, the [X] outside the cell would equal the [X] inside the cell.

49. **Which of the following determines the distance that a graded potential will travel down an axon?**
   A. increasing the axon diameter
   B. decreasing the axon's internal resistance
   C. decreasing the membrane resistance
   D. increasing the space constant
   E. increasing the amplitude of the graded potential

50. **Which of the following manipulations would *decrease* the endplate potential at the neuromuscular junction?**
   A. increase the synaptic vesicle content of acetylcholine (assume no change in the number of vesicles released)
   B. increase the number of accessible acetylcholine binding sites in myasthenia gravis
   C. increase Ca entry at the presynaptic neuron terminal
   D. pharmacologically inactivate acetylcholinesterase
   E. apply a nicotinic antagonist to the postsynaptic membrane

51. **Upon arrival of the action potential, acetylcholine released from a presynaptic nerve terminal results from:**
   A. Cl$^-$ entry
   B. acetylcholinesterase
   C. synapsin I phosphorylation
   D. opening of channels allowing Na/K to flow down their concentration gradients
   E. postsynaptic inhibition

52. **Reciprocal innervation is most accurately described as:**
   A. inhibition of flexor muscles during activation of the extensor
   B. activation of contralateral extensors during activation of contralateral flexors
   C. reduction in Ia fiber activity during a contraction
   D. simultaneous stimulation of alpha motor neurons to flexor and extensor muscles
   E. Renshaw inhibition

53. **Which of the following statements is true regarding a situation in which 500 presynaptic neurons synapse onto a single postsynaptic neuron?**
   A. This is an example of divergence on the postsynaptic neuron.
   B. Temporal summation could not occur in the postsynaptic neuronal soma.
   C. If 250 of the synapses were excitatory and 250 were inhibitory, the postsynaptic neuron would never generate an action potential.
   D. The closer a synapse is to the axon hillock, the greater the influence on the frequency of action potentials generated.
   E. This scenario would never occur because postsynaptic neurons have only one presynaptic neuron.

54. **The receptor potential of a given cell (receptor cell) that transduces environmental stimuli is:**
   A. not affected by changes in the receptor cell space constant
   B. fixed in amplitude regardless of stimulus intensity
   C. self-propagating
   D. nonincremental
   E. due to a change in the receptor cell ion permeability

55. **A surgeon washes out a surgical wound from which a tumor has been removed with sterile distilled water (no ions) rather than sterile physiologic saline (similar to extracellular solution). She does this in order to cause any remaining tumor cells to:**
   A. depolarize and decrease action potential frequency
   B. increase the activity of secondary active transport and destroy normal cell function
   C. swell and burst
   D. inhibit voltage-dependent K^+ channels and decrease the duration of action potentials
   E. wash off any neurotransmitter and increase synaptic activity

56. **If the vagus nerve (preganglionic cell body in the brain stem) is severed, then:**
   A. the size of the pupils will decrease
   B. heart rate will decrease
   C. movement of food through the gut will decrease
   D. airway resistance will increase (more difficult to breath)
   E. skeletal muscle weakness will occur

Use Fig. 1-4, which represents the intracellular concentration of phosphate with time, to answer question 57. Assume that the extracellular concentration of phosphate is 2 mM.

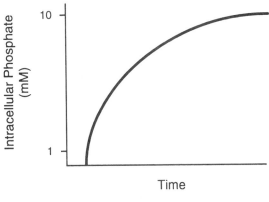

FIG. 1-4

57. **Phosphate is transported through:**
   A. diffusion
   B. facilitated diffusion
   C. secondary active cotransport
   D. osmosis

58. **Renshaw inhibition:**
   A. is an example of presynaptic inhibition
   B. is an example of contralateral inhibition
   C. is an example of positive feedback in the nervous system
   D. involves an interneuron in its reflex arc
   E. involves only EPSP generation

59. **A patient presents with a very slow and weak patellar tendon reflex. One cause of this may be:**
   A. degradation of Schwann cells
   B. ingestion of an anti-acetylcholinesterase
   C. inhalation of nicotine
   D. decreased IPSPs on the motor efferent
   E. increased acetylcholine synthesis

60. **Decongestants, which dilate airways, cause sympathetic postganglionic nerves to release their neurotransmitter. One symptom of a decongestant overdose might be:**
   A. decreased heart rate
   B. contracted pupils
   C. decreased blood levels of norepinephrine and dopamine β-hydroxylase
   D. increased blood pressure due to constriction of blood vessels
   E. decreased blood levels of glucose

61. Drug-induced skeletal muscle relaxation is sometimes required when aligning fractured or dislocated bones. Which of the following causes skeletal muscle relaxation?
    A. an adrenergic antagonist
    B. a muscarinic agonist
    C. a dopaminergic antagonist
    D. a nicotinic antagonist
    E. an increase in $[K^+]$

62. Under normal conditions, a miniature endplate potential:
    A. is the smallest EPSP possible
    B. is due to the presynaptic release of a molecule of acetylcholine
    C. is equal in magnitude in the presence and absence of anti-acetylcholinesterase
    D. is equal in magnitude in the presence and absence of acetylcholinesterase
    E. causes an action potential postsynaptically

63. The postsynaptic graded potential in neuron 3 during presynaptic inhibition is an (*first answer*), while during postsynaptic inhibition it would be an (*second answer*).

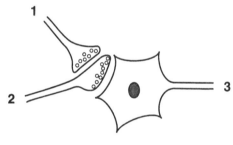

FIG. 1-5

    A. IPSP, IPSP
    B. IPSP, action potential
    C. EPSP, EPSP
    D. IPSP, EPSP
    E. EPSP, IPSP

64. When two neurons synapse on a single postsynaptic neuron and cause EPSPs and IPSPs, then:
    A. temporal summation cannot occur
    B. an action potential will never occur postsynaptically
    C. the presynaptic neuron ending farthest from the postsynaptic axon hillock will have a greater effect on the frequency of action potentials generated
    D. upon activation, the presynaptic nerves will have opposite effects on postsynaptic frequency of action potential generation
    E. spatial summation cannot occur

65. Ion X^- has equal intracellular and extracellular concentrations. When the cell membrane potential is -60 mV, ion X^- will (assume that no active transport pump exists for X^-):
    A. have no net flux
    B. have a net outward flux
    C. have a net inward flux
    D. be in a steady state
    E. be in equilibrium

66. Removal of the Na^+ channel inactivation gate would result in:
    A. a decrease in the duration of the action potential
    B. a resting membrane potential more negative than normal
    C. an action potential (if initiated) that would not propagate a distance greater than a few space (length) constants
    D. an increase in time the Na^+ channel would be open
    E. an inhibition of the opening of voltage-dependent potassium channels

67. GABA opens Cl^- channels on a postsynaptic membrane in which resting membrane potential is -40 mV. Assume the extracellular Cl^- is 110 mM and intracellular Cl^- is 11 mM. GABA would lead to:
    A. an IPSP
    B. an EPSP
    C. no change in membrane potential since Cl^- is in equilibrium
    D. opening of voltage-dependent Na^+ channels
    E. net Cl^- efflux

68. When a neurotransmitter opens a ligand-gated channel to an unknown ion^+ and no change in the membrane potential of -60 mV is observed, then the unknown ion^+ (assume that $[K^+]_{out} = 12$ mM, $[K^+]_{in} = 120$ mM, $[Na^+]_{out} = 140$ mM, and $[Na^+]_{in} = 14$ mM):
    A. has a greater electrical than chemical potential
    B. has a net outward flux
    C. is at equilibrium
    D. is in equal concentrations in and outside the nerve
    E. is at a greater concentration outside the nerve than inside the nerve

69. During the absolute refractory period of a nerve action potential:
    A. Na^+ channels have a high resistance
    B. the Na/K ATPase is inactive
    C. the Na^+ equilibrium potential is negative
    D. the reflection coefficient for all solutes is 1.0
    E. K^+ channels are inactivated

70. Cobra venom directly inhibits endplate potentials. The venom from this snake contains:
    A. a nicotinic agonist
    B. a nicotinic antagonist
    C. a muscarinic agonist
    D. a muscarinic antagonist
    E. an acetylcholinesterase inhibitor

71. **The voltage-gated K$^+$ channels in nerves are:**
    A. necessary for facilitated diffusion
    B. activated by membrane depolarization
    C. inactivated by any change in membrane potential
    D. directly activated by neurotransmitter
    E. none of the above

72. **Within the autonomic nervous system:**
    A. all preganglionic parasympathetic neurons are adrenergic
    B. all preganglionic sympathetic neurons are cholinergic
    C. all postganglionic parasympathetic neurons are adrenergic
    D. all postganglionic sympathetic neurons are cholinergic
    E. All of the above answers are correct.

73. **At the neuromuscular junction, the influx of sodium ions that partially determines the endplate potential is due to:**
    A. hyperpolarization of the postsynaptic membrane
    B. a net outward driving force for sodium
    C. potassium efflux
    D. high intracellular Na concentrations in the endplate region
    E. a ligand-activated process

74. **On the postsynaptic membrane of a normal neuron, an increase in K permeability:**
    A. would depolarize the membrane potential
    B. would make the neuron less likely to generate an action potential
    C. would generate an excitatory postsynaptic potential
    D. leads to a potential that would not summate with other postsynaptic potentials
    E. leads to a potential that would not degrade with distance traveled

75. **Which of the following ion channels would produce the greatest amount of membrane depolarization when opened by a neurotransmitter (assume a typical cell with a membrane potential of -60 mV)?**
    A. channels permeable to Cl only
    B. channels permeable to K and Na
    C. channels permeable to K only
    D. channels permeable to Na only
    E. channels equally permeable to Na, K, and Cl

76. **Athletes have been known to self-inject steroids. One side effect of this abusive behavior is a change in the number of postsynaptic neurotransmitter receptors for GABA (possibly accounting for the alterations in behavior observed with steroid use). Steroids in this case are acting as a:**
    A. neurotransmitter
    B. neuromodulator
    C. neuroactive peptide
    D. biogenic amine
    E. paracrine hormone

77. **In resting cells, intracellular concentrations of K$^+$ and Na$^+$ are in a steady state due to:**
    A. the law of electroneutrality
    B. membranes being impermeable to K$^+$ and Na$^+$
    C. zero net electrochemical driving force on K$^+$ and Na$^+$
    D. Na/K ATPase counteracting leakage of K$^+$ and Na$^+$
    E. Gibbs-Donnan equilibrium

78. **Farmer Brown arrives at the emergency room after inhaling insecticide that she was spraying on her fields. She has constricted pupils, wheezy breathing (constricted airway), and a slowed heart rate. An appropriate treatment would be:**
    A. acetylcholine
    B. a muscarinic antagonist
    C. anti-acetylcholinesterase
    D. a β-receptor antagonist
    E. a sodium channel blocker

79. **In a typical nerve, increasing the resting membrane potential from -60 mV to -65 mV will:**
    A. increase the probability of generating an action potential
    B. have the same effect on nerve excitability as the relative refractory period
    C. not allow that cell to develop an IPSP
    D. not allow that cell to develop an EPSP
    E. cause sodium channels to open

80. **If the chloride ion is at electrochemical equilibrium in a nerve, an increase in the number of open chloride channels will cause:**
    A. a decrease in its membrane potential
    B. an increase in its chloride content
    C. a decrease in its chloride content
    D. an increase in the unidirectional flux of chloride from the inside to the outside of the nerve
    E. no change in the unidirectional flux of chloride from the outside to the inside of the nerve

81. **A substance with a partition coefficient that is greater than 1:**
    A. is more water-soluble than lipid-soluble
    B. has a lower permeability coefficient than that of a similar-size molecule with a partition coefficient less than 1
    C. is more concentrated in the cell membrane than in the adjacent extracellular fluid
    D. is more concentrated in the cell cytoplasm than in the cell membrane
    E. is usually a charged particle

82. **All the following statements concerning the passive flux of an ion across a cell plasma membrane are true EXCEPT:**
   A. Passive flux is directly proportional to the electrical potential gradient across the membrane.
   B. Passive flux is directly proportional to the concentration gradient of the ion across the membrane.
   C. An active transport system is required for the ion if passive flux is to be maintained at a constant level.
   D. Passive flux is directly proportional to membrane permeability of the ion.
   E. Passive flux of the ion occurs primarily through the lipid bilayer portion of the membrane.

83. **Voltage-dependent activation of which membrane ion channel will result in the efflux of positively charged ions from the cell?**
   A. sodium channel
   B. potassium channel
   C. calcium channel
   D. sodium/potassium cation channel
   E. chloride channel

84. **In order to function normally in vivo (i.e., within the body), the living mammalian cell:**
   A. will always be in a state of thermodynamic equilibrium with its extracellular environment
   B. must maintain a zero electrochemical potential difference between cytoplasm and extracellular fluid for each permeable molecule or ion
   C. must maintain a high permeability across its plasmalemmal membrane for passive diffusion of each essential nutrient and metabolic waste product
   D. must maintain a cytoplasmic Na^+ concentration approximately 10-fold higher than extracellular Na^+ concentration and vice versa for K^+
   E. must be in a state of osmotic equilibrium with its extracellular environment

85. **The cell membrane permeability coefficient of an uncharged solute molecule is inversely proportional to:**
   A. the length of the pathway taken by the solute particle in its passage through the membrane
   B. the diffusion coefficient for the solute molecule and membrane
   C. the partition coefficient for the solute and membrane
   D. the solubility of the solute molecule within the membrane phase
   E. the concentration gradient of the solute molecule across the membrane

86. **The electrical potential difference for a single permeable cation–anion pair moving across a cell plasmalemmal membrane:**
   A. requires no energy to maintain its value constant
   B. would be reduced to zero if the membrane diffusion coefficients of the cation and anion were made equal
   C. would be reduced to zero if the membrane diffusion coefficient for the cation were reduced to zero
   D. would be reduced to zero if the membrane diffusion coefficient for the anion were reduced to zero

87. **At equilibrium what will be the relative change in volume of cells placed in each of the following solutions? (Assume cell osmolarity is 300 mOsm/l, Na^+ and Cl^- are impermeable, and urea is permeable.)**
   Solution 1: 150 mM NaCl, 100 mM urea
   Solution 2: 100 mM NaCl, 150 mM urea
   Solution 3: 300 mM NaCl, 100 mM urea
   Solution 4: 100 mM NaCl, 50 mM urea
   Solutions that would cause cells to:

	Swell	No change in volume	Shrink
A.	—	—	Solutions 1,2,3,4
B.	Solutions 3,4	Solution 1	Solution 2
C.	Solutions 1,4	Solution 3	Solution 2
D.	Solutions 2,4	Solution 1	Solution 3
E.	Solutions 1,3,4	Solution 2	—

88. **A patient presents with sensory loss and weakness. An electromyogram (EMG) shows an increase in compound action potential amplitude and a slowed conduction velocity. Which of the following is the most likely explanation?**
   A. neuropathy
   B. myopathy
   C. disease of the neuromuscular junction

89. **A drug that blocks the chloride channel leads to a slight depolarization of the resting membrane potential of certain neurons. In which direction is the net electrochemical driving force on chloride?**
   A. inward
   B. outward
   C. no net electrochemical driving force

90. **Which of the following occurs during osmosis in a cell that is not permeable to all ions?**
   A. Water moves from a region of low to high solute concentration.
   B. Water is pumped by active transport into the cell.
   C. Water moves from a region of low to high water concentration.
   D. Volume on both sides of the membrane remains the same.
   E. Osmolarity on both sides of the membrane is unchanged.

91. **In two cases (1 and 2), the initial concentrations of solute X separated by a membrane permeable to X are:**

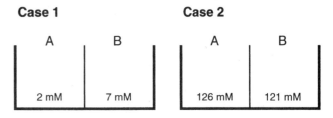

FIG. 1-6

Which one of the following statements is true?

A. All other conditions being equal, Cases 1 and 2 will reach equilibrium at the same rate.

B. All other conditions being equal, Case 2 will reach equilibrium sooner than Case 1.

C. Prior to equilibrium, net flux is directly proportional to the molecular weight of X.

D. Prior to equilibrium, the direction of net flux (A to B) is the same in both cases.

E. Prior to equilibrium, net flux does not depend on permeability.

92. **Each of the following statements concerning the passive flux (leak) of an ion across the cell membrane is true EXCEPT:**

A. Passive flux is directly proportional to the electrical potential gradient across the membrane under conditions of a constant chemical gradient.

B. Passive flux is directly proportional to the concentration gradient of the ion across the membrane under conditions of a constant electrical gradient.

C. An active transport system is required for the ion if passive flux is to be maintained at a constant level.

D. Passive flux increases as a function of the net electrochemical driving force on an ion.

E. Passive flux of ions is independent of ion channel conductances.

93. **In an isolated unmyelinated nerve axon preparation, tetrodotoxin (TTX) is locally applied to a 2-mm segment on the axon that has a space constant of 20 mm. If an action potential is initiated proximal to the area of TTX, then an intracellular electrode placed 18 mm distal to the area of TTX would record:**

A. no action potential, but a normal resting membrane potential

B. an action potential identical to the action potential at the proximal area

C. an action potential reduced by 37% in amplitude as compared to the action potential at the proximal area

D. an action potential of greater amplitude as compared to the action potential at the proximal area

E. a longer-duration action potential with no after-hyperpolarization

94. **Assuming the typical concentration gradients of ions in nerves, an excitatory endplate potential, in principle, could be produced by:**

A. a decreased permeability in K^+

B. a decreased permeability in Na^+

C. activation of voltage-dependent K^+ channels

D. activation of the Na^+ channel inactivation gate

E. inactivation of the calcium channel activation gate

95. **Nerve A makes an excitatory synaptic contact with nerve B. Tetraethylammonium (TEA) is injected into the presynaptic terminal of nerve A. An action potential in nerve A would:**

A. lead to an IPSP in nerve B

B. lead to an action potential in nerve B of longer duration than a normal action potential

C. decrease the duration that the neurotransmitter is present in the synaptic cleft

D. increase the neurotransmitter concentration in the synaptic cleft

E. inhibit action potentials in nerve B

96. **All the following are true of both the somatic and autonomic nervous systems EXCEPT:**

A. presence of peripheral ganglia

B. presence of afferent and efferent nerves

C. use of acetylcholine as a neurotransmitter

D. innervation of muscle

E. presence of EPSPs

97. **What directly determines the value of the resting membrane potential?**

A. the concentration gradient of uncharged molecules

B. the concentration gradient of impermeable negatively charged proteins

C. the concentration gradient of impermeable ions

D. the relative conductances of ion channels

E. the osmolarity of a cell

98. **Which of the lines (A–E) in Fig. 1-7 represents the dependence of the resting membrane potential on extracellular K^+ concentration in a typical nerve? Assume intracellular K^+ concentration stays constant at 120 mM.**

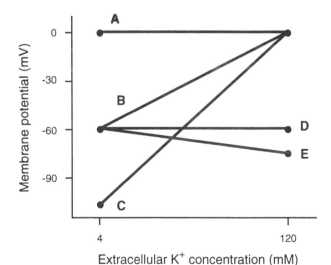

FIG. 1-7

99. **Myelin:**
   A. decreases the probability of graded potentials falling below threshold along an axon
   B. covers the axons of all nerves
   C. is formed from membranes of adjacent neurons
   D. shields the entire length of an axon from direct contact with extracellular fluid
   E. increases the internal resistance of an axon

100. **In a cell, the resting membrane potential is -60 mV and the extracellular H^+ concentration is 39.8 nM (pH 7.4). If H^+ is in equilibrium across the plasma membrane, what is the pH inside the cell?**
   A. 0.398 nM (pH 9.4)
   B. 3.98 nM (pH 8.4)
   C. 39.8 nM (pH 7.4)
   D. 398 nM (pH 6.4)
   E. 3,980 nM (pH 5.4)

101. **At a neuromuscular junction, the addition of a drug that blocks Ca^{2+} channels would be associated with a decrease in each of the following EXCEPT:**
   A. postsynaptic duration of the EPP
   B. postsynaptic amplitude of the EPP
   C. postsynaptic amplitude of the MEPP
   D. presynaptic Ca^{2+} influx
   E. presynaptic release of neurotransmitter during an action potential

102. **Counter-transporters:**
   A. would increase their activity if the Na^+ concentration gradient increased
   B. cannot transport substances against their concentration gradient
   C. do not show saturation kinetics
   D. transport a cation and an anion in the same direction
   E. transport glucose in both directions across the membrane

103. **In general, a specific neurotransmitter:**
   A. binds to voltage-gated Na^+ channels responsible for nerve action potentials
   B. is involved in electrical synapses
   C. has effects that are independent of their rate of removal from the synaptic cleft
   D. is released from the postsynaptic terminals
   E. can be excitatory in some cells and inhibitory in others

104. **One factor that increases the propagation velocity of an action potential is:**
   A. decreasing the length of the axon
   B. decreasing the membrane capacitance of the axon
   C. increasing the threshold of an action potential in the axon
   D. increasing the frequency of stimulation of the axon
   E. increasing the number of IPSPs occurring on the axon

105. **What is one reason patients who suffer from severe and extensive burns develop tachycardia?**
   A. Burns selectively stimulate the parasympathetic nervous system.
   B. Burns increase the activity of acetylcholinesterase at the skeletal neuromuscular junction.
   C. Burns hyperpolarize nerves within the sympathetic nervous system.
   D. Burns destroy many cells and cause a mass release of K^+ into the extracellular space.
   E. Burns inhibit adrenal medulla function.

Match the descriptions in questions 106–108 with the appropriate lettered point on this nerve action potential.

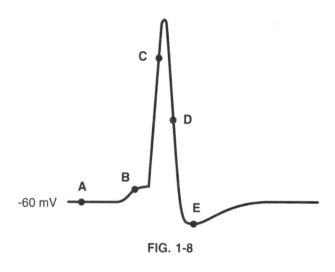

FIG. 1-8

106. **The point at which Na^+ permeability is highest**

107. **The point at which the net ion flux across the membrane is zero**

108. **The point at which the net electrochemical driving force on K^+ is greatest**

For questions 109–114, match the appropriate figure (A–E) with the situation that it most closely describes.

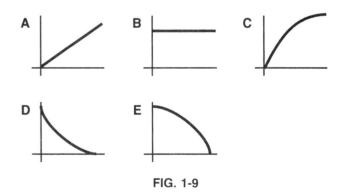

FIG. 1-9

109. The pressure (y-axis) necessary to prevent water flow as a function of solute concentration (x-axis) for a membrane bathed on one side by pure water and on the other side by a solution containing an impermeable solute.

110. The rate of urea diffusion (y-axis) across a membrane as a function of the concentration difference for urea (x-axis) across the membrane.

111. The relationship between the rate of d-glucose uptake across a red cell membrane (y-axis) as a function of the galactose concentration in the extracellular fluid (x-axis) if the glucose concentration in the extracellular fluid is kept constant and glucose and galactose *share* the same transporter.

112. The relationship between the rate of d-glucose uptake across a red cell membrane (y-axis) as a function of the galactose concentration in the extracellular fluid (x-axis) if the glucose concentration in the extracellular fluid is kept constant and glucose and galactose *do not share* a common transporter.

113. The electrical potential difference across a membrane (y-axis) as a function of the time (x-axis) if the membrane is bathed on one side with a solution of 10 mM NaCl and on the other side with a solution of 100 mM NaCl and if both Na and Cl can cross the membrane but the permeability to Na is greater than that to Cl.

114. The relation between the rate of glucose transport across a red blood cell membrane (y-axis) and the concentration of d-glucose in the extracellular medium (x-axis).

For questions 115–119, assume that a hypothetical cell contains 150 mM NaCl and that the cell membrane is impermeable to Na^+ and sucrose but permeable to Cl^- and urea.

115. If this cell were immersed in a solution containing 300 mM urea, the cell would:
   A. undergo no change in volume
   B. swell and ultimately burst
   C. double in volume
   D. shrink to one-third its original volume
   E. shrink to one-half its original volume
   F. initially shrink and then swell
   G. initially swell and then shrink

116. If this cell were immersed in a solution containing 300 mM NaCl, the cell would:
   A. undergo no change in volume
   B. swell and ultimately burst
   C. double in volume
   D. shrink to one-third its original volume
   E. shrink to one-half its original volume
   F. initially shrink and then swell
   G. initially swell and then shrink

117. If this cell were immersed in a solution containing 300 mM sucrose, the cell would:
   A. undergo no change in volume
   B. swell and ultimately burst
   C. double in volume
   D. shrink to one-third its original volume
   E. shrink to one-half its original volume
   F. initially shrink and then swell
   G. initially swell and then shrink

118. Assuming that the reflection coefficient of urea is 0.8, if this cell were immersed in a solution containing 500 mM urea, the cell would:
   A. undergo no change in volume
   B. swell and ultimately burst
   C. double in volume
   D. shrink to one-third its original volume
   E. shrink to one-half its original volume
   F. initially shrink and then swell
   G. initially swell and then shrink

119. Assuming that the reflection coefficient of urea is 0.3, if this cell were immersed in a solution containing 500 mM urea, the cell would:
   A. undergo no change in volume
   B. swell and ultimately burst
   C. double in volume
   D. shrink to one-third its original volume
   E. shrink to one-half its original volume
   F. initially shrink and then swell
   G. initially swell and then shrink

120. Exposure of red cells to ouabain will lead to all of the following *EXCEPT:*
   A. a decrease in the electrical potential across the membrane
   B. cell swelling
   C. a decrease in cell Cl^-
   D. a loss of cell K^+
   E. a gain of cell Na^+

121. If an ion is passively distributed across a cell membrane:
   A. transport across the membrane must be the result of simple diffusion
   B. a change in the permeability of the membrane to that ion will not change the distribution of that ion
   C. the distribution of that ion will not be affected by metabolic inhibitors
   D. the steady-state intracellular concentration of that ion will be halved if the volume of the cell doubles
   E. none of the above

122. Drug X, when applied to a nerve axon, results in both a gradual decrease in the amplitude of the individual action potentials and a slow (several hours) depolarization of the resting membrane potential. The drug is most likely:
    A. blocking the voltage-gated sodium channels
    B. blocking the voltage-gated potassium channels
    C. blocking the Na/K pump
    D. blocking Na inactivation
    E. increasing the rate at which voltage-dependent changes in K^+ permeability occur

123. For a motor neuron to initiate an action potential in a skeletal muscle, there must be:
    A. release of norepinephrine
    B. temporal summation
    C. spatial summation
    D. release of acetylcholine
    E. none of the above is needed

124. In hypertension, an adrenergic antagonist (blocker) is given to vasodilate blood vessels and reduce blood pressure. One common side effect of this antihypertensive medication is diarrhea (increased gastrointestinal motility). This is likely due to:
    A. the adrenal medulla, located near the GI tract, increasing its activity
    B. decreased blood flow to the GI tract
    C. predominance of parasympathetic activity
    D. an overall increase in autonomic activity
    E. increased blood flow to the GI tract

125. Excessive vomiting in the short term can lead to hypokalemia with no change in intracellular $[K^+]$. One possible result of this is:
    A. an increase in the Na/K ATPase activity
    B. a decreased probability of action potential generation
    C. a decrease in net K^+ efflux
    D. an increase in the number of IPSPs at the neuromuscular junction
    E. an increase in the number of EPSPs at the neuromuscular junction

126. A patient presents with a very strong patellar tendon reflex (i.e., a larger than normal reflex reaction). One cause of this might be:
    A. degradation of Schwann cells
    B. ingestion of an anti-acetylcholinesterase
    C. long duration of presynaptic inhibition
    D. increased Renshaw inhibition of the motor efferent
    E. decreased number of Na^+/K^+ channels

127. Axon A has a longer time constant than Axon B. The action potentials:
    A. have a slower conduction velocity in Axon A than in Axon B
    B. demonstrate differing degrees of temporal summation
    C. travel farther down Axon A than Axon B since the space constant is lower
    D. have a lower overshoot in Axon A
    E. in Axon B have a shorter after-hyperpolarization

128. Action potential propagation velocity increases with an increase in an axon's:
    A. capacitance
    B. partition coefficient
    C. myelination
    D. intracellular resistance
    E. time constant

129. TEA application to the presynaptic neuromuscular junction leads to an endplate potential that is:
    A. greater than normal due to TEA's indirectly increasing Ca^{2+} influx
    B. less than normal due to TEA's indirectly decreasing Ca^{2+} influx
    C. less than normal due to TEA's directly blocking Na^+ channels
    D. greater than normal due to TEA's directly blocking Na^+ channels
    E. unchanged since TEA has no effect on presynaptic action potentials

130. A hypothetical cell contains 150 mM NaCl and is bathed in a solution of 500 mM urea. For this cell, the reflection coefficients are: $Na^+ = 1.0$, $Cl^- = 0$, urea $= 0.8$. This cell will:
    A. have 75 mM Cl^- inside and outside at equilibrium
    B. initially swell and then shrink
    C. initially shrink and then swell
    D. shrink with no further change in volume
    E. undergo no change in volume

131. Which of the following statements is true for the compound action potential illustrated in Fig. 1-10?

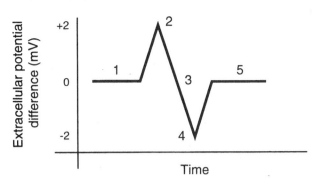

FIG. 1-10

A. Phase 4 is due to after-hyperpolarization.
B. For a single action potential, the intracellular membrane potential is -2 mV.
C. The resting intracellular membrane potential is 0 mV.
D. The phase 2 peak is dependent on nerve and muscle mass.
E. During phase 3, no action potentials are occurring.

132. Facilitated diffusion of a substance:
A. moves it from an area of low concentration to an area of high concentration
B. does not require a carrier protein
C. is not saturable
D. does not exhibit specificity
E. is subject to competition

133. Many symptoms of cystic fibrosis are due to a genetic defect in which membrane ion channel?
A. sodium channel
B. potassium channel
C. calcium channel
D. sodium/potassium cation channel
E. chloride channel

134. A 60-year-old man develops diplopia (double vision), difficulty in chewing and swallowing, and weakness of his limbs. All these symptoms are made worse by exercise and occur more frequently late in the day. A drug that could potentially alleviate these symptoms is:
A. curare, a nicotinic antagonist
B. atropine, a muscarinic antagonist
C. neostigmine, an anti-acetylcholinesterase
D. cocaine, to functionally increase the Na^+ channel threshold
E. valium, to increase the number of IPSPs

135. If the membrane potential is equal to the equilibrium potential for a given ion, then the net flux of the ion through the membrane will:
A. depend on the number of activated voltage-gated channels
B. be zero
C. be greater in the inward direction
D. be greater in the outward direction
E. be determined by the concentration (chemical) gradient alone

136. With regard to osmosis:
A. osmotic pressure gradients are proportional to the concentration gradient of permeable ions
B. osmosis is the net movement of water from an area of high osmolarity to one of low osmolarity
C. osmotic pressure is increased by the Na/K ATPase
D. water will usually flow against its concentration gradient
E. the osmotic pressure gradient is zero when all molecules are permeable

137. Which group of substances constitutes the catecholamines?
A. norepinephrine, epinephrine, and acetylcholine
B. norepinephrine, epinephrine, and serotonin
C. norepinephrine, epinephrine, and dopamine
D. norepinephrine, epinephrine, dopamine, and serotonin
E. dopamine and serotonin

138. The voltage-gated Na^+ channel of nerves:
A. can be influenced by extracellular $[Ca^{2+}]$
B. possesses an inactivation mechanism that is faster than the process of activation
C. is directly activated by neurotransmitters
D. is identical to the voltage-gated K^+ channel
E. is activated by any change in voltage in the cell

139. In a cell that is in steady state, the chloride equilibrium potential (V_{Cl}) is -60 mV, and the resting membrane potential (V_m) is -80 mV. If the cell is permeable to chloride, which of the following is a true statement regarding this cell?
A. Chloride ions are at equilibrium; therefore, there is no need to postulate the existence of a chloride pump.
B. There must be an active transport mechanism to pump chloride *out* in order to balance the net *inward* movement of chloride ions.
C. There must be an active transport mechanism to pump chloride *in* to balance the net *outward* movement of chloride ions.
D. There must be an active transport mechanism to pump chloride *out* to balance the net *outward* movement of chloride ions.
E. There must be an active transport mechanism to pump chloride *in* to balance the net *inward* movement of chloride ions

140. Applying a single threshold stimulus to a somatic efferent neuron will cause:
   A. a twitch contraction of a group of muscle fibers
   B. a twitch of a single muscle fiber
   C. a tetanic contraction of a group of muscle fibers
   D. a tetanic contraction of a single muscle fiber
   E. None of the above will occur.

141. All of the following are ways to physiologically increase active tension in muscle *EXCEPT*:
   A. in cardiac muscle, increase contractility
   B. in smooth muscle, increase the number of cells recruited
   C. in skeletal muscle, increase length
   D. in cardiac muscle, increase length
   E. in skeletal muscle, increase the number of cells recruited

142. Tetanic force in slow skeletal muscle will:
   A. not increase further with increasing stimulation frequency
   B. increase with increasing extracellular calcium concentration
   C. decrease further with increasing stimulation frequency
   D. increase with increasing Golgi tendon organ afferent nerve activity
   E. not decrease with decreasing intracellular calcium concentration

143. All of the following statements are true about the role of Ca^{2+} in muscle contraction *EXCEPT*:
   A. Ca^{2+} from outside the cell contributes to activation of contraction in both cardiac and smooth muscle.
   B. Ca^{2+} is conducted by specific membrane channels in smooth muscle.
   C. Ca^{2+} binds directly to troponin C in skeletal muscle.
   D. Ca^{2+} is stored in the sarcoplasmic reticulum in cardiac muscle.
   E. Ca^{2+} binds directly to myosin light-chain kinase in smooth muscle.

144. Calcium channel blockers are widely prescribed to facilitate coronary vasodilation. A potential side effect could be:
   A. decreased contractility of skeletal muscle
   B. increased blood pressure
   C. pupillary constriction
   D. increased gut peristalsis
   E. decreased contractility of cardiac muscle

145. Which one of the following events will cause contraction of smooth muscle?
   A. inhibition of the myosin light-chain kinase
   B. inhibition of the myosin light-chain phosphatase
   C. inhibition of calmodulin
   D. inhibition of calcium channels
   E. activation of troponin C

146. All the following events will lead to contraction of skeletal muscle *EXCEPT*:
   A. depolarization of the T-tubules
   B. Ca^{2+} release from troponin C
   C. Ca^{2+} release by the sarcoplasmic reticulum
   D. cross-bridge formation between myosin and actin
   E. depolarization of the sarcolemma

147. Large motor units:
   A. are recruited first
   B. produce tetanic tension at low stimulation frequencies
   C. have fewer muscle fibers
   D. produce more force than small motor units
   E. use ATP less quickly

148. Which one of the following statements describes the motor units that are recruited to maintain posture?
   A. They contain small-diameter fibers.
   B. They have primarily a glycogenolytic metabolism.
   C. They produce large forces over a long period of time.
   D. They use ATP quickly.
   E. They produce large forces over a short period of time.

149. The skeletal muscle α-motoneuron must:
   A. respond to excitatory Golgi tendon organ afferents but not to excitatory muscle spindle afferents
   B. respond to inhibitory inputs but not to excitatory inputs
   C. spatially sum postsynaptic potentials
   D. respond to excitatory muscle spindle afferents but not to excitatory Golgi tendon organ afferents
   E. temporally sum presynaptic potentials

150. When more motor units are recruited to maintain a constant velocity of contraction against an increasing load, which of the following must be true?
   A. Fewer muscle fibers are active.
   B. Greater force is generated by the newly recruited fibers.
   C. The slower fibers are derecruited in favor of the faster fibers.
   D. Increasing the frequency of firing increases velocity.
   E. Less force is generated by the newly recruited fibers to increase velocity.

151. Which of the following must be true during successive recruitment of motor units to produce more force?
   A. α-motor neurons become less active.
   B. All motor units fire at the same frequency.
   C. Slow motor units receive more inhibitory feedback.
   D. Newly recruited motor units fire at a lower frequency.
   E. Slow motor units fire at a lower frequency.

152. The T-tubule system:
   A. stores calcium in smooth muscle
   B. is a part of the sarcoplasmic reticulum in cardiac muscle but not in smooth muscle
   C. is a part of the sarcoplasmic reticulum in smooth muscle but not in cardiac muscle
   D. conducts the action potential in smooth muscle
   E. conducts the action potential in skeletal muscle

153. **Curare, a substance that competitively blocks the acetylcholine receptor, is occasionally used to relax muscles during surgery. Which one of the following postoperative treatments aids in recovery from curare?**
   A. botulinus toxin, to block ACh release
   B. neostigmine, an acetylcholinesterase inhibitor
   C. nifedipine, to block Ca^{2+} channels
   D. tetrodotoxin, to block Na^+ channels
   E. none of the above

Use Fig. 1-11, which shows motor unit recruitment, to answer questions 154 and 155.

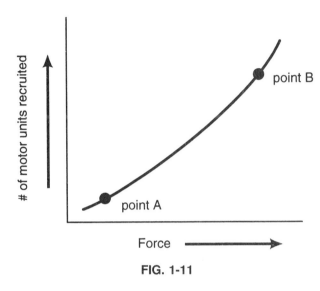

FIG. 1-11

154. **Compared to the motor units recruited at point B, the motor units recruited at point A:**
   A. have greater glycogenolytic metabolism
   B. are larger
   C. use more ATP
   D. produce more force
   E. have greater oxidative metabolism

155. **When the motor units at point B are recruited, the motor units that were recruited at point A are:**
   A. fatigued
   B. generating no force
   C. firing at a higher frequency
   D. larger
   E. in rigor

156. **Calcium influx across a muscle cell membrane is important for:**
   A. the rapid upstroke of the skeletal muscle action potential
   B. skeletal muscle relaxation
   C. the plateau phase of the smooth muscle action potential
   D. smooth muscle relaxation
   E. the falling phase of the smooth muscle action potential

157. **Afferent nerves from the muscle spindles provide information about:**
   A. tension only
   B. length, velocity, and tension
   C. length only
   D. length and velocity
   E. tension and velocity

Questions 158–161. Use Fig. 1-12 and the key to identify the muscles described in questions 158–161.

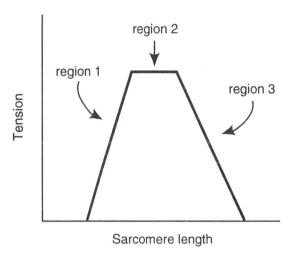

FIG. 1-12

Key for questions 158–161:
   ''A'' = skeletal muscle
   ''B'' = cardiac muscle
   ''C'' = smooth muscle
   ''D'' = none of the muscle types
   ''E'' = all three of the muscle types

158. **Muscle that normally operates in region 1**

159. **Muscle that normally operates in region 3**

160. **Muscle that is not described by the diagram**

161. **Muscle that normally operates in region 2**

Questions 162–164. Use the following diagram and key to match with questions 162–164.—A muscle lifts two different weights and generates the following data:

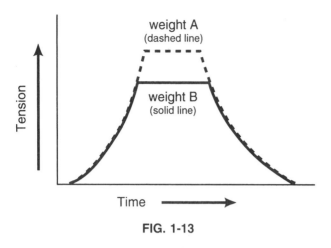

FIG. 1-13

Key for questions 162–164:
"A" = weight A
"B" = weight B
"C" = A and B are equal

162. The contraction(s) with the shortest isotonic phase

163. The contraction(s) with the fastest velocity of shortening

164. The contraction(s) that move(s) the weight the greatest distance

165. A motor unit is:
    A. a single muscle fiber innervated by several motor neurons
    B. all the muscle fibers innervated by several motor neurons
    C. all the muscle fibers innervated by a single motor neuron
    D. a single muscle fiber innervated by a single motor neuron

166. The skeletal muscle α-motor neuron is the "final common pathway" for a motor unit for all the following reasons EXCEPT:
    A. it integrates information from muscle spindle afferents
    B. it responds to only one neurotransmitter
    C. all its muscle fibers contract at the same time
    D. it integrates information from Golgi tendon afferents
    E. it integrates information from the brain

167. The channels opened by acetylcholine at the neuromuscular junction conduct:
    A. Na^+ and Ca^{2+} to raise the membrane voltage to a positive potential
    B. K^+ and Ca^{2+} to raise the membrane voltage to zero potential
    C. Na^+ and Ca^{2+} to raise the membrane voltage to a negative potential
    D. K^+ and Na^+ to raise the membrane voltage to a positive potential
    E. Na^+ and K^+ to raise the membrane voltage to zero potential

168. The neuromuscular junction contains:
    A. acetylcholine receptors but no regenerative sodium channels
    B. no acetylcholine receptors
    C. both acetylcholine receptors and regenerative sodium channels
    D. regenerative sodium channels
    E. neither acetylcholine receptors nor regenerative sodium channels

169. The graded potential at the neuromuscular junction:
    A. opens Ca^{2+} channels in the T-tubules
    B. is conducted some distance from the motor endplate
    C. hyperpolarizes the endplate membrane below threshold for an action potential
    D. opens acetylcholine channels in the membrane surrounding the motor endplate
    E. opens Ca^{2+} channels in the sarcoplasmic reticulum

Questions 170–172 are based on your evaluation of Fig. 1-14.

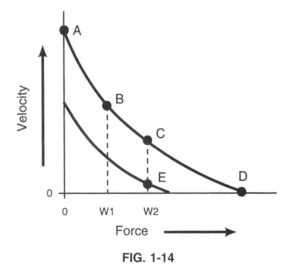

FIG. 1-14

170. Point corresponding to the peak force during an isometric contraction.

171. **Point corresponding to the muscle generating the greatest type II afferent nerve activity while lifting weight 2 (W2)**

172. **Point corresponding to the greatest distance moved when lifting *EITHER* weight 1 (W1) or weight 2 (W2)**

173. **Muscle contraction in the patellar tendon reflex (a deep tendon reflex) results from:**
    A. activation of motor units due to stretch of the Golgi tendon organs
    B. activation of motor units due to stretch of the muscle spindles
    C. increased type Ib afferent nerve activity inhibiting the contracting motor units
    D. decreased type Ia afferent nerve activity inhibiting the contracting motor units
    E. increased type II afferent nerve activity inhibiting the contracting units

174. **A patient places her hands together, palm to palm, and pushes. If the muscles of one arm are fast and the muscles of the other are slow, what must happen to maintain her hands in a steady position?**
    A. more slow motor units must be recruited at a higher frequency
    B. more fast motor units must be recruited at a higher frequency
    C. more fast motor units must be recruited at a lower frequency
    D. fewer slow motor units must be recruited at a lower frequency
    E. fewer fast motor units must be recruited at a higher frequency

CARDIOVASCULAR PHYSIOLOGY

1. **Which of the following would both decrease heart rate?**
   A. cutting the sympathetic nerves to the heart; infusion of acetylcholine
   B. stimulation of sympathetic nerves to the heart; infusion of a drug that blocks the effects of acetylcholine
   C. infusion of epinephrine; infusion of a drug that blocks the effects of acetylcholine
   D. infusion of a drug that blocks the effects of norepinephrine; cutting the vagus nerve
   E. stimulation of the vagus nerve; the infusion of epinephrine

2. **If no action potential reached the AV node, a QRS interval that is abnormally long would suggest that the ectopic pacemaker driving the ventricle is located:**

   A. in the common bundle of His
   B. just before the branch point for the left and right bundle of His
   C. in a Purkinje cell located at the end of the left bundle branch
   D. in the AV node
   E. in any ventricular area, but probably firing at a rate of > 70 beats/min

3. **In cardiac muscle, the strength of a contraction would be increased by all the following EXCEPT:**
   A. inhibition of Na:Ca exchange
   B. lengthening the sarcomeres
   C. phosphorylation of the SR calcium pump
   D. inhibition of the Na:K pump
   E. a decrease in heart rate

Questions 4–7. Refer to Fig. 2-1.

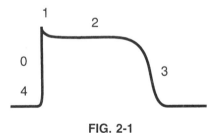

FIG. 2-1

4. **A decrease in potassium conductance is associated with which of the following phases of the ventricular action potential?**
   A. 0
   B. 1
   C. 2
   D. 3
   E. 4

5. **Phase 2 corresponds to which component of the EKG?**
   A. P-wave
   B. P-R interval
   C. QRS complex
   D. S-T segment
   E. T-wave

6. **An increase in sodium conductance produces which phase of the ventricular action potential?**
   A. 0
   B. 1
   C. 2
   D. 3
   E. 4

7. **What is the major effect that tetrodotoxin would have on the above action potential?**
   A. completely prevent the action potential
   B. decrease the slope of phase 0
   C. greatly suppress the amplitude of phase 2
   D. greatly prolong the duration of the action potential
   E. depolarize the membrane potential during phase 4

8. **During stimulation of the sympathetic nerves to the heart:**
   A. heart rate decreases
   B. heart rate increases, but contractility does not change
   C. heart rate and contractility increase
   D. heart rate and contractility decrease
   E. heart rate increases, but contractility decreases

9. **The electrical silence observed during the P-R interval is due to the fact that:**
   A. all the cardiac cells are at the resting membrane potential
   B. the action potential in AV node cells has a small magnitude
   C. the action potential is conducted through a small mass of tissue
   D. there is a lack of fast sodium channels in AV node cells
   E. all the ventricular muscle cells are depolarized

10. **Stimulation of the parasympathetic nerves to the heart has the greatest effect on the rate of action potential conduction in:**
    A. atrial muscle cells
    B. the AV node
    C. the bundle of His
    D. ventricular cells
    E. The effect is similar for all cardiac cells.

11. **Stimulation of the vagus nerve may result in a decrease in contractility of the ventricle because:**
    A. the muscle cells in the ventricles are heavily innervated by parasympathetic fibers, which directly inhibit calcium influx
    B. the decrease in heart rate leads to enhanced calcium efflux via the Na:Ca exchanger
    C. the decrease in heart rate leads to an increase in calcium influx via calcium channels
    D. acetylcholine causes a receptor-mediated inhibition of the calcium pump that is located on the SR
    E. The statement is false; stimulation of the vagus nerve increases the contractility of the ventricle because it enhances calcium influx.

Questions 12–17. Refer to Fig. 2-2.

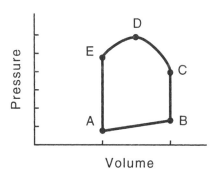

FIG. 2-2

12. **In a healthy individual at rest, which phase of the above pressure-volume loop occupies the most time?**
    A. A–B
    B. B–C
    C. C–D
    D. D–E
    E. E–A

13. **During which interval can dP/dt be used to evaluate the strength of myocardial contraction?**
    A. A–B
    B. B–C
    C. –D
    D. D–E
    E. E–A

14. **All the valves of the heart are closed during which of the following periods?**
    A. A–B
    B. C–D
    C. C–E
    D. D–E
    E. E–A

15. **Anemia produces an increased likelihood of a bruit in the base of the aorta. During which part of the pressure-volume loop would you expect to hear such a bruit?**
    A. A–B
    B. B–C
    C. C–D
    D. D–E
    E. E–A

16. **The mitral valve opens at which point on the pressure-volume loop?**
    A. A
    B. B
    C. C
    D. D
    E. E

17. **If only contractility increased before the next beat of this heart, you would expect for the next beat that:**
    A. point E would shift to the left
    B. point B would shift to the right
    C. point C would shift upward
    D. point C would shift downward
    E. stroke volume would decrease

18. **The following pairs relate a specific tissue to one of its most intense vasodilator stimuli. All the pairs are correct *EXCEPT*:**
    A. brain:hypocapnia
    B. intestine:ingested lipids
    C. skeletal muscle:metabolic factors
    D. skin:decreased sympathetic tone
    E. kidney:decrease in arterial pressure

19. **A resting normal adult receives an intravenous infusion of isotonic saline at a rate of 1 1/h over a three-hour period. This would cause:**
    A. reduction of plasma atrial natriuretic peptide (ANP)
    B. renal antidiuresis
    C. a significant rise of arterial pressure
    D. an increase of lymph flow
    E. a rise of plasma renin activity

20. **Which of the following is true about the baroreflex mechanism?**
    A. Acute increases in arterial pressure cause a decrease in heart rate.
    B. Acute increases in arterial pressure cause an increase in heart rate.
    C. Acute decreases in arterial pressure cause a decrease in heart rate.
    D. Acute changes in arterial pressure do not alter heart rate.
    E. Acute decreases in arterial pressure cause arterial vasodilation.

21. **An increase in the number of perfused capillaries:**
    A. decreases the oxygen diffusion distance
    B. increases the surface area for exchange
    C. increases the arterial oxygen content
    D. choices A and B only
    E. choices B and C only

22. **An *increase* in capillary filtration coefficient is likely to occur when:**
    A. plasma oncotic pressure falls
    B. the number of capillary pores increases
    C. interstitial fluid pressure rises
    D. capillary surface area decreases
    E. there is a decrease in arterial blood pressure

23. **Which of the following is most likely to produce delayed diastolic filling of the left ventricle?**
    A. aortic stenosis
    B. tricuspid regurgitation
    C. mitral stenosis
    D. pulmonic stenosis
    E. increasing heart rate from 80 to 100 beats/min

24. **Which of the following factors contribute(s) to the maintenance of balance between the outputs of the left and right ventricles?**
    A. reflex activity via sympathetic nerves
    B. reflex activity via parasympathetic nerves
    C. circulating epinephrine levels
    D. Frank-Starling law of the heart
    E. All of the above factors contribute.

25. **In a healthy individual, a 10 mm Hg increase in venous pressure across a skeletal muscle vascular bed will result in a decrease in its:**
    A. interstitial pressure
    B. interstitial volume
    C. interstitial protein concentration
    D. movement of fluid into its interstitial space
    E. lymph flow

26. **The amplitude of the pulse pressure in the aorta is:**
    A. directly proportional to stroke volume
    B. directly proportional to aortic capacitance
    C. directly proportional to peripheral resistance
    D. calculated by adding 1/3 of the difference between the systolic and the diastolic pressure to the diastolic pressure
    E. greater in the proximal than in the distal aorta

27. **All the following are true for the venous system compared to the arterial system *EXCEPT* that in the veins:**
    A. pressure is lower
    B. compliance is greater
    C. flow is greater
    D. blood volume is greater
    E. wall tension is less

28. **If cardiac output remained constant, a decrease in left ventricular end-diastolic volume would occur over time if:**
    A. contractility decreased
    B. the afterload on the heart decreased
    C. heart rate decreased
    D. a calcium channel blocking drug were administered
    E. None of the above would cause a decrease in left ventricular end-diastolic volume.

29. **A patient has a normal arterial blood pressure and cardiac output at rest, but the mitral valve is leaky (insufficient). You would expect all the following *EXCEPT*:**
    A. an increase in left ventricular end-diastolic pressure
    B. an increase in left ventricular end-diastolic volume
    C. a systolic murmur
    D. a decrease in afterload
    E. a decrease in mean pulmonary venous pressure

30. **An increase in preload alone should be associated with an increase in all the following *EXCEPT*:**
    A. stroke volume
    B. end-systolic volume
    C. arterial pulse pressure
    D. end-diastolic volume
    E. end-diastolic pressure

31. **A patient receives a transfusion of 1,000 ml of whole blood. Which of the following would be expected to decrease?**
    A. left atrial pressure
    B. cardiac output
    C. mean circulatory filling pressure
    D. arterial pressure
    E. arterial resistance

32. **A patient is inadvertently given an infusion of 1,000 ml of 0.9% saline. All of the following will help restore right atrial pressure to normal *EXCEPT*:**
    A. stress relaxation
    B. increase in capillary pressure
    C. increase in lymph flow
    D. increase in urine flow
    E. decrease in sympathetic nerve activity to peripheral venous tissues

33. **During the rapid ejection phase of the cardiac cycle:**
    A. the mitral valve is open
    B. aortic pressure is rising
    C. the aortic valve is closed
    D. ventricular volume is at its lowest volume
    E. the first heart sound starts during this phase

34. A patient absorbs 300 ml/min of oxygen. The oxygen content of blood taken from the femoral artery = 18 ml/100 ml; blood taken from the pulmonary artery has an oxygen content of 13 ml/100 ml; and blood taken from the femoral vein has an oxygen content of 140 ml/100 ml. If the patient has a heart rate of 60 beats per minute, the patient's stroke volume is:
  A. 10 ml
  B. 12.5 ml
  C. 80 ml
  D. 100 ml
  E. 120 ml

35. The viscosity of blood:
  A. increases when streaming occurs
  B. decreases with increases in hematocrit
  C. is less than that of plasma
  D. increases at very low flow rates
  E. has no influence on Reynolds' number

36. Assuming the arterial-venous pressure gradient remains constant, flow through a vessel will decrease:
  A. if a vessel in parallel constricts
  B. 8-fold if the radius is halved
  C. if the hematocrit is decreased
  D. 16-fold if the radius is doubled
  E. if another vessel is added in series

37. Assume at this point in the capillary network that filtration equals absorption, plasma oncotic pressure = 30 mm Hg, interstitial oncotic pressure = 8 mm Hg, and interstitial hydrostatic pressure = −2 mm Hg,. What is the capillary hydrostatic pressure (in mm Hg)?
  A. 20 mm Hg
  B. 22 mm Hg
  C. 24 mm Hg
  D. 36 mm Hg
  E. 40 mm Hg

38. An increase in protein concentration in the interstitial fluid would tend to cause all the following EXCEPT:
  A. an increase in lymph flow
  B. an increase in interstitial oncotic pressure
  C. a decrease in capillary filtration
  D. edema
  E. a decrease in net transcapillary oncotic pressure gradient

39. Vasoconstriction of all arterioles, with no change in aortic or venous pressure, would decrease all the following EXCEPT:
  A. cardiac output
  B. pressure at the venous end of the capillary
  C. filtration across capillaries
  D. pressure at the arterial end of the capillary
  E. arterial-venous oxygen difference.

40. Vascular permeability is highest in the:
  A. liver
  B. skin
  C. heart
  D. skeletal muscle
  E. kidney

41. The function of the papillary muscles and chordae tendinae is to:
  A. hold open the semilunar valves during systole
  B. keep the AV valves from bulging into the aorta and pulmonary arteries during systole
  C. keep the AV valves from bulging into the atria during ventricular contraction
  D. increase backflow into the ventricles during diastole
  E. hold the AV valves open during diastole

42. Under normal circumstances, the largest drop in blood pressure in the systemic circulatory system occurs over which of the following vascular segments?
  A. venae cavae
  B. small and large veins and venules
  C. aorta
  D. small arteries and arterioles
  E. capillaries and venules

43. In the SA node, the dominant event that causes the sharp change in membrane potential from −45 to +20 millivolts is the:
  A. opening of voltage-gated TTX (tetrodotoxin)-sensitive sodium channels
  B. opening of potassium channels
  C. opening of chloride channels
  D. opening of ligand-gated sodium channels
  E. opening of voltage-gated calcium channels

44. Even through blood pressure may fall as a result of hemorrhage, cerebral blood flow is maintained constant because of:
  A. autoregulation
  B. reactive hyperemia
  C. active hyperemia
  D. Starling equilibrium
  E. increased metabolism

45. All the following processes or mechanisms help the body regulate mean arterial blood pressure EXCEPT:

  A. sympathetic outflow to the splanchnic bed
  B. parasympathetic outflow to the heart
  C. activation of the renin-angiotensin system
  D. locally induced alteration in organ blood flow
  E. carotid baroreceptor

46. **In an otherwise healthy individual at rest, an increase in afterload is likely to be associated with all the following EXCEPT:**
    A. a decrease in stroke volume
    B. a decrease in ventricular end-diastolic volume
    C. an increase in diastolic blood pressure
    D. an increase in end-systolic volume
    E. an increase in cardiac mass

47. **When comparing the right ventricle to the left ventricle, all the following are true for the left ventricle EXCEPT:**
    A. muscle mass is greater in the left ventricle
    B. depolarization starts first in the left ventricle
    C. pressure generated in the left ventricle is greater
    D. the left ventricle does more work
    E. the left ventricle starts to eject blood first

48. **Endothelium-derived relaxing factor (EDRF) influences blood flow by:**
    A. increasing blood pressure
    B. directly increasing cardiac output
    C. dilating resistance vessels upstream of capillaries
    D. dilating capillaries
    E. decreasing tissue oxygen utilization

49. **The most important physiological regulator of resistance in cutaneous (skin) blood vessels is:**
    A. lactic acid
    B. adenosine
    C. potassium
    D. norepinephrine
    E. carbon dioxide

50. **During vigorous exercise, all the following organs are likely to have greatly increased blood flow EXCEPT the:**
    A. heart
    B. skeletal muscles
    C. lungs
    D. kidneys
    E. skin

Questions 51–52. Refer to Fig. 2-3.

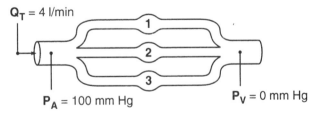

Q_T = 4 l/min

P_A = 100 mm Hg P_V = 0 mm Hg

FIG. 2-3

51. **If pressure at P_A and P_V remains constant, the resistance in circuit 1 is decreased, and the resistances in circuit 2 and 3 do not change, then:**
    A. flow through circuit 1 decreases
    B. flow through circuit 2 increases
    C. total flow (Q_T) increases
    D. none of the above occurred
    E. cannot determine from the data given

52. **If total flow (Q_T) remains constant, resistance in circuit 1 increases, and the resistances in circuit 2 and 3 do not change, then:**
    A. flow through circuit 1 decreases
    B. flow through circuit 2 decreases
    C. flow through circuit 3 decreases
    D. both B and C are correct
    E. P_A decreases

53. **When a well conditioned athlete at rest is placed in a warm environment, the following will occur:**
    A. increased total peripheral resistance
    B. decreased heart rate
    C. increased cardiac output
    D. increased blood pressure
    E. none of the above

54. **The major factor that explains the decrease of total peripheral resistance during exercise is:**
    A. decreased sympathetic nervous activity
    B. increased systemic filling pressure
    C. local regulation of the skeletal muscle vascular bed
    D. increased arterial pressure
    E. increased muscle capillary hydrostatic pressure

Questions 55–57. Refer to Fig. 2-4.

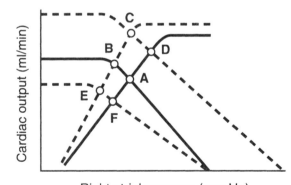

Right atrial pressure (mm Hg)

FIG. 2-4

SECTION I: QUESTIONS

The following represent various cardiovascular changes shown in Fig. 2-4. Please match the moves shown below with the statements given subsequently. Assume that unmentioned variables are constant.
A. A to C
B. A to B
C. C to D
D. A to F
E. E to A

55. Increased blood volume together with increased contractility:

56. Increased parasympathetic nerve activity to heart together with decreased arterial resistance:

57. Increased peripheral resistance:

58. A patient receives a strong blow to the head and is brought to the hospital, complaining of headache and various neurological symptoms. Upon examination, you find a blood pressure of 220/160 (this patient's normal value is 120/80). Appropriate treatment for this patient is:
A. intravenous infusion of a drug that decreases arterial pressure
B. intravenous infusion of a drug that increases renal function
C. an X-ray to determine whether the patient has a subdural hematoma
D. using leeches to decrease blood volume
E. intravenous infusion of a drug that dilates the arterioles

59. A 25% loss of blood volume is likely to:
A. increase unstressed volume
B. decrease the plasma levels of vasopressin
C. increase tissue interstitial pressure
D. increase the plasma levels of angiotensin II
E. increase the plasma levels of ANF

60. Assuming that cardiovascular reflexes are allowed to operate, a decrease in cardiac output due to an infarct is likely to cause an increase in all the following EXCEPT:
A. parasympathetic nerve activity
B. venous pressure
C. mean systemic filling pressure
D. release of renin
E. heart rate

61. The QT interval shortens with increases in heart rate because:
A. norepinephrine directly shortens the duration of ventricular muscle action potentials
B. the duration of ventricular muscle cell action potentials intrinsically decreases as heart rate increases
C. parasympathetic stimulation shortens the duration of ventricular muscle action potentials
D. sodium channels inactivate faster as heart rate increases
E. potassium channels fail to open during the plateau phase (phase 2) of the ventricular action potential

62. Increasing the rate at which cardiac muscle cells are electrically stimulated causes the strength of contraction to (X) because the amount of calcium that (Y) during phase 4 (Z)

	X	Y	Z
A.	increase	influxes	increases
B.	increase	influxes	decreases
C.	increase	effluxes	decreases
D.	decrease	effluxes	increases
E.	increase	influxes	remains constant

Question 63. Refer to Fig. 2-5.

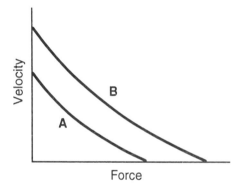

FIG. 2-5

63. Which of the following would cause the heart to go from curve A to curve B in Fig. 2-5?
A. activation of the parasympathetic nervous system
B. infusion of a drug that blocks calcium channels
C. release of epinephrine from the adrenal medulla
D. decrease in the intracellular sodium concentration
E. infusion of an acetylcholine esterase inhibitor

64. An increase in preload is likely to be associated with:

A. a decrease in stroke volume
B. an increase in end systolic volume
C. a decrease in diastolic arterial blood pressure
D. a decrease in ventricular end diastolic volume
E. an increase in the ejection fraction

Questions 65–67. Refer to Fig. 2-6.

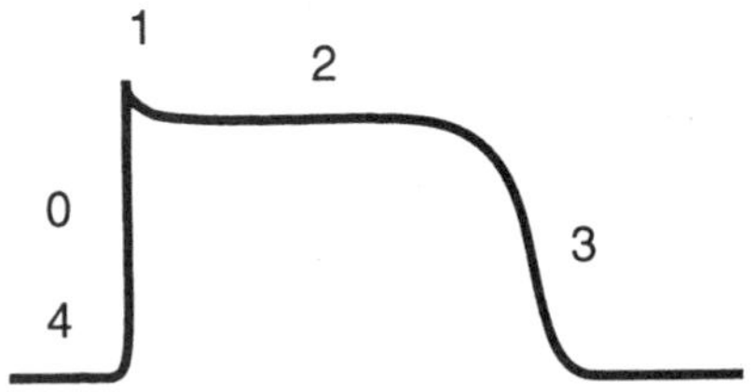

FIG. 2-6

Questions 70–71. Refer to Fig. 2-7.

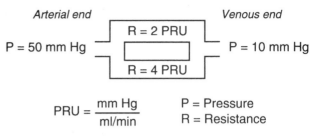

FIG. 2-7

65. The T wave of the EKG is caused by which phase of the ventricular action potential?
   A. 1
   B. 2
   C. 3
   D. 4
   E. none of the above

66. The P wave of the EKG is caused by which phase of the ventricular action potential?
   A. 1
   B. 2
   C. 3
   D. 4
   E. none of the above

67. A change in extracellular potassium concentration would have the greatest effect on which phase of the ventricular action potential?
   A. 1
   B. 2
   C. 3
   D. 4
   E. none of the above

68. A patient's EKG has an upward deflection of the P wave in the lead II and lead III recordings, but no P wave is present in the lead I recording. The most likely cause is:
   A. atrial repolarization occurs completely vertically
   B. atrial depolarization occurs completely horizontally
   C. ventricular depolarization occurs completely horizontally
   D. atrial repolarization occurs completely horizontally
   E. atrial depolarization occurs completely vertically

69. An increase in the rate of intraventricular pressure development during isovolumic contractions could be caused by:
   A. inhibition of the Na:Ca exchanger
   B. a decrease in afterload
   C. stimulation of the parasympathetic vagus nerve
   D. decreasing the heart rate
   E. increasing the duration of ventricular action potentials

70. Total flow through this network would equal:
   A. 6.67 ml/min
   B. 53.3 ml/min
   C. 37.5 ml/min
   D. 30 ml/min
   E. 15 ml/min

71. If the pressure at the venous end increased from 10 to 20 mm Hg without any changes in resistance, the flow through the vessel with a resistance of 2 PRU would equal:
   A. 7.5 ml/min
   B. 22.5 ml/min
   C. 5 ml/min
   D. 11.25 ml/min
   E. 15 ml/min

72. The coronary circulation has a relatively high resistance to blood flow because:
   A. coronary blood vessels are smaller in diameter than blood vessels to other organs
   B. cardiac venous pressure is less than that in other organs
   C. perfusion of the left ventricle occurs mainly during diastole
   D. epinephrine, which dilates the blood vessels in other organs, causes constriction in the heart
   E. coronary blood vessels are especially sensitive to the constrictor effect of angiotensin II

73. Blood flow to resting skeletal muscles is:
   A. independent of the central nervous system
   B. likely to decrease with increased carotid sinus nerve activity
   C. likely to increase in response to locally administered norepinephrine
   D. likely to increase in response to locally administered vasopressin
   E. none of the above

74. Decreased blood volume is likely to be associated with all the following EXCEPT:
   A. decreased arterial blood pressure
   B. increased systemic filling pressure
   C. decreased firing of the carotid sinus nerve
   D. reabsorption of interstitial fluid into the vascular compartment
   E. increased heart rate

SECTION I: QUESTIONS

75. If heart rate, end-diastolic pressure, and total periph-eral resistance remain constant but mean arterial pressure increases, which of the following must also occur?
   A. decreased venous return
   B. decreased mean venous pressure
   C. decreased end-systolic volume
   D. increased right atrial pressure
   E. decreased stroke work

Questions 76–77. Refer to the renal function curves in Fig. 2-8.

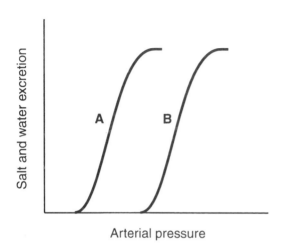

FIG. 2-8

76. A hypothetical substance shifts the renal function curve from A to B. Assuming that caloric, salt, and water intakes remain constant, this causes:
   A. a long-term reduction in arterial blood pressure
   B. an initial decrease of renal salt and water excretion
   C. an decrease in body weight
   D. a decrease in arterial resistance
   E. none of the above

77. All the following may be true for this hypothetical substance EXCEPT:
   A. it may be a diuretic acting on the distal nephron
   B. it may stimulate hormone secretion by glomerulosa cells
   C. it may increase the secretion of renin
   D. it may vasoconstrict the afferent arteriole
   E. it may increase secretion from the adrenal medulla

78. A generalized systemic inflammatory condition (known as anaphylaxis) will cause:
   A. increased renal fluid output
   B. hypertension
   C. decreased blood volume
   D. decreased interstitial fluid pressure
   E. increased level of atrial natriuretic factor

79. An individual with anaphylaxis (see question 78) would benefit from all of the following EXCEPT:
   A. an intravenous infusion of fluid having a high protein content
   B. a drug that increases arterial resistance
   C. a drug that decreases capillary permeability
   D. a drug that decreases heart rate
   E. a drug that increases cardiac contractility

80. A drug that reduces arrhythmia could act by:
   A. decreasing (making more negative) the threshold for calcium channels
   B. shortening the duration of the relative refractory period
   C. partially inhibiting the K_1 potassium channel
   D. activating β-adrenergic receptors in the heart
   E. activating muscarinic receptors in the heart

81. An inverted T wave (downward deflection) in the EKG would most likely be caused by:
   A. ventricular repolarization occurring from endocardium to epicardium
   B. ventricular repolarization occurring from epicardium to endocardium
   C. ventricular depolarization occurring from epicardium to endocardium
   D. ventricular depolarization occurring from endocardium to epicardium
   E. an abnormal delay in AV nodal conduction

82. The average critical closing pressure of an arterial bed is about _____ mm Hg and would be significantly (higher or lower) if the sympathetic nerves were stimulated.

	Average Closing Pressure	Effect of Sympathetic Nerve Stimulation
A.	0 mm Hg	Higher
B.	7 mm Hg	Higher
C.	7 mm Hg	Lower
D.	20 mm Hg	Higher
E.	20 mm Hg	Lower

83. Which of the following is most likely to produce a diastolic murmur?
   A. aortic stenosis
   B. pulmonic stenosis
   C. ventricular septal defect
   D. mitral stenosis
   E. tricuspid regurgitation

Questions 84–85. Refer to Fig. 2-9 showing a slow action potential for a normal individual with a heart rate of 60 beats/min.

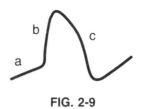

FIG. 2-9

84. Blocking the parasympathetic activity to the heart would:
   A. increase the height of the depolarization in phase b
   B. make the threshold of the action potential more positive
   C. increase the rate of depolarization during phase a
   D. prolong the duration of the action potential
   E. increase the interval between action potentials

85. Voltage-gated sodium channels that can be blocked with tetrodotoxin are responsible for phase:
   A. phase a
   B. phase b
   C. phase c
   D. Voltage-gated sodium channels are not involved in action potentials in sinoatrial cells

86. Compared to sinoatrial cells, ventricular contractile cells will have:
   A. an action potential with a shorter duration
   B. a more negative resting membrane potential
   C. a slower depolarization during the action potential
   D. a slower conduction velocity
   E. a smaller amplitude action potential

87. The tension in the wall of an aneurysm *increases* with:

   A. increasing luminal diameter
   B. decreasing transmural pressure
   C. increasing wall thickness
   D. decreasing intravascular pressure
   E. increasing interstitial pressure

Questions 88–89. Please refer to Fig. 2-10. The solid lines refer to the normal situation, while the dashed lines refer to an undiagnosed pathologic situation.

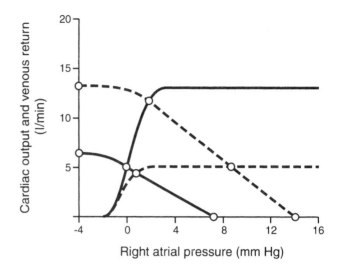

FIG. 2-10

88. This individual's normal values for cardiac output, right atrial pressure, and mean systemic filling pressure are, respectively:
   A. 4.5 l/min, 1 mm Hg, and 7 mm Hg
   B. 5 l/min, 0 mm Hg, and 7 mm Hg
   C. 5 l/min, 9 mm Hg, and 14 mm Hg
   D. 12 l/min, 8 mm Hg, and 14 mm Hg
   E. 12 l/min, 0 mm Hg, and 7 mm Hg

89. The most likely explanation for the change in cardiac output for an individual with cardiac function and venous return curves indicated by the dashed lines is:

   A. increased arterial resistance and decreased contractility
   B. increased venomotor tone and decreased contractility
   C. increased venomotor tone and decreased myocardial fiber length
   D. increased arterial resistance and increased extracardiac pressure
   E. increased arterial resistance and increased myocardial fiber length

SECTION I: QUESTIONS

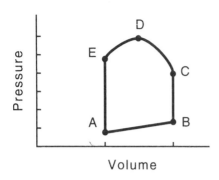

FIG. 2-11

90. If only afterload increased before the next beat of this heart, you would expect for the next beat that:
    A. point E would shift to the left
    B. point B would shift to the right
    C. point A would shift to the left
    D. point C would shift downward
    E. stroke volume would decrease

91. If only preload increased before the next beat of this heart, you would expect for the next beat that:
    A. point E would shift to the left
    B. point B would shift to the right
    C. point A would shift to the left
    D. point C would shift downward
    E. stroke volume would decrease

92. A patient develops an insufficient (leaky) aortic valve. Where along the pressure-volume loop would you expect to hear a murmur?
    A. B–C
    B. C–D
    C. C–E
    D. E–A
    E. E–B

93. A patient develops an insufficient (leaky) mitral valve. You would expect to hear a murmur during all phases of the pressure-volume loop *EXCEPT:*
    A. A–B
    B. B–C
    C. B–E
    D. E–A
    E. E–B

94. A patient develops a stenosis of the mitral valve. You would expect to hear a murmur during which phases of the pressure-volume loop?
    A. A–B
    B. B–C
    C. C–D
    D. D–E
    E. E–A

95. A patient develops a stenosis of the aortic valve. You would expect to hear a murmur during which phase of the pressure-volume loop?
    A. A–B
    B. B–C
    C. C–E
    D. E–A

96. When systemic arterial blood pressure increases, the myogenic response:
    A. is inhibited by elevations in circulating angiotensin II produced by the blood vessel renin-angiotensin system
    B. augments the rise in arterial pressure by redistributing blood from veins to arteries, thus increasing venous return and causing a rise in cardiac output
    C. reduces the luminal diameter of arterioles, which causes a rise in total peripheral resistance and thus a normalization of blood flow
    D. acts to maintain blood flow to the brain and heart and thus balances the demands of an increased sympathetic nerve activity
    E. all of the above

97. A patient with no baroreceptor function would most likely suffer from:
    A. hypertension
    B. hypotension
    C. increased blood pressure lability
    D. no obvious problem in regulating arterial blood pressure

98. Which of the following is most likely to produce sinus bradycardia (rate below 60/min)?
    A. removal of three units of blood
    B. moderate exercise
    C. standing erect from a supine position
    D. carotid sinus massage
    E. painful fracture of left arm

99. The blood-brain barrier:
    A. is part of the cerebral autoregulatory system that protects the brain from large increases in arterial pressure
    B. occurs because cerebral arterioles are surrounded by a thick basement membrane and a large mass of vascular smooth muscle
    C. is produced by the impermeable type IV collagen secreted by cerebral endothelial cells
    D. results in a diminished movement of vasoactive peptides into the brain tissue
    E. none of the above

100. Which of the following is most likely to occur in anaphylactic shock?
    A. a rise in total peripheral resistance and a rise in the resistance to venous return
    B. hypotension and tachycardia
    C. reduced plasma levels of angiotensin and aldosterone
    D. a decrease in hematocrit
    E. none of the above

101. **Left ventricular heart failure is associated with an increased:**
    A. left ventricular contractility
    B. left ventricular end-diastolic pressure
    C. left ventricular stroke volume
    D. output from the right heart
    E. venous return

102. **During a run of several miles at a strenuous pace, all the following hemodynamic variables would be elevated EXCEPT:**
    A. mean systemic filling pressure
    B. arterial blood pressure
    C. stroke volume
    D. cerebral blood flow
    E. coronary blood flow

103. **Under normal physiological conditions, the most important underlying determinant of cardiac output is:**
    A. mean systemic pressure
    B. blood volume
    C. heart rate
    D. stroke volume
    E. V_{O_2}

Questions 104–107. An adult man weighing 70 kg and having a normal resting cardiac output of 5 l/min has been observed to have a long-standing (years) elevation of his aortic systolic pressure (160 mm Hg) and a diastolic pressure of 55 mm Hg. Match the following words and phrases to questions 104–107.
    A. renal hypertension
    B. normal flow
    C. laminar flow
    D. turbulent flow
    E. atherosclerosis
    F. high sympathetic nerve activity
    G. arterial-venous fistula
    H. aortic valve regurgitation
    I. aortic stenosis
    J. increased
    K. decreased
    L. normal

104. **What is the most likely diagnosis?**

105. **Upon x-ray of the heart, the size of the left ventricle would be:**

106. **Stroke volume of this patient would be:**

107. **You would expect the mean arterial pressure to be:**

108. **Stroke work of the human left ventricle is likely increased by:**
    A. severe hemorrhage
    B. ventricular tachycardia (heart rate >250/min)
    C. pulmonary valve stenosis
    D. mitral stenosis
    E. chronic hypertension

109. **Which of the following is most likely seen in ventricular septal defect without cyanosis?**
    A. a decrease in pulmonary artery pressure
    B. a decrease in oxygen saturation of left ventricular blood
    C. a mid-diastolic heart murmur
    D. an increase in oxygen saturation of right ventricular blood
    E. a decrease in right ventricular stroke work

110. **All the following will be found in aortic stenosis EXCEPT:**
    A. increased left ventricular stroke work
    B. increased rate of rise in systolic aortic blood pressure
    C. increased systolic pressure gradient across the aortic valve
    D. EKG evidence of left axis deviation
    E. a systolic ejection heart murmur

111. **Which of the following is likely to exhibit the shortest phase 4 of the cardiac action potential?**
    A. Purkinje fiber
    B. SA node cell
    C. atrial muscle
    D. ventricular muscle
    E. AV node cell

112. **According to the Laplace relation for the heart, if pressure doubles and the radius of the left ventricle remains constant, what must happen to wall thickness for wall tension to remain constant?**
    A. increase 1.5-fold
    B. increase 2-fold
    C. increase 4-fold
    D. decrease 2-fold
    E. decrease 4-fold

113. **Movement of fluid from the capillaries to the interstitial space:**
    A. occurs because the capillary wall is only slightly permeable to fluid
    B. occurs when the balance of forces favors filtration over reabsorption
    C. requires that the capillary wall be impermeable
    D. occurs only in cases that produce edema, such as heart failure or hypertension

114. **Blood flow to skeletal muscle:**
   A. accounts for approximately 70% of the cardiac output at rest
   B. is greater at rest than renal blood flow on a per gram basis
   C. stays constant during exercise because oxygen extraction increases
   D. is elevated in chronically hypertensive patients
   E. depends primarily on local metabolic activity

115. **Which of the following is most likely associated with an increase in the area under the left ventricular pressure-volume loop, left axis deviation in the EKG pattern, and a systolic ejection murmur?**
   A. mitral stenosis
   B. tricuspid stenosis
   C. aortic regurgitation
   D. pulmonic regurgitation
   E. aortic stenosis

116. **Complete left bundle branch block is most likely associated with which of the following EKG changes?**
   A. prolonged duration of QRS complex
   B. increased amplitude of T wave
   C. lengthened ST interval
   D. prolonged P-R interval
   E. elevated ST segment

117. **Which of the following principles puts a dilated heart at a clear disadvantage?**
   A. Starling's law of the heart
   B. Poiseuille's law
   C. Fick's law
   D. Laplace's law
   E. Reynolds' number

118. **Rapid expansion of extracellular volume is compensated for by all the following EXCEPT:**
   A. increased secretion of atrial natriuretic peptide
   B. reduced secretion of renin
   C. reduced secretion of vasopressin
   D. increased renal sympathetic nerve activity
   E. reduced aldosterone secretion

119. **Drugs that block L-type calcium channels would be expected to:**
   A. increase heart rate by enhancing the firing rate of the sinoatrial node
   B. trigger vasoconstriction
   C. lower blood pressure
   D. increase the force of contraction of the heart
   E. lengthen the plateau phase of the cardiac action potential

120. **The portion of the cardiac conductile system with the slowest rate of conduction is the:**
   A. atrial muscle
   B. atrioventricular node
   C. bundle of His
   D. Purkinje system
   E. ventricular muscle

121. **What effect does tetrodotoxin (TTX) have on the firing rate of isolated sinoatrial nodal cells?**
   A. increases the rate
   B. decreases the rate
   C. no change in rate

Questions 122–126. These questions concern the cardiac action potential and related electrophysiological occurrences. Match the ionic events listed below (phrases A–L) to the items in questions 122–125. A phrase may be used once, twice, or not at all. Some questions may be answered by two phrases.
   A. decrease in the outward potassium current
   B. increase in the outward potassium current
   C. decrease in the inward potassium current
   D. increase in the inward potassium current
   E. decrease in the inward fast sodium current
   F. increase in the inward fast sodium current
   G. decrease in the outward fast sodium current
   H. increase in the outward fast sodium current
   I. decrease in the inward calcium current
   J. increase in the inward calcium current
   K. decrease in the outward calcium current
   L. increase in the outward calcium current

122. **The early-to-mid portion of the pacemaker potential of the sinoatrial node:**

123. **The QRS complex of the electrocardiogram:**

124. **The T wave of the electrocardiogram:**

125. **The ST segment of the EKG:**

126. **The "rapid" upstroke of the sinoatrial nodal action potential:**

127. **Which of the following produces a decrease in the slope of phase 4 depolarization of SA node pacemaker cells?**
   A. direct application of epinephrine
   B. direct application of norepinephrine
   C. cardiac sympathetic nerve stimulation
   D. direct application of acetylcholine
   E. direct application of atropine

Use Fig. 2-12 to answer questions 128–129.

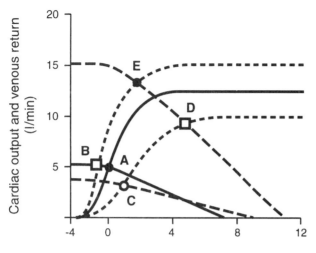

FIG. 2-12

128. Which point would represent the expected value for cardiac output during the first 10 minutes of an angiotensin II infusion? (Assume no direct cardiac effects of angiotensin II, but that all compensatory cardiovascular systems are working.)
   A. point A
   B. point B
   C. point C
   D. point D
   E. point E

129. Point B in Fig. 2-12 could best be described as the cardiac output during:
   A. acute volume expansion
   B. withdrawal of cardiac vagal tone
   C. moderate sustained isometric exercise
   D. left ventricular heart failure
   E. an i.v. infusion of norepinephrine

130. At a heart rate of 70 beats/min, coronary artery blood flow is greatest:
   A. immediately after the second heart sound
   B. when dP/dt has reached its maximum
   C. immediately after the mitral valve has closed
   D. immediately after the aortic valve has opened
   E. during the rapid ejection phase of the cardiac cycle

131. An increase in arterial pulse pressure is mostly like to be found in:
   A. aortic insufficiency
   B. aortic stenosis
   C. mitral insufficiency
   D. mitral stenosis
   E. pulmonary insufficiency

132. A person with no innervation of the heart and a person with a normally innervated heart run at an identical pace. Which of the following would be greater in the person with no innervation of the heart?
   A. blood flow to the active muscle masses
   B. venous return
   C. stroke volume
   D. cardiac output
   E. heart rate

133. Closure of the aortic valve is associated with all the following EXCEPT:
   A. dicrotic notch on the aortic pressure wave
   B. the second heart sound
   C. relaxation of the ventricle
   D. rapid filling of the left ventricle
   E. T-wave of the EKG

134. A decrease in cardiac output due to a large hemorrhage that results in a sustained decrease in arterial blood pressure is likely to be associated with a decrease in all the following EXCEPT:
   A. parasympathetic nerve activity
   B. venous pressure
   C. mean systemic filling pressure
   D. release of renin
   E. plasma pH

135. A generalized systemic inflammatory condition (known as anaphylaxis) will cause all the following EXCEPT:
   A. increased sympathetic nerve activity
   B. arterial vasodilatation
   C. decreased blood volume
   D. protein accumulation in the interstitial fluid
   E. increased level of atrial natriuretic factor

136. All patients in shock are suffering from an inadequate cardiac output. The intravenous infusion of fluid to help restore blood pressure is logical for all types of shock EXCEPT:
   A. anaphylactic shock
   B. cardiogenic shock
   C. loss of autonomic control due to a CNS lesion
   D. hemorrhagic shock
   E. shock induced by severe burns

137. All of the following are likely to occur in hemorrhagic shock EXCEPT:
   A. a rise in total peripheral resistance
   B. hypotension and tachycardia
   C. increased plasma levels of angiotensin
   D. a decrease in hematocrit
   E. increased mean systemic filling pressure

138. **Left ventricular heart failure due to a stenotic aortic valve is associated with:**
    A. eccentric hypertrophy
    B. pulmonary edema
    C. decreased pulmonary wedge pressure
    D. expanded jugular neck veins when the patient is in the upright position
    E. increased diastolic compliance

139. **In a patient suffering from heart failure induced by a stenotic pulmonary valve, all the following procedures or treatments might be beneficial *EXCEPT*:**
    A. administering digitalis
    B. administering a diuretic
    C. administering a catecholamine
    D. administering an angiotensin-converting enzyme inhibitor
    E. placing the patient on a low-salt diet

140. **In an arterial blood sample, which of the following would be expected to decrease during hemorrhagic shock?**
    A. epinephrine
    B. angiotensin II
    C. anion gap
    D. P_{CO_2}
    E. cortisol

141. **At rest, patients with a mild form of right ventricular congestive heart failure will have:**
    A. hypotension
    B. elevated central venous pressure
    C. reduced cardiac output
    D. increased cardiac reserve
    E. elevated left atrial pressure

RESPIRATORY PHYSIOLOGY

1. **Pulmonary edema forms preferentially at the lung base because:**
   A. P_{O_2} is less at the base
   B. P_{CO_2} is higher at the base
   C. intravascular pressure is greater at the base
   D. lymphatic drainage is less at the base
   E. vascular resistance is higher at the base

2. **If $PA_{O_2} = 200$ mm Hg and $PA_{CO_2} = 20$ mm Hg, what is PI_{O_2}?**
   A. 180 mm Hg
   B. 225 mm Hg
   C. 153 mm Hg
   D. 250 mm Hg
   E. 32 mm Hg

3. **An increase in Pa_{CO_2} is caused by:**
   A. decreased diffusing capacity for CO
   B. increased V_{CO_2}/V_A
   C. increased shunt fraction
   D. V_A/Q mismatch
   E. decreased physiological dead space

4. **The normal pattern of phrenic nerve activity is generated by impulses from the:**
   A. pons
   B. cerebrum
   C. medulla
   D. cerebellum
   E. hypothalamus

5. **Contraction of the diaphragm would cause:**
   A. a decrease in the volume of air in the lungs
   B. an increase in airways pressure
   C. a decrease in intrapleural pressure
   D. movement of the ribs toward the spinal cord
   E. a decrease in intraabdominal pressure

6. **The V_A of an 80-inch tall, 200-pound man with a tidal volume of 700 ml and a breathing rate of 20 breaths/min is about:**
   A. 140,000 ml/min
   B. 12,400 ml/min
   C. 4,000 ml/min
   D. 10,000 ml/min
   E. 14,000 ml/min

7. **On the accompanying compliance curve of a lung, the middle of expiration is:**

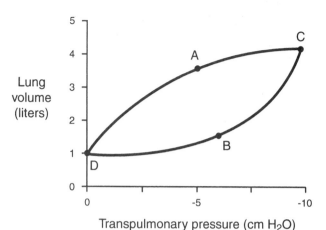

FIG. 3-1

   A. A
   B. B
   C. C
   D. D

8. **All the following are true of V_A and Q in the lungs of a healthy, standing individual *EXCEPT*:**
   A. Q is greater at the base than at the apex
   B. V_A is greater at the apex than at the base
   C. V_A/Q is greater at the apex than at the base
   D. differences in V_A/Q from apex to base are less during exercise
   E. the V_A/Q distribution causes higher PA_{O_2} at the apex than at the base

9. **If the P_{O_2} in a blood sample is not changed, which of the following will cause a decrease in the content of oxygen in the blood?**
   A. an increase in 2,3 diphosphoglycerate (DPG)
   B. a decrease in temperature
   C. an increase in pH
   D. a decrease in P_{CO_2}
   E. an increase in hemoglobin

10. **Most of the lung volume is in the:**
   A. alveoli
   B. bronchioles
   C. segmental bronchi
   D. lobar bronchi
   E. trachea

11. If the water vapor pressure in saturated air is 47 mm Hg when barometric pressure is 760 mm Hg and the temperature is 37°C, what is the water vapor pressure at 380 mm Hg in saturated air at the same temperature?
   A. 47 mm Hg
   B. 23.5 mm Hg
   C. 35.3 mm Hg
   D. 11.8 mm Hg
   E. Insufficient information is available to answer.

12. One hundred percent O_2 administration will reverse hypoxemia in all of the following conditions EXCEPT:
   A. arterial–venous shunt
   B. V_A/Q mismatch
   C. hypoventilation
   D. decreased D_{CO}
   E. loss of cabin pressure in an airplane

13. To accomplish a metabolic compensation for a respiratory acidosis, there would be:
   A. an increase in plasma bicarbonate
   B. a decrease in plasma bicarbonate
   C. an increase in Pa_{CO_2}
   D. a decrease in Pa_{CO_2}
   E. a decrease in hemoglobin concentration

14. If one were to inflate the lungs of a lightly anesthetized adult human to 2 liters over FRC:
   A. a forced expiration would occur within 10 sec
   B. no breathing movements would occur after 10 sec
   C. rapid inspiratory and expiratory movements would occur within 10 sec
   D. inspiration would continue for about 1 more liter
   E. airways resistance would be increased from the value at FRC

15. All else being equal, which of the following gases will equilibrate most quickly across an alveolar membrane?
   A. O_2
   B. He
   C. CO
   D. CO_2
   E. All gases diffuse at the same rate.

16. Airways resistance:
   A. is greater during inspiration than during expiration
   B. is lower when near FRC than when near TLC
   C. is increased by sympathetic stimulation
   D. is decreased in asthma
   E. is increased by histamine

17. The equilibrium point of the lungs and chest wall is at:
   A. residual volume
   B. tidal volume
   C. total lung capacity
   D. functional residual capacity
   E. vital capacity

18. Which of the following is transformed to the active state during passage through the pulmonary circulation?
   A. angiotensin I
   B. norepinephrine
   C. vasopressin
   D. endothelin I
   E. prostaglandin E_2

19. Occlusion of the left pulmonary artery would cause:
   A. an increase in shunt fraction
   B. an increase in PI_{O_2}
   C. an increase in anatomical dead space
   D. a decrease in anatomical dead space
   E. an increase in physiological dead space

20. All the following will cause an increase in pulmonary vascular resistance EXCEPT:
   A. a decrease in Pa_{O_2}
   B. a decrease in Pa_{CO_2}
   C. a decrease in FI_{O_2}
   D. a decrease in cardiac output
   E. a decrease in arterial pH

21. Which of the following is always true of normal blood?
   A. An increase in P_{CO_2} causes an increase in Cl^- inside red blood cells.
   B. An increase in P_{CO_2} causes a decrease in HCO_3^- inside red blood cells.
   C. A decrease in P_{CO_2} causes a decrease in O_2 bound to hemoglobin.
   D. The P_{CO_2} inside the red blood cell is higher than in the plasma.
   E. The P_{O_2} inside the red blood cell is higher than in the plasma.

22. When people are very cold, their lips and nail beds may turn blue. This occurs because:
   A. the rate of oxygen removal from the blood is increased
   B. skin metabolism is decreased
   C. the oxygen dissociation curve is shifted to the left by a decrease in temperature
   D. the blood pH is increased by a decrease in temperature
   E. deoxygenated hemoglobin has a different three-dimensional structure than oxygenated hemoglobin

23. **During acclimation to altitude:**
    A. the sensitivity of carotid bodies to hypoxia increases
    B. the sensitivity of central chemoreceptors to hypoxia increases
    C. the sensitivity of carotid sinuses to hypoxia increases
    D. the HCO_3^- concentration in the blood increases
    E. the HCO_3^- concentration in the brain decreases

24. **Which of the following arterial gases and pH most likely were obtained from a person who arrived at an altitude of 10,000 ft. 30 min before the sample was taken?**

	P_{O_2}	P_{CO_2}	pH
A.	55	36	7.42
B.	70	20	7.42
C.	33	50	7.28
D.	70	20	7.53
E.	55	25	7.53

25. **Chronic severe hypoxia would be expected to cause or lead to all of the following EXCEPT:**
    A. pulmonary hypertension
    B. right ventricular hypertrophy
    C. increase in mean circulatory filling pressure
    D. decrease in right ventricular end diastolic pressure
    E. increase in hematocrit

26. **Which of the following would cause the greatest immediate increase in V_A?**
    A. an increase in arterial pressure to 150 mm Hg evoked by i.v. injection of saline
    B. ventilation with 10% O_2
    C. ventilation with 10% CO_2
    D. injection of mild acid to decrease arterial pH to 7.30
    E. ventilation with 80% N_2, 20% O_2

27. **All the following are true of pulmonary surfactant EXCEPT that it:**
    A. floats on water
    B. is lipoproteinaceous
    C. is formed in alveolar type II cells
    D. decreases lung compliance
    E. is insufficient in premature babies

28. **In an individual with an obstructive ventilatory defect, all the following would be increased EXCEPT:**
    A. TLC
    B. FRC
    C. FEV_1
    D. RV
    E. airways resistance

29. **If the barometric pressure is 300 mm Hg, the PI_{O_2} of a healthy subject will be:**
    A. 63 mm Hg
    B. 53 mm Hg
    C. 3 mm Hg
    D. 13 mm Hg
    E. 45 mm Hg

30. **According to Fick's Law, if the partial pressure difference across a membrane does not change but both the surface area and thickness are doubled, the rate of transfer of the gas across the membrane will:**
    A. be halved
    B. be doubled
    C. increase 4-fold
    D. decrease 4-fold
    E. not change

31. **Which of the following changes in P_{O_2} would have the greatest effect on the amount of O_2 (ml O_2/100 ml) in the blood?**
    A. from 0 mm Hg to 20 mm Hg
    B. from 20 mm Hg to 40 mm Hg
    C. from 50 mm Hg to 70 mm Hg
    D. from 80 mm Hg to 100 mm Hg
    E. from 100 mm Hg to 150 mm Hg

32. **If a person with PA_{O_2} = 125 mm Hg and PA_{CO_2} = 20 mm Hg doubles V_A without changing metabolic rate, PA_{O_2} will become:**
    A. 75 mm Hg
    B. 110 mm Hg
    C. 115 mm Hg
    D. 132 mm Hg
    E. 138 mm Hg

33. **An individual has a residual volume of 2 liters, a vital capacity of 6 liters, and a functional residual capacity of 3 liters. What is the total lung capacity?**
    A. 3 liters
    B. 4 liters
    C. 8 liters
    D. 9 liters
    E. 11 liters

34. **All the following are true of pulmonary vascular resistance EXCEPT that it:**
    A. increases with increasing cardiac output
    B. increases with decreasing Pa_{O_2}
    C. increases with increasing Pa_{CO_2}
    D. is greater at the top than at the bottom of the lungs
    E. is more affected by alveolar gases than by blood gases

35. **FEF 25–75% (MMFR) is a reflection of:**
    A. lung compliance only
    B. airways resistance only
    C. both lung compliance and airways resistance
    D. expiratory muscle force
    E. CO_2 retention

36. **A patient has the following blood gases and pH: Pa$_{CO_2}$ = 64 mm Hg, Pa$_{CO_2}$ = 62 mm Hg, pH = 7.36. Which of the following best fits these data?**
   A. respiratory compensation for hypoxemia
   B. respiratory compensation for metabolic alkalosis
   C. metabolic compensation for respiratory acidosis
   D. uncompensated metabolic acidosis
   E. uncompensated respiratory acidosis

37. **All the following can be measured with just an air-filled spirometer EXCEPT:**
   A. FRC
   B. FEV$_1$
   C. FVC
   D. tidal volume
   E. FEF 25–75% (MMFR)

38. **A patient has the following blood gases and pH:**
   Pa$_{O_2}$ = 48 mm Hg
   Pa$_{CO_2}$ = 43 mm Hg
   pH = 7.38
   The patient was placed on a ventilator and given 100% O$_2$. The blood gases became:
   Pa$_{O_2}$ = 68 mm Hg
   Pa$_{CO_2}$ = 36 mm Hg
   pH = 7.41
   You should conclude that the patient's primary (i.e., most severe) problem is:
   A. hypoventilation
   B. a shunt
   C. V$_A$/Q mismatch
   D. an obstructive ventilatory defect
   E. anemia

39. **A diver is breathing 10% O$_2$ at a pressure of 1,500 mm Hg. The diver's body temperature is 37°C, and Pa$_{CO_2}$ = 32 mm Hg. What is the Pa$_{O_2}$?**
   A. 63 mm Hg
   B. 105 mm Hg
   C. 110 mm Hg
   D. 113 mm Hg
   E. 145 mm Hg

40. **Bacteria penetrating the respiratory zone of otherwise healthy lungs are removed by:**
   A. cilia
   B. white blood cells
   C. lymphocytes
   D. macrophages
   E. platelets

41. **A 130-pound Olympic racer at the end of the Super G has a tidal volume of 2,500 ml and a breathing rate of 25 breaths/min. What is the racer's alveolar ventilation (to the nearest l/min)?**
   A. 6 l/min
   B. 9 l/min
   C. 59 l/min
   D. 62 l/min
   E. 63 l/min

42. **Respiratory compensation for metabolic acidosis occurs as a result of effects of pH on:**
   A. peripheral chemoreceptors only
   B. central chemoreceptors only
   C. both central and peripheral chemoreceptors
   D. pontine chemoreceptors
   E. carotid baroreceptors

43. **The apneustic center is:**
   A. located in the medulla and provides inspiratory drive
   B. located in the medulla and provides expiratory drive
   C. located in the pons and provides inspiratory drive
   D. located in the pons and provides expiratory drive
   E. located in the hypothalamus and provides expiratory drive

44. **Which of the following would you expect to find in an individual who has lived at 10,000 feet above sea level for three weeks?**
   A. increased CSF pH
   B. decreased CSF pH
   C. decreased plasma pH
   D. decreased CSF bicarbonate concentration
   E. increased CSF bicarbonate concentration

45. **The greatest flow during forced expiration occurs near total lung capacity:**
   A. due to dynamic compression of airways
   B. due to maximal diaphragmatic force
   C. because minimal intraalveolar pressure is achieved
   D. because greatest intrapleural pressure achieved
   E. because maximal surface tension is achieved

46. **A patient transported to your emergency room is unconscious and cyanotic; the initial blood gases and pH are Pa$_{O_2}$ = 36 mm Hg, Pa$_{CO_2}$ = 90 mm Hg, pH = 7.01. You place the patient on a ventilator with room air, a tidal volume of 800 ml/breath, and a rate of 10 breaths/min. The second blood gas reading, 10 min later, is: Pa$_{O_2}$ = 101 mm Hg, Pa$_{CO_2}$ = 36 mm Hg, pH = 7.30. This history is consistent with:**
   A. carbon monoxide poisoning
   B. adult respiratory distress syndrome
   C. diabetes mellitus
   D. barbiturate poisoning
   E. emphysema

47. **A decrease in blood pressure stimulates breathing by effects on:**
   A. the carotid bodies
   B. the central chemosensitive cells
   C. the gamma efferents
   D. the cerebrum
   E. the carotid sinuses

48. **A liquid-ventilated lung compared to a gas-ventilated lung:**
  A. has reduced airways resistance
  B. has pronounced hysteresis
  C. is more compliant
  D. requires greater pressure to inflate
  E. has increased residual volume

49. **If the V_A of an individual with a Pa_{O_2} of 100 mm Hg and a Pa_{CO_2} of 40 mm Hg were doubled, Pa_{O_2} would become:**
  A. 50 mm Hg
  B. 80 mm Hg
  C. 125 mm Hg
  D. 150 mm Hg
  E. 200 mm Hg

50. **All the following would decrease airways resistance *EXCEPT*:**
  A. positive pressure inflation of the lungs
  B. negative pressure inflation of the lungs
  C. sympathetic stimulation
  D. vagal stimulation
  E. spontaneous inspiration

51. **A decrease in diffusing capacity will cause:**
  A. hypoxemia only
  B. hypercapnia only
  C. hypoxemia and hypercapnia
  D. a decrease in 2,3 DPG
  E. anemia

52. **A 170-pound man with a body temperature of 37°C has a tidal volume of 800 ml and a breathing rate of 10 breaths/min. What is his minute volume?**
  A. 0.6 liters
  B. 7.5 liters
  C. 8.0 liters
  D. 6.3 liters
  E. 7.8 liters

53. **The primary respiratory control center is located in the:**
  A. cerebrum
  B. medulla
  C. pons
  D. carotid body
  E. hypothalamus

54. **Pa_{O_2} is greater at the apex than at the base of the lung because:**
  A. blood flow is greater at the apex
  B. ventilation is greater at the apex
  C. D_{CO} is less at the apex
  D. V_A/Q is greater at the apex
  E. shunt fraction is greater at the base

55. **A patient with a body temperature of 37°C is ventilated with 30% O_2 when the barometric pressure is 754 mm Hg. What is the patient's PI_{O_2}?**
  A. 98 mm Hg
  B. 148 mm Hg
  C. 162 mm Hg
  D. 212 mm Hg
  E. 226 mm Hg

56. **If the length of a tube is reduced to half and the diameter is also reduced by half, the resistance to flow through the tube will:**
  A. not change
  B. decrease 4-fold
  C. increase 2-fold
  D. increase 8-fold
  E. increase 16-fold

57. **All the following are true for CO_2 *EXCEPT*:**
  A. approximately 60% is in the form of HCO_3^-
  B. an increase in Pa_{CO_2} increases Cl^- in red blood cells
  C. less than 3% is in the dissolved form
  D. about 30% is bound to hemoglobin
  E. the CO_2 carrying capacity of blood is decreased by increasing P_{O_2}

58. **A 130-lb patient has a Pa_{CO_2} of 80 mm Hg, a tidal volume of 1.5 liters, and a ventilation rate of 40 breaths per min; metabolic rate is approximately 80% elevated for a resting person of this size. Which of the following must be true for this patient?**
  A. decreased diffusing capacity
  B. increased anatomical dead space
  C. anemia
  D. increased shunt fraction
  E. increased physiological dead space

59. **At FRC, the intrapleural pressure of a healthy person lying in bed is about (compared to atmospheric pressure):**
  A. -20 cm H_2O
  B. -5 cm H_2O
  C. 0 cm H_2O
  D. 5 cm H_2O
  E. 20 cm H_2O

60. **Which of the following would have the greatest effect on Pa_{CO_2}?**
  A. a 50% reduction in V_A
  B. a 50% reduction in hemoglobin concentration
  C. a decrease in FI_{O_2} to 18%
  D. an increase in inspired CO_2 to 5%
  E. a 100% increase in 2,3 DPG

SECTION I: QUESTIONS

61. **A patient with a moderately severe reduction in diffusing capacity will mostly like have which of the following?**
   A. a near normal resting P_{O_2}, which will decrease markedly during severe exercise.
   B. a very low resting P_{O_2} that prevents the patient from performing even light exercise
   C. hypoxemia, which will not become more severe during exercise
   D. hypercapnea that will become very severe during exercise
   E. equally severe hypoxemia and hypercapnea, both of which will become more severe during exercise

62. **Tuberculosis grows best in areas of high P_{O_2}. Where in the lung does tuberculosis usually concentrate?**
   A. base
   B. apex
   C. near the heart
   D. near lymphatic vessels
   E. near pulmonary veins

63. **An individual is diagnosed as having pulmonary hypertension/cor pulmonale. The most likely cause of this condition is:**
   A. hypoxia
   B. hypercapnea
   C. ketoacidosis
   D. Kussmaul respiration
   E. tricuspid valve stenosis

Questions 64–67. Match the following laboratory values with the conditions listed for the next four questions (*use each answer no more than once*).

	Pa_{O_2} (mm Hg)	Pa_{CO_2} (mm Hg)	Arterial pH	Ca_{O_2} (ml/100 ml)	Hemoglobin) (g/100 ml)
A.	120	20	7.19	20	15
B.	95	38	7.36	5	16
C.	52	30	7.34	17	16
D.	50	80	7.21	16	15
E.	108	34	7.51	10	8

64. **Hypoventilation**

65. **Diabetes mellitus (metabolic acidosis)**

66. **Carbon monoxide poisoning**

67. **Adult respiratory distress syndrome (ARDS)**

68. **Which condition do the following values for an arterial blood sample represent?**
   $P_{O_2} = 52$ mm Hg
   $P_{CO_2} = 60$ mm Hg
   pH = 7.05
   $[HCO_3-] = 16$ mM/l
   A. respiratory acidosis only
   B. metabolic acidosis only
   C. respiratory acidosis and metabolic acidosis
   D. respiratory acidosis and metabolic alkalosis
   E. respiratory alkalosis and metabolic acidosis

69. **An average intrapleural pressure of -1 cm H_2O at FRC suggests:**
   A. decreased lung compliance
   B. increased lung compliance
   C. increased airways resistance
   D. decreased airways resistance
   E. decreased residual volume

70. **Arteriovenous oxygen extraction is increased by a decrease in:**
   A. pH
   B. CO_2
   C. 2,3 diphosphoglycerate
   D. temperature

71. **Within zone II in the lung, flow occurs:**
   A. during diastole only
   B. during systole and diastole
   C. during systole only
   D. periodically during diastole

Questions 72–74. Use the following data to answer questions 72–74.

   A patient was attached to a spirometer that had an initial volume of 10 liters of air. One liter of pure He was added to the spirometer when the patient was at functional residual capacity (FRC), and the patient rebreathed into the spirometer for 12 min while CO_2 was absorbed and replaced by oxygen to maintain constant spirometer volume at end expiration. At the end of the 12-min breathing period, the He concentration was 7%. The patient then exhaled into the spirometer as completely as possible from FRC; the exhalation increased the spirometer volume by 1.1 liters. The patient then took a maximal inspiration and then exhaled as completely as possible. The total volume exhaled during this latter maneuver was 5.0 liters.

72. **The patient's functional residual capacity was closest to which of the following?**
   A. 5.00 liters
   B. 6.00 liters
   C. 2.36 liters
   D. 3.29 liters
   E. 3.63 liters

73. **The patient's residual volume was closest to which of the following?**
   A. 1.10 liters
   B. 1.80 liters
   C. 2.19 liters
   D. 3.29 liters
   E. 5.26 liters

74. **The patient's total lung capacity was approximately:**
   A. 8 liters
   B. 7 liters
   C. 6 liters
   D. 5 liters
   E. 4 liters

75. **A patient's test reveals a blood hemoglobin of 15 g/100 ml, a Pa_{O_2} of 55 mm Hg, a Pa_{CO_2} of 31 mm Hg, an arterial pH of 7.43, and an arterial O_2 saturation of 78%. As each gram of hemoglobin binds 1.34 ml of O_2, and as the solubility coefficient for O_2 is 0.003 ml/100 ml/mm Hg, this patient's arterial O_2 content is:**
   A. 20.1 ml/100 ml
   B. 0.17 ml/100 ml
   C. 20.3 ml/100 ml
   D. 15.9 ml/100 ml

76. **Referring to the patient in question 75, one would conclude that the patient:**
   A. is anemic
   B. is hypoventilating
   C. has an alveolar–arterial P_{O_2} difference that is greater than normal
   D. has an arterial O_2 content that is greater than normal

77. **Which of the following has the least effect on Pa_{O_2}?**
   A. V_A
   B. FI_{O_2}
   C. V_{O_2}
   D. hemoglobin concentration

78. **When someone is breathing 100% oxygen instead of room air:**
   A. the tendency of alveoli to collapse is significantly reduced
   B. the oxygen content in normal blood is more than doubled
   C. the total gas pressure of the systemic venous blood is significantly increased
   D. mixed venous P_{O_2} will be less than 100 mm Hg
   E. the quantity of CO_2 added to the blood in the systemic capillaries is significantly increased

79. **A compensatory mechanism for reducing V_A/Q_C mismatch in a region of the lung with higher than average V_A/Q ratio is:**
   A. bronchoconstriction caused by high PA_{CO_2}
   B. bronchoconstriction caused by low PA_{CO_2}
   C. bronchodilation caused by high PA_{CO_2}
   D. vasoconstriction caused by low PA_{O_2}
   E. vasoconstriction caused by high PA_{O_2}

80. **In obstructive lung disease, a patient is most likely to have:**
   A. low lung compliance
   B. high functional residual capacity
   C. high forced expiratory flow rate
   D. high transpulmonary pressure at a given lung volume
   E. high ventilation perfusion ratio

81. **During a forced exhalation:**
   A. the pleural pressure can be greater than atmospheric pressure
   B. the alveolar pressure is always less than pleural pressure
   C. the transpulmonary pressure increases as the lung volume decreases
   D. the pressure in the bronchi is greater than alveolar pressure
   E. the flow rate increases as the lung volume decreases

82. **During heavy muscular exercise, there is an increased production of lactic acid by the muscles. The lactic acid:**
   A. is excreted as lactic acid by the kidneys into the urine
   B. results in a reduction in plasma HCO_3^-
   C. results in hypoventilation
   D. leads to increased hemoglobin affinity for oxygen
   E. causes the anion gap to decrease

83. **The following data were obtained regarding a patient: arterial pH = 7.52; Pa_{CO_2} = 50 mm Hg; Pa_{O_2} = 75 mm Hg. This patient:**
   A. is hyperventilating
   B. has respiratory alkalosis
   C. must have an increased plasma HCO_3^- concentration
   D. has a relatively increased V_A
   E. has respiratory acidosis

84. **A normal subject is allowed to breathe a primary mixture of inert gas and 15% oxygen for 10 min before switching to a secondary mixture of inert gas with 15% oxygen and 3% carbon dioxide. The effect on the subject's ventilation is most likely to be:**
   A. an increase after breathing the secondary mixture for several minutes
   B. a decrease after breathing the secondary mixture for several minutes
   C. an increase after breathing the secondary mixture for several hours
   D. a decrease after breathing the secondary mixture for several hours

85. The following arterial blood gas data were obtained regarding a healthy human and a human COPD patient.

	Breathing Room Air	Breathing a 40% O_2 Mixture
Healthy	$Pa_{O_2} = 100$ mm Hg	$Pa_{O_2} = 200$ mm Hg
	$Pa_{CO_2} = 40$ mm Hg	$Pa_{CO_2} = 40$ mm Hg
COPD	$Pa_{O_2} = 40$ mm Hg	$Pa_{O_2} = 70$ mm Hg
	$Pa_{CO_2} = 65$ mm Hg	$Pa_{CO_2} = 75$ mm Hg

Based on the above data, all the following statements are true *EXCEPT*:
A. the COPD patient is hypoventilating while breathing room air
B. breathing the 40% O_2 mixture results in hypoventilation in both the healthy human and the COPD patient
C. O_2 chemoreceptors are a greater determinant of V_A in the COPD patient than in the healthy human while the persons are breathing room air
D. while breathing room air and while breathing 40% O_2 mixture, the COPD patient is breathing less than the healthy human

86. A patient is found to have a lowered arterial oxygen partial pressure (hypoxemia). Each of the following could be considered as a possible cause of this condition *EXCEPT*:
A. ventilation–perfusion mismatch
B. low blood hemoglobin concentration
C. hypoventilation
D. physiological shunting
E. high altitude exposure

87. Increasing tidal volume, while keeping all other factors constant, will result in:
A. decreased minute ventilation
B. increased dead space ventilation
C. increased alveolar ventilation
D. increased P_{CO_2} in arterial blood
E. increased inspiratory reserve volume

88. Tissue PO_2 is determined by a balance between:
A. cardiac output and venous return
B. tissue oxygen use and carbon dioxide production
C. tissue metabolism and tissue blood flow
D. lung ventilation and perfusion

89. If tissue oxygen consumption increases to four times normal and tissue blood flow increases to 2 times normal, then:
A. tissue interstitial fluid P_{O_2} will decrease
B. tissue interstitial fluid P_{O_2} will not change
C. tissue interstitial fluid P_{O_2} will increase
D. the amount of oxygen removed from the blood each minute will not change

90. Each of the following conditions causes increased ventilatory drive due to low arterial P_{O2} (hypoxemia) *EXCEPT*:
A. severe chronic obstructive pulmonary disease
B. immediate breathing of a low oxygen level (acute hypoxia)
C. prolonged breathing of a low oxygen level (chronic hypoxia)
D. carbon monoxide poisoning
E. adaptation to high altitude

91. Normally, the arterial blood gases do not change significantly during strenuous exercise. Which of the following is thought to stimulate the respiratory center the proper amount to supply the extra oxygen requirements for strenuous exercise and to blow off the extra carbon dioxide?
A. hydrogen ions from lactic acid produced by exercising muscles
B. the central and peripheral chemoreceptors
C. neurogenic factors involving the higher brain centers and proprioceptive reflexes
D. hypoxia developing within the exercising muscles

92. A condition in which hypoxia is always accompanied by hypercapnia is:
A. diffusion impairment
B. V_A/Q_C mismatch
C. physiologic shunt
D. hypoventilation
E. anemia

Questions 93–95. Figure 3-2 shows pressure changes for a single tidal breath. From the figure, determine the pressures in questions 93–95.

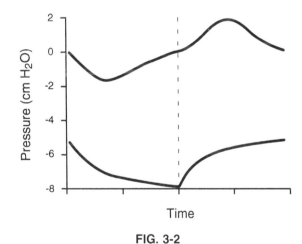

FIG. 3-2

93. Transpulmonary pressure at the end of inspiration
A. −8 cm H_2O
B. −5 cm H_2O
C. 0 cm H_2O
D. 3 cm H_2O
E. 8 cm H_2O

94. **Pleural pressure immediately before inspiration**
    A. -8 cm H_2O
    B. -5 cm H_2O
    C. 0 cm H_2O
    D. 3 cm H_2O
    E. 8 cm H_2O

95. **Alveolar pressure at the end of expiration**
    A. -8 cm H_2O
    B. -5 cm H_2O
    C. 0 cm H_2O
    D. 3 cm H_2O
    E. 8 cm H_2O

96. **During inspiration, all the following increase EX-CEPT:**
    A. intrapleural pressure
    B. stroke volume
    C. venous return
    D. intra-abdominal pressure
    E. pulmonary vascular resistance

97. **During normal expiration, which of the following increases?**
    A. metabolic rate of the diaphragm
    B. bronchial diameter
    C. pulmonary vascular diameter
    D. alveolar pressure
    E. height of the xiphoid process above the ground

98. **In a normal subject after 10 min of exposure to hypoxia (PA_{O_2} = 50 mm Hg), you would expect that compared to the initial response (first 15 sec) there would be:**
    A. an increase in arterial P_{CO_2}
    B. a decrease in arterial pH
    C. a decrease in activity of the medullary chemoreceptors
    D. a decrease in the pH of the CSF
    E. a decrease in the activity of the peripheral chemoreceptors

99. **A lightly anesthetized patient still capable of spontaneous breathing is artificially ventilated for 10 min at his normal tidal volume but at twice his normal frequency with a gas mixture of 50% O_2 and 50% N_2. On cessation of this artificial ventilation, the patient fails to breathe for 1 min. The most important cause of this temporary apnea is a decreased activity of the:**
    A. peripheral chemoreceptors because of the high P_{O_2}
    B. peripheral chemoreceptors because of the low P_{CO_2}
    C. medullary chemoreceptors because of the high P_{O_2}
    D. medullary chemoreceptors because of the low P_{CO_2}
    E. peripheral chemoreceptors because of the decrease in arterial pH

100. **Prolonged hypoxia may result in:**
    A. pulmonary vasodilation
    B. reduced proportion of pulmonary blood flow to the lung apex
    C. coronary vasoconstriction
    D. decreased right ventricular end diastolic pressure
    E. increased mean circulatory filling pressure

RENAL PHYSIOLOGY

Questions 1–4. Data were obtained on one of your classmates who volunteered to participate in a renal clearance study in order to pay for medical school expenses.

Two hours following the initiation of an inulin infusion:
Plasma inulin = 20 mg/dl
Plasma glucose = 150 mg/dl
Urine flow = 2 ml/min
Urine inulin = 500 mg/dl
Urine glucose = 30 mg/dl

1. **What is the GFR?**
   A. 130 ml/min
   B. 100 ml/min
   C. 50 ml/min
   D. 25 ml/min
   E. 12 ml/min

2. **If you then simply doubled the rate at which the inulin solution was being infused into this otherwise normal medical student, all the following would be expected to change EXCEPT:**
   A. plasma inulin concentration
   B. urine inulin concentration
   C. excretion of inulin in the urine
   D. GFR

3. **What was the clearance of glucose?**
   A. 60 ml/min
   B. 6 ml/min
   C. 0.6 mg/min
   D. 0.4 ml/min
   E. 0.15 ml/min

4. **Which is true for the reabsorption of glucose by this student?**
   A. approximately 75 mg/min is being reabsorbed
   B. approximately 20 mg/min is being reabsorbed
   C. approximately 150 mg/min is being reabsorbed
   D. glucose reabsorption must be at its maximum level
   E. cannot determine the rate of glucose reabsorption from the data presented

5. **You discover a new drug that causes GFR to increase but renal blood flow to decrease. This drug does not affect arterial blood pressure. The drug causes:**
   A. constriction of the afferent arteriole
   B. dilation of the afferent arteriole
   C. constriction of the efferent arteriole
   D. dilation of the efferent arteriole
   E. equal constriction of both the afferent and efferent arterioles

6. **The macula densa is an important component for all the following EXCEPT:**
   A. autoregulation of GFR
   B. secretion of renin
   C. regulation of afferent arteriole tone
   D. sensing fluid delivery to the distal tubule
   E. sensing plasma osmolarity

7. **A patient has the following clinical data:**
   urine volume/24 h = 600 ml
   urine osmolality = 1,100 mOsm
   plasma osmolality = 260 mOsm
   blood pressure = 120/80 mm Hg
   plasma potassium = 4.1 mM

   Which of the following could produce these data?
   A. a large increase in antidiuretic hormone secretion
   B. a large increase in aldosterone secretion
   C. a large increase in angiotensin II
   D. the total absence of aldosterone
   E. the total absence of antidiuretic hormone

8. **A patient has a tumor of the adrenal gland, causing a sustained hypersecretion of aldosterone (primary aldosteronism). Which of the following parameters is elevated above that found in a normal individual ingesting an identical diet?**
   A. plasma renin concentration
   B. plasma angiotensin II concentration
   C. plasma K
   D. plasma ANF concentration
   E. plasma chloride concentration

9. **When you are excreting a maximally concentrated urine, the greatest amount of water is being reabsorbed by the:**
   A. proximal tubule
   B. descending limb of Henle's loop
   C. ascending thin limb of Henle's loop
   D. thick ascending limb of Henle's loop
   E. collecting ducts

10. **When you are excreting a maximally concentrated urine, the fluid in the thin ascending limb of Henle's loop has:**
    A. a lower urea concentration than that found in the fluid within an adjacent descending limb
    B. a lower sodium concentration than that in the adjacent interstitial fluid
    C. a lower osmolality than that found in the fluid within an adjacent collecting duct
    D. an osmolality identical to that of the adjacent interstitial fluid
    E. a lower osmolality than that found in the afferent arteriolar blood

11. **With ADH present, which of the following is correct for the tubular fluid/plasma ratio for osmolality at the *end* of the structure mentioned?**
    A. distal tubule ___ the ratio is greater than 1
    B. proximal tubule ___ the ratio is less than 1
    C. cortical collecting duct ___ the ratio is 1
    D. thick ascending loop of Henle ___ the ratio is 1
    E. medullary collecting duct ___ the ratio is less than 1

12. **For a patient who has an acute increase in P_{CO_2} (acute respiratory acidosis), you would expect all the following *EXCEPT*:**
    A. a small decrease in plasma HCO_3^-
    B. a significant initial decrease in plasma pH
    C. increased HCO_3^- reabsorption by the kidney
    D. a gradual increase in plasma pH over the next several days
    E. an increase in titratable acid excretion for several days

13. **Upon changing from a normal diet to a diet with a very high potassium content, you would expect:**
    A. a large decrease in the amount of potassium being reabsorbed by the proximal tubule
    B. a decrease in plasma aldosterone, causing increased K secretion by collecting duct cells
    C. a rapid development of a metabolic alkalosis
    D. a slight increase in plasma K, causing increased K secretion by cells along the collecting duct
    E. a parallel increase in urinary sodium excretion

14. **A decrease in renal arterial blood pressure of 10 mm Hg in a normal kidney will lead to all the following responses *EXCEPT*:**
    A. a decrease in urinary sodium excretion
    B. a decrease in efferent arteriolar resistance
    C. an increase in renin secretion
    D. a decrease in afferent arteriolar resistance
    E. a response that maintains GFR and renal blood flow near normal values

15. **Which of the following acts to decrease GFR and renal blood flow below normal levels?**
    A. autoregulation
    B. a small increase in efferent arteriolar resistance
    C. prostaglandin E_2
    D. a decrease in afferent arteriolar resistance
    E. a high plasma catecholamine level

16. **Following hemorrhage, renal blood flow is normally reduced because of:**
    A. a decrease in activity of the parasympathetic nerves to the kidney
    B. an increase in sympathetic nerve activity to the kidneys
    C. a decrease in hematocrit
    D. an increase in aldosterone secretion
    E. a decrease in renin secretion

17. **Phosphate reabsorption by the kidney:**
    A. occurs primarily along the distal tubule and collecting duct
    B. has a genetically fixed transport maximum like that of glucose
    C. is controlled by the secretion of angiotensin II
    D. is influenced by the level of parathyroid hormone
    E. occurs primarily along the thick ascending limb of Henle

18. **The initial increase (first 15 min) in plasma HCO_3^- following hypoventilation is associated with:**
    A. a rapid (first 15 min) increase in the production of ammonium by the kidney
    B. an increase in arterial pH
    C. a shift of K^+ into cells
    D. a decrease in the concentration of protein bases ($Prot^-$)
    E. a rapid (first 15 min) increase in the amount of titratable acid excreted by the kidney

19. **Which process enables us to produce a urine with a final pH of 4.5?**
    A. Na^+/H^+ exchange pump
    B. diffusion of H^+ from the tubular cell into the tubular fluid
    C. ATP-powered proton pump
    D. cotransport of Na^+ and H^+ into the tubular fluid
    E. cotransport of K^+ and H^+ into the tubular fluid

20. **The carbonic acid/bicarbonate system is considered the most important body buffer because:**
    A. both the acid and base components can be independently regulated
    B. it is the only buffer in the body that has a pK close to the normal pH of plasma
    C. it is present in large quantities
    D. carbonic acid is a gas, while HCO_3^- is an electrolyte
    E. none of the above

21. **Any substance that is filtered by the glomerulus and reabsorbed and not secreted by the renal tubules will have a renal clearance that is:**
    A. equal to the clearance of urea
    B. equal to the clearance of inulin
    C. less than the clearance of inulin
    D. greater than the clearance of inulin
    E. equal to the glomerular filtration rate

22. **As tubular fluid passes along the ascending limb of the loop of Henle:**
    A. osmolarity increases
    B. water is always reabsorbed
    C. urea concentration increases more than 3-fold
    D. in the presence of ADH, water is reabsorbed
    E. chloride is reabsorbed

Questions 23–24. A patient has a pH of 7.49 and an arterial P_{CO_2} of 50 mm Hg. Using these data, answer questions 23 and 24.

23. **The HCO_3^- concentration is:**
    A. 40 mM
    B. 37 mM
    C. 30 mM
    D. 46 mM
    E. 16 mM

24. **What type of acid/base disturbance does this patient have?**
    A. acute respiratory alkalosis
    B. chronic respiratory alkalosis
    C. chronic respiratory acidosis
    D. metabolic acidosis
    E. metabolic alkalosis

25. **Which of the following might be a cause of this patient's problem?**
    A. ingestion of NaCl
    B. increased production of ketoacids
    C. decrease in plasma potassium
    D. decreased aldosterone secretion
    E. decrease in plasma angiotensin II levels

Questions 26–27. To answer questions 26 and 27, use the data presented in Fig. 4-1 for the renal handling of glucose.

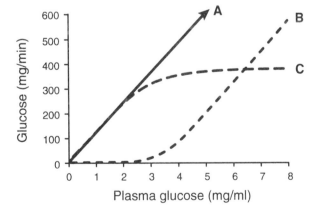

FIG. 4-1

26. **Which of the following properly identifies the three curves presented in the figure?**
    A. A = excretion of glucose; B = filtration of glucose; C = reabsorption of glucose
    B. A = filtration of glucose; B = excretion of glucose; C = reabsorption of glucose
    C. A = filtration of glucose; B = reabsorption of glucose; C = excretion of glucose
    D. A = reabsorption of glucose; B = excretion of glucose; C = filtration of glucose
    E. A = reabsorption of glucose; B = filtration of glucose; C = excretion of glucose

27. **When the plasma level of glucose was increased from 5 to 7 mg/ml, the:**
    A. clearance of glucose increased
    B. excretion of glucose remained constant
    C. reabsorption of glucose decreased
    D. filtered load of glucose remained constant
    E. T_{max} was finally exceeded

28. **PAH is secreted by a T_{max}-limited system. When the plasma concentration of PAH is above that required for the T_{max}, any further increase in the plasma concentration of PAH will cause all the following *EXCEPT*:**
    A. the amount of PAH secreted each minute will remain constant
    B. the excretion of PAH will increase
    C. the clearance of PAH will decrease
    D. the filtered load of PAH will increase
    E. the extraction ratio for PAH will increase

29. **After a large hemorrhage, you would expect all the following *EXCEPT*:**
    A. increased ADH secretion
    B. increased osmolar excretion
    C. increased renin secretion
    D. decreased urine flow
    E. increased aldosterone secretion

30. **A patient has a head injury that has damaged the medullary respiratory center. His breathing is very rapid and deep. The most likely finding upon analysis of the blood would be:**
    A. elevated pH and elevated P_{CO_2}
    B. elevated pH and low P_{CO_2}
    C. low pH and low P_{CO_2}
    D. low pH and elevated P_{CO_2}
    E. none of the above

Questions 31–32. Use the following data obtained from a patient to answer questions 31 and 32.

Urine Data	Plasma Data	Renal Function
VOLUME = 0.1 l/h	HCO_3^- = 24 mM	GFR = 100 ml/min
HCO_3^- = 0.7 mMol/h	pH = 7.38	
NH_4^+ = 2.0 mMol/h	Na^+ = 138 mM	
Titratable acid = 3.0 mMol/h	K^+ = 4.1 mM	

31. The net HCO_3^- generation for the patient was:
   A. 4.7 mMol/h
   B. 50 mMol/h
   C. 5 mMol/h
   D. 146.3 mMol/h
   E. 4.3 mMol/h

32. How many mMol of H^+ per hour did this patient secrete?
   A. 148.3 mMol/h
   B. 4.3 mMol/h
   C. 146.3 mMol/h
   D. 150 mMol/h
   E. 5.0 mMol/h

33. One of the consequences of the deranged metabolism in diabetes mellitus is an excessive production of acid. After this condition has been untreated for several days, all the following will be observed EXCEPT:
   A. decreased plasma pH
   B. increased anion gap
   C. decreased plasma P_{CO2}
   D. increased NH_4^+ excretion
   E. increased HCO_3^- excretion

34. Aldosterone:
   A. secretion is increased by converting enzyme inhibitors
   B. acts through basolateral membrane receptors to increase luminal membrane sodium channels
   C. increases Na^+ entry into intercalated cells along the late distal tubule and collecting duct
   D. increases the amount of Na^+/K^+ ATPase in the principal cells
   E. decreases the number of K^+ channels on the luminal membrane of the principal cells

Questions 35–38. Use the following data to answer questions 35–38. Both patients complain of intense thirst and a constant desire to urinate.

Item	Patient 1	Patient 2
Plasma osmolality	290 mOsm	280 mOsm
Urine osmolality	98 mOsm	170 mOsm
Urine volume	3 ml/min	2.2 ml/min

35. What is the osmolar clearance for Patient 1?

   C_{osm} = _____

36. What is the free water clearance for Patient 1?

   C_{H_2O} = _____

Question 37. One hour following the administration of excess antidiuretic hormone, the following data were obtained for these two patients. Use these data to answer question 37.

Item	Patient 1	Patient 2
Plasma osmolality	288 mOsm	275 mOsm
Urine osmolality	500 mOsm	700 mOsm

37. Which of the following is true regarding the two patients?
   A. Both patients have nephrogenic diabetes insipidus (inability of the kidney to respond to ADH).
   B. Patient 1 has nephrogenic diabetes insipidus, but Patient 2 does not have nephrogenic diabetes insipidus.
   C. The endogenous plasma ADH concentration was high in both patients before administering the ADH.
   D. Patient 2 had a higher medullary interstitial osmolality than did Patient 1.
   E. Both patients have primary diabetes insipidus (inability to make ADH).

Question 38. Following an overnight dehydration (no water available), the following data were obtained for these two patients. Use these data to answer question 38.

Item	Patient 1	Patient 2
Plasma osmolality	315 mOsm	290 mOsm
Urine osmolality	140 mOsm	600 mOsm

38. Which of the following is true regarding the two patients?
   A. Patient 1 has primary diabetes insipidus (inability to make ADH).
   B. Patient 2 would benefit from receiving ADH treatment.
   C. Patient 2 has primary diabetes insipidus (inability to make ADH).
   D. Patient 1 should not be given ADH treatment
   E. Both A and B are true.

39. Following 24 hours without any fluid intake, you would expect plasma osmolarity to 1, which would cause the secretion of 2, and also a (an) 3.

	1	2	3
A.	increase	more ADH	increased thirst
B.	increase	less ADH	decreased thirst
C.	decrease	less ADH	decreased thirst
D.	decrease	more ADH	increased thirst
E.	remain the same	less ADH	increased thirst

40. An increase in plasma potassium would stimulate the secretion of *1*, which would cause potassium secretion by the *2* to *3*.

	1	*2*	*3*
A.	ADH	distal nephron	increase
B.	renin	proximal tubule	decrease
C.	aldosterone	distal nephron	increase
D.	renin	distal nephron	decrease
E.	aldosterone	proximal tubule	increase

41. Assume a normal GFR. The afferent arterial concentration of substance X = 100 mg/dl, and the efferent arterial concentration of substance X = 100 mg/dl. Substance X is most likely:
   A. secreted by the renal tubules
   B. metabolized by the glomerulus
   C. not reabsorbed by the renal tubules
   D. freely filtered
   E. reabsorbed by the renal tubules

42. At the distal end of the proximal tubule, which of the following substances would normally have a lower concentration in tubular fluid than in the original glomerular filtrate?
   A. urea
   B. bicarbonate
   C. hydrogen ions
   D. creatinine
   E. chloride

43. The appearance of protein molecules in the urine depends on:
   A. molecular size
   B. net charge on the protein
   C. reabsorption along the proximal tubule
   D. answers A and B are correct
   E. answers A, B, and C are correct

44. If the activity of carbonic anhydrase in the kidney is inhibited by the drug acetazolamide, which of the following would be most correct?
   A. clearance of bicarbonate would decrease
   B. urine would become more acidic
   C. plasma bicarbonate would decrease
   D. titratable acid excretion would increase
   E. NH_4^+ excretion would increase

45. If the production of creatinine by the body decreased from 1,000 mg/day to 500 mg/day and plasma creatinine decreased from 2 mg/dl to 1 mg/dl, then:
   A. the glomerular filtration rate would decrease approximately 50%
   B. the glomerular filtration rate would approximately double
   C. no change in glomerular filtration would occur
   D. it is impossible to estimate what would happen to the glomerular filtrate from these data

46. The percentage of fluid reabsorbed by the proximal tubule can be increased by:
   A. aldosterone
   B. angiotensin II
   C. an increase in peritubular capillary pressure
   D. AVP
   E. a decrease in oncotic pressure in the peritubular capillaries

47. A patient is inadvertently given 2 liters of isotonic saline (0.9% NaCl) over a 4-h period of time. This infusion should cause an increase in:
   A. AVP
   B. plasma oncotic pressure
   C. angiotensin II
   D. atrial natriuretic factor
   E. aldosterone

48. A patient is given the drug furosemide, which blocks the $Na^+/K^+/2\ Cl^-$ cotransporter. After a few hours (drug is still effective), you would expect all the following EXCEPT:
   A. a decreased plasma volume
   B. an increase in angiotensin II
   C. an increase in potassium excretion
   D. a large volume of hypertonic urine
   E. an increase in sodium excretion

49. It has been found that a nephron segment studied in a dish does not actively transport Na and is impermeable to water. This segment is the:
   A. proximal tubule
   B. thin descending limb of Henle
   C. thin ascending limb of Henle
   D. thick ascending limb of Henle
   E. distal tubule

Questions 50–53. The following data were obtained in a subject. Assume that GFR is 100 ml/min throughout.

	Period 1	Period 2	Period 3	Period 4
Plasma concentration of X	100 mg/dl	200 mg/dl	300 mg/dl	400 mg/dl
Urinary X excretion	0 mg/min	20 mg/min	100 mg/min	200 mg/min

50. The filtered load of X in period 3 was:
   A. 3 mg/min
   B. 30 mg/min
   C. 100 mg/min
   D. 200 mg/min
   E. 300 mg/min

51. The T_{max} for X was:
   A. 100 mg/min
   B. 180 mg/min
   C. 200 mg/min
   D. 20 mg/min
   E. cannot estimate from the above data

52. An increase in aldosterone can affect H^+ secretion by the proximal tubule by:
  A. direct stimulation of the H^+/ATP pump
  B. direct stimulation of the Na^+/H^+ exchanger
  C. causing hypokalemia
  D. causing hyponatremia
  E. causing an increase in angiotensin II

53. A large increase in sympathetic nerve activity to the kidney is noted, but glomerular capillary pressure does not change (i.e., it remains at 60 mm Hg). In view of this information, you would predict that the:
  A. filtration fraction will increase
  B. protein concentration in the efferent artery will decrease
  C. Hct in the efferent arteriole will decrease
  D. peritubular capillary pressure will increase
  E. renal plasma flow will remain constant

Questions 54–55. A patient is aggressively treated with a diuretic for several weeks, and the following data are obtained.

Patient	Normal
Plasma Na = 130 mM	138–145 mM
Plasma Cl = 81 mM	95–105 mM
Plasma K = 2.5 mM	3.5–5.0 mM
P_{osm} = 265 mOsm	285–290 mOsm
Blood pressure = 105/65 mm Hg	—
Plasma pH = 7.52	7.40
P_{CO2} = 50 mm Hg	40 mm Hg
Plasma HCO_3 = 39 mM	22–26 mM

54. This patient has:
  A. metabolic acidosis
  B. acute respiratory alkalosis
  C. chronic respiratory alkalosis
  D. chronic respiratory acidosis
  E. metabolic alkalosis

55. All the following might be expected in this patient EXCEPT:
  A. decreased extracellular volume
  B. increased intracellular volume
  C. increased renin secretion
  D. urine pH >7.4
  E. increased H^+ secretion

Question 56. A sample of blood is obtained from a blood vessel within the kidney of a normal individual, and the following data are obtained:

Hct	60%
Protein concentration	7.2 g%
Pressure within the vessel	35 mm Hg

56. The arterial blood of this individual has a Hct of 50% and a protein concentration of 6.0 g%. The sample was obtained from the:
  A. afferent arteriole
  B. glomerular capillary
  C. efferent arteriole
  D. peritubular capillary
  E. vasa recta

Questions 57–58. To answer questions 57 and 58, use the following laboratory data obtained in a patient.

Arterial pH	7.2
P_{CO_2}	26 mm Hg
Plasma Na	140 mM
Plasma K	5 mM
Plasma Cl	105 mM

57. What is the plasma HCO_3?
  A. 7 mM
  B. 10 mM
  C. 14 mM
  D. 18 mM
  E. 22 mM

58. What is a possible cause of this patient's condition?
  A. ingestion of HCl acid
  B. excretion of an alkaline urine
  C. ingestion of $NaHCO_3$
  D. increased production of lactic acid
  E. vomiting HCl

59. The H^+ ions secreted by the Na^+/H^+ exchanger in the kidney are most likely to:
  A. combine with $HPO_4^=$
  B. combine with HCO_3^-
  C. lower tubule pH to below 6.0
  D. combine with Cl^-
  E. combine with $SO_4^=$

60. Ca^{2+} handling by the distal tubule and collecting duct involves all the following EXCEPT:
  A. a passive Ca^{2+} entry mechanism in the luminal membrane
  B. maintenance of a low intracellular Na^+ concentration by Na^+/K^+ ATPase
  C. Ca^{2+} ATPase in the basolateral cell membrane
  D. a Ca^{2+} secretory process similar to that for potassium
  E. a parathyroid hormone-sensitive reabsorptive process

61. A sample of tubular fluid was obtained by micropuncture of a segment of the nephron in a normal mammal. The fluid had an osmolarity of 900 mOsm/l and a pH of 5.5. The tubular fluid came from the:
  A. proximal tubule
  B. tip of the loop of Henle
  C. upper portion of the ascending limb of the loop of Henle
  D. papillary collecting duct
  E. late portion of the distal tubule

62. **Relative to the plasma in the efferent arteriole, the fluid in Bowman's capsule has a:**
    A. higher glucose concentration
    B. higher sodium concentration
    C. higher potassium concentration
    D. lower oncotic pressure
    E. all of the above

63. **Inulin is infused intravenously in a normal subject. The concentration of inulin in the plasma in the peritubular capillaries is:**
    A. zero
    B. higher than the concentration of inulin in the fluid in Bowman's capsule
    C. lower than the concentration of inulin in the fluid in Bowman's capsule
    D. the same as the concentration of inulin in the fluid in Bowman's capsule

64. **In a person on a very high potassium intake, the urine at the end of the ascending limb of the loop of Henle will:**
    A. contain approximately 10% of the filtered potassium
    B. contain approximately 50% of the filtered potassium
    C. contain approximately 100% of the filtered potassium
    D. contain approximately 200% of the filtered potassium
    E. have a potassium concentration higher than that of the plasma

65. **A drug that blocks angiotensin-converting enzyme (ACE) is given to a patient. All the following are likely to decrease EXCEPT:**
    A. peripheral arterial resistance
    B. plasma aldosterone concentration
    C. arterial blood pressure
    D. plasma renin concentration
    E. plasma angiotensin II concentration

Questions 66–68. Match the following lettered sets of data with the condition (shown in questions 66–68) that best fits the data. The subjects are humans, and normal values are shown in the first row of data.

	Urine Flow (ml/min)	$[Osm]_U$ mOsm/kg	Hct %	$[Osm]_P$ mOsm/kg	$[Na]_P$ mM
Normal Values	1.0	560	46	290	142
A.	4.5	110	38	270	130
B.	4.7	100	54	310	151
C.	4.3	720	42	308	138
D.	0.4	780	54	310	151
E.	0.3	790	38	270	130

66. _____ **Diabetes insipidus**

67. _____ **Diabetes mellitus**

68. _____ **Inappropriate ADH secretion (SIADH)**

69. **At the end of the proximal tubule, which of the following substances would normally have a higher concentration in tubular fluid than in the original glomerular filtrate?**
    A. glucose
    B. amino acids
    C. phosphate
    D. creatinine
    E. sodium

70. **If you place a patient on a low-sodium diet, you would expect a decrease in:**
    A. glucose reabsorption
    B. amino acid reabsorption
    C. hydrogen ion secretion by the proximal tubule
    D. bicarbonate reabsorption
    E. none of the above would be decreased

71. **The major factor determining the long-term ECF volume is:**
    A. the amount of sodium retained in the ECF
    B. the ECF sodium concentration
    C. the amount of K^+ retained in the ECF
    D. the osmolality of the ECF

Questions 72–75. The table below gives arterial blood gas findings and pertinent electrolytes for patients with acid-base disturbances. Use these data for questions 72–75.

	pCO_2 mm Hg	HCO_3^- mM	pH U	Na^+	K^+ mEq/l	Cl^-	Creatinine mg/dl
Patient A	35	19	7.35	140	5.5	110	1
Patient B	40	30	7.50	140	3.0	99	4
Patient C	15	5	7.15	140	6.0	105	2
Patient D	60	30	7.32	140	5.5	99	1
Patient E	25	20	—	140	4.8	109	1

72. **The patient with metabolic acidosis consistent with uncontrolled diabetes mellitus is:**
    A. Patient A
    B. Patient B
    C. Patient C
    D. Patient D
    E. Patient E

73. **Characterize Patient E.**
    A. metabolic acidosis without increased anion gap
    B. respiratory alkalosis, compensated
    C. metabolic acidosis with increased anion gap
    D. metabolic alkalosis, compensated
    E. respiratory acidosis, uncompensated

74. **Total H^+ secretion would be highest in which patient?**
    A. Patient A
    B. Patient B
    C. Patient C
    D. Patient D
    E. Patient E

75. In a hydropenic state (water scarcity) and relative to the renal artery, the renal vein would be:
    A. the same tonicity
    B. slightly hypertonic
    C. slightly hypotonic

76. What are the putative events in the tubuloglomerular feedback hypothesis of renal autoregulation? (DTF = distal tubule flow; MD = macula densa; JG = juxtaglomerular apparatus; AR = afferent arteriole resistance; ER = efferent arteriole resistance.)
    A. ↓DTF→MD response→↑AR→↓GFR
    B. ↑DTF→↑renin→↑aldosterone→↓GFR
    C. ↑DTF→MD response→↑AR→↓GFR
    D. ↑DTF→JG response→↑AR→↓GFR
    E. ↓DTF→JG response→↑AR→↓GFR

77. The rate of inulin excretion is dependent upon which two variables?
    A. urine flow and arterial blood pressure
    B. GFR and proximal reabsorption
    C. urine flow and plasma concentration
    D. plasma concentration and proximal secretion
    E. plasma concentration and GFR

78. Two hours after ingestion of 1 liter of an unknown fluid, urine flow increased from 1 to 10 ml/min, urine osmolality decreased from 1,000 to 250 mOsmol/kg•H_2O, sodium excretion was unchanged, potassium excretion increased from 75 to 175 mEq/min, and urinary pH increased from 5.6 to 7.3. The fluid ingested was probably:
    A. water
    B. 0.15 M NaCl
    C. 0.5 M glucose
    D. 0.05 M $NaHCO_3$
    E. 0.3 M urea

79. A 60-kg subject runs a 10-km race on a hot day. At the end of the race, plasma osmolarity is elevated to 320 mOsmol/l from a control value of 280 mOsmol/l. Assuming that total body water initially was 60% of body weight and that the subject lost only water during the race, estimate the extracellular fluid volume after the race.
    A. 24 liters
    B. 12 liters
    C. 36 liters
    D. 10.5 liters
    E. 8.5 liters

80. Which of the following inhibits the secretion of aldosterone?
    A. i.v. infusion of 1 liter of isotonic NaCl solution
    B. a fall in plasma osmolality
    C. an increase in plasma potassium concentration
    D. stimulation of renal nerves
    E. decrease in sodium delivery to the macula densa

81. The nephron segment in which the sodium concentration in the tubular fluid is greater than that in the surrounding interstitial fluid is the:
    A. late proximal tubule
    B. thick ascending loop of Henle
    C. medullary collecting duct
    D. thin ascending loop of Henle
    E. distal tubule

82. All of the following will increase GFR EXCEPT?
    A. constriction of the efferent arteriole
    B. a marked rise in K_f
    C. a rise in arterial pressure
    D. dilation of the afferent arteriole
    E. a fall in plasma oncotic pressure

83. Two lean patients are of the same height, age, sex, and body weight. However, one of the patients has a 75% reduction in renal tissue, while the other patient has normal renal function. Each patient is then given an identical inulin infusion (i.e., the same amount in milligrams of inulin/min). Which of the following statements is true?
    A. Plasma inulin concentration would be higher in the normal patient 1 h after starting the infusion.
    B. Urine inulin concentration would be higher in the patient with the reduced renal function 1 h after starting the infusion.
    C. At the time that plasma inulin concentration is constant in both patients, the rate of inulin excretion in the urine would be equal as well.
    D. At the time that plasma inulin concentration is constant in both patients, the clearance of inulin also would be equal.
    E. After 2 h of inulin infusion, the plasma inulin concentration of both patients would be equal.

84. Which of the following elevates the filtration fraction?
    A. dilation of the afferent arteriole
    B. an increase in the ultrafiltration coefficient of the glomerulus
    C. dilation of the efferent arteriole
    D. a marked rise in arterial pressure
    E. an increase in tubular pressure

Questions 85–88. Use the following data to answer questions 85–88.
    Urine flow = 1 ml/min
    Urine sodium concentration = 75 mMol/l
    Urine inulin concentration = 100 mg/ml
    Urine potassium concentration = 200 mMol/l
    Plasma sodium concentration = 150 mMol/l
    Plasma potassium concentration = 5 mMol/l
    Plasma inulin concentration = 1 mg/ml

85. The amount of sodium filtered at the glomerulus is:
    A. 15 mMol/min
    B. 75 mMol/min
    C. 7500 mMol/min
    D. 100 ml/min
    E. 2 ml/min

86. **What percentage of the filtered potassium is excreted in the urine?**
   A. 25.7%
   B. 40%
   C. 60%
   D. 100%
   E. 20%

87. **The renal clearance of sodium is:**
   A. 1 ml/min
   B. 100 ml/min
   C. 75 μMol/min
   D. 150 mMol/min
   E. 0.5 ml/min

88. **The net rate of tubular reabsorption of potassium is:**
   A. 100 μMol/min
   B. 500 μMol/min
   C. 300 μMol/min
   D. 200 μMol/min
   E. 50 μMol/min

89. **A 25-year-old patient presents in the walk-in clinic with polydipsia and polyuria (5 liters/day of dilute urine, 50–100 mOsm/kg water, Sp. Gr. = 1.002–1.005). The initial diagnosis is primary (pituitary) diabetes insipidus. Which one of the following observations is consistent with this diagnosis?**
   A. A concentrated urine is elaborated in response to an i.v. infusion of hypertonic saline.
   B. A concentrated urine is produced in response to an infusion of hypotonic saline.
   C. A concentrated urine is produced after i.v. vasopressin.
   D. A concentrated urine is voided upon overnight restriction of fluid intake.
   E. Both A and C of the above choices are correct.

90. **Patients with cirrhosis of the liver typically exhibit edema formation. Which of the following must occur in order to establish this edema?**
   A. increased cell membrane K^+ permeability
   B. increased plasma oncotic pressure
   C. decreased plasma renin activity
   D. Na^+ retention
   E. stimulation of ADH release

91. **Three patients have been diagnosed with severe chronic renal failure. These patients all exhibit plasma creatinine concentrations exceeding 6 mg/dl, hematocrits less than 38%, and plasma potassium concentrations between 4.3 and 5.8 mEq/l. Assuming a normal diet and physical activity for each of these patients, you would expect their creatinine excretion rates to be:**
   A. widely disparate
   B. similar to normal GFR
   C. less than those of normal individuals
   D. greater than those of normal individuals
   E. similar to those of normal individuals

92. **In a normal subject, 24 hours of water deprivation results in:**
   A. an osmolality of the tubular fluid at the end of the thick ascending loop of Henle equal to that of the plasma
   B. increased urea reabsorption in the papillary collecting duct
   C. increased osmolality of the cortical interstitium
   D. decreased osmolality of the papillary interstitium
   E. none of the above

93. **Sodium in the proximal tubule:**
   A. is reabsorbed exclusively through the paracellular pathway
   B. moves from lumen to cell actively against a concentration gradient
   C. is transported across the basolateral cell membrane actively by a Na^+/K^+ ATPase
   D. is reabsorbed exclusively by cotransport with glucose
   E. is reabsorbed exclusively by counter-transport with hydrogen ions

94. **A compound that has a renal clearance 25 times that of creatinine is probably:**
   A. only filtered at the glomerulus
   B. only secreted by the nephron
   C. both filtered and secreted
   D. synthesized by the nephron and secreted
   E. filtered, secreted and reabsorbed

95. **All the following have an established transport T_m EXCEPT:**
   A. glucose
   B. sodium
   C. albumin
   D. para-aminohippuric acid (PAH)
   E. lactate

GASTROINTESTINAL PHYSIOLOGY

1. **Gastrointestinal hormones are:**
   A. steroids
   B. released into the lumen of the GI tract
   C. destroyed in their passage through the liver
   D. found in endocrine cells distributed over wide areas of mucosa
   E. members of either one or the other of two chemically related families

2. **Members of the secretin family of peptides:**
   A. act either as hormones or neurocrines
   B. contain fragments possessing full biological activity
   C. stimulate gastric acid secretion
   D. function physiologically as paracrines
   E. can be released by distention of the stomach

3. **A substance released from nerves that stimulates contraction of the ileocecal sphincter is likely to be:**
   A. VIP (vasoactive intestinal peptide)
   B. GRP (gastrin-releasing peptide)
   C. one of the enkephalins
   D. peptide YY
   E. motilin

4. **A muscle cell that has no striations and has a ratio of thin to thick filaments of 15:1 most likely would be found in the:**
   A. external anal sphincter
   B. lower esophageal sphincter
   C. pharynx
   D. tongue
   E. upper esophageal sphincter

5. **A lesion results in loss of primary peristaltic contractions of the pharynx and esophagus; however, secondary peristalsis of the lower esophagus still occurs upon distention of the esophageal body. The lesion most likely is in the:**
   A. cortical region of the brain
   B. cricopharyngeal muscle (upper esophageal sphincter)
   C. enteric nerves
   D. nucleus ambiguus
   E. pharyngeal muscle

6. **A catheter that monitors pressure at its tip is inserted through the nose and passed an unknown distance. The catheter records a pressure between swallows that is subatmospheric and that decreases during inspiration and increases during expiration. The catheter tip is most likely in the:**
   A. upper esophageal sphincter
   B. esophageal body above the diaphragm
   C. esophageal body below the diaphragm
   D. lower esophageal sphincter
   E. orad region of the stomach

7. **In fasting subjects, the period of intense contractions of the MMC (migrating motility complex), when compared to the period of minimal contractions, is characterized by:**
   A. a decrease in the apparent propagation velocity of control slow waves
   B. a decrease in the frequency of duodenal slow waves
   C. an increase in the amplitude of antral slow waves
   D. an increase in the frequency of antral slow waves
   E. the occurrence of slow waves in the orad stomach

8. **Which of the following solutions would empty most rapidly from the stomach?**
   A. 100 mN HCl
   B. water
   C. isotonic starch
   D. hypertonic NaCl
   E. isotonic NaCl

9. **A region of the intestine contracts weakly upon stimulation of its extrinsic nerves. Distention of the region elicits a peristaltic reflex, but with weak contractions. Slow wave activity is absent. These findings suggest a disorder of the:**
   A. enteric nerves
   B. parasympathetic nerves
   C. release of CCK
   D. smooth muscle cells
   E. sympathetic nerves

10. **Intraluminal pressure is monitored from a region of the colon that exhibits a relatively constant resting pressure of about 20 mm Hg. When an adjacent region of colon is distended, resting pressure falls to near 0 and then increases slowly back toward 20 mm Hg, even though the distention persists. The region being monitored is most likely the:**
    A. ileocecal sphincter
    B. ascending colon
    C. transverse colon
    D. internal anal sphincter
    E. external anal sphincter

11. **Compared to fluid in a salivary gland acinus, the fluid at the duct opening in the mouth will have a:**
    A. lower concentration of K^+
    B. higher concentration of water
    C. higher concentration of Na^+
    D. higher concentration of Cl^-
    E. lower pH

12. **A substance found in saliva that increases blood flow to the salivary glands is:**
    A. kallikrein
    B. bradykinin
    C. lactoferrin
    D. lysozyme
    E. acetylcholine

13. **Salivary amylase:**
    A. digests starch into glucose units
    B. is an endopeptidase
    C. is activated by low gastric pH
    D. is essential for normal starch digestion
    E. remains active in unmixed contents of the orad stomach

14. **A cell isolated from the gastric mucosa contains granules localized between its nucleus and the basal membrane. That cell is most likely a:**
    A. parietal cell
    B. gastrin cell
    C. chief or peptic cell
    D. mucous neck cell
    E. surface epithelial cell

15. **During the interdigestive phase, a subject is injected with a dose of histamine that is sufficient to stimulate acid secretion. Compared to the period before stimulation:**
    A. the potential difference across the gastric mucosa will be less
    B. the pH of the gastric venous blood will be less
    C. the concentration of Na^+ in the gastric juice will be greater
    D. there will be more tubulovesicles in the parietal cells
    E. none of the above

16. **Following the stimulation of gastric secretion, the concentration of H^+ in gastric juice increases because:**
    A. the volume of secretion from the parietal cells increases
    B. the concentration of H^+ being secreted by the parietal cells increases
    C. the gastric mucosal barrier tightens and prevents a loss of H^+
    D. the nonparietal component of gastric secretion is inhibited
    E. H^+ is exchanged for Na^+ as the juice moves up the gastric gland

17. **Enterokinase is directly responsible for the activation of:**
    A. carboxypeptidase A
    B. enterokinase
    C. colipase
    D. trypsin
    E. all of the above

18. **Histamine-2 (H_2) receptor blockers, such as cimetidine, inhibit the acid secretory response to:**
    A. histamine and gastrin but not acetylcholine
    B. histamine but not gastrin
    C. the stimuli present during the cephalic phase
    D. somatostatin
    E. none of the above

19. **Each of the following is decreased by vagotomy EXCEPT:**
    A. receptive relaxation of the orad stomach
    B. pepsin secretion in response to a meal
    C. gastrin release in response to distention
    D. gastrin release in response to luminal amino acids
    E. pancreatic secretion in response to fat and amino acids in the duodenum

20. **During the gastric phase of acid secretion, each of the following occurs EXCEPT:**
    A. acetylcholine directly stimulates the parietal cells
    B. acetylcholine releases gastrin from the G cells
    C. GRP releases gastrin from the G cells
    D. histamine potentiates the effect of acetylcholine on the parietal cells
    E. digested protein directly stimulates the parietal cells

21. **Each of the following is inhibited by ouabain (blocks Na^+/K^+ ATPase) EXCEPT:**
    A. diarrhea caused by cholera toxin
    B. diarrhea caused by lactose intolerance
    C. intestinal Na^+ uptake by diffusion through membrane channels
    D. intestinal glucose uptake
    E. K^+ secretion in the colon

22. **Acidification of the antral mucosa will not reduce serum gastrin in patients with:**
    A. pernicious anemia
    B. duodenal ulcer (normal peptic ulcer)
    C. atrophic gastritis
    D. Zollinger-Ellison syndrome
    E. gastric cancer

23. **Pancreatic enzymes are:**
    A. all secreted as inactive proenzymes
    B. all secreted by acinar cells
    C. synthesized in response to a secretory stimulus
    D. secreted from condensing vacuoles
    E. important for only protein digestion

24. **Which of the following combination of agents will produce the highest rate of pancreatic bicarbonate secretion?**
    A. secretin plus histamine
    B. cholecystokinin plus acetylcholine
    C. gastrin plus vagal stimulation
    D. secretin plus vagal stimulation
    E. cholecystokinin plus phenylalanine in the duodenum

25. **Compared to hepatic bile, gallbladder bile will differ in that its:**
    A. bile salt concentration will be less
    B. cholesterol to bile salt ratio will be greater
    C. osmolality will be greater
    D. phospholipid concentration will be less
    E. sodium concentration will be greater

26. **Bile acid A has less solubility in intestinal fluid than bile acid B. Compared to bile acid B, bile acid A is more likely to be:**
   A. a primary bile acid
   B. a trihydroxy rather than dihydroxy bile acid
   C. absorbed passively in the jejunum
   D. conjugated
   E. deoxycholic rather than lithocholic acid

27. **Removal of the distal ileum will increase bile acid:**
   A. levels in hepatic venous blood
   B. levels in the portal vein
   C. secretion by hepatocytes
   D. storage in the gallbladder
   E. synthesis by hepatocytes

28. **Colipase:**
   A. is secreted as an inactive enzyme
   B. hydrolyzes the 2'-ester linkage of triglycerides
   C. binds to fat digestion products
   D. binds to pancreatic lipase
   E. is a constituent of micelles

29. **Which of the following is an integral part of the intestinal brush border membrane?**
   A. carboxypeptidase A
   B. enterokinase
   C. colipase
   D. elastase
   E. amylase

30. **The addition of glucose to the lumen of an intestinal segment is found to increase the potential difference across the mucosa. The addition of compound X to the lumen decreases the absorption of glucose but causes a further increase in the potential difference. Compound X is most likely:**
   A. an amino acid
   B. fructose
   C. galactose
   D. palmitic acid
   E. glycerol

31. **If the intestinal absorption of 10 mMol of glycine were compared to the absorption of 5 mMol of the dipeptide glycylglycine:**
   A. the concentration of glycine in the blood would increase at the same rate in each case
   B. the concentration of dipeptide in the blood would increase at half the rate of that of the free amino acid
   C. the concentration of glycine in the blood would increase faster when the dipeptide was being absorbed
   D. the concentration of glycine in the blood would increase faster when the free amino acid was being absorbed
   E. the dipeptide, if added at the same time as free glycine, would decrease the absorption of the free amino acid

32. **Fatty acid binding proteins:**
   A. directly aid in the uptake of fatty acids and monoglycerides by the brush border
   B. transport fatty acids to chylomicrons
   C. are cofactors in the resynthesis of triglycerides
   D. preferentially bind medium-chain fatty acids
   E. transport fatty acids to the smooth endoplasmic reticulum

33. **The major mechanism for the uptake of Na^+ in the colon is:**
   A. exchange with H^+
   B. cotransport with Cl^-
   C. cotransport with organic solutes
   D. primary active transport
   E. diffusion through membrane channels

Questions 34–37: Matching. Each choice may be used once, more than once, or not at all.
   A. histamine
   B. acetylcholine
   C. gastrin
   D. secretin
   E. bombesin (GRP)

34. **Inhibits gastric acid secretion:**

35. **Amino acid derivative released from ECL cells:**

36. **Stimulates the growth of the oxyntic gland mucosa:**

37. **Acts as a paracrine:**

38. **Swallowing:**
   A. initiates primary esophageal peristalsis
   B. is entirely voluntary
   C. is primarily controlled by feedback via the sympathetic system
   D. is initiated by receptors on the tongue
   E. can occur in the absence of any material to be swallowed

39. **The esophageal muscle immediately above the diaphragm:**
   A. receives vagal input directly
   B. relaxes as a bolus approaches
   C. is tonically contracted
   D. is normally flaccid between swallows so that the pressure inside is less than atmospheric
   E. generates secondary peristaltic waves in response to hormones released by material distending it

40. Intact vagal innervation is required for each of the following *EXCEPT:*
   A. receptive relaxation of the stomach
   B. peristalsis in the lower third of the esophagus
   C. stimulation of acid secretion by food in the mouth
   D. a portion of gastrin release stimulated by distending the stomach
   E. pancreatic secretion during the cephalic phase of digestion

41. The rate of gastric emptying of a test meal is increased by:
   A. increasing the fat content of the meal
   B. increasing the volume of the meal
   C. increasing the size of the food particles in the meal
   D. making the meal hypotonic
   E. decreasing the pH of the meal from 7.0 to 4.0

42. Slow waves of the small intestine:
   A. trigger contractions
   B. always contain spike potentials
   C. are produced with a lower frequency proximally than distally
   D. occur at approximately 90-min intervals
   E. set the maximal frequency of small intestinal contractions

43. During fasting, the predominant motility activity of the small intestine is:
   A. receptive relaxation
   B. segmentation
   C. brief sporadic contractions interrupted periodically by migrating motility complexes
   D. strong peristaltic contractions repeated over the length of the gut at frequencies of 11 to 12 cycles per minute
   E. periods of quiet followed by mass movements

44. Propulsion of colonic contents into the rectum:
   A. is caused by a migrating motility complex
   B. causes an involuntary contraction of the external anal sphincter
   C. initiates defecation
   D. is voluntary
   E. causes the internal anal sphincter to relax

45. Salivary secretion:
   A. is produced at high volumes relative to the mass of the glands
   B. is usually hypertonic
   C. is primarily regulated by hormones
   D. is inhibited by sympathetic stimulation
   E. has a lower concentration of Na^+ as the rate of flow increases

46. Stimulation of the parasympathetic nerves to the salivary glands results in each of the following *EXCEPT:*
   A. increased output of saliva
   B. increased growth of the glands
   C. contraction of the myoepithelial cells
   D. increased metabolism of the glands
   E. vasoconstriction of the blood vessels to the glands

47. As a fasted individual begins eating, each of the following occurs within the parietal cells *EXCEPT:*
   A. increased H^+/K^+ ATPase activity
   B. increased activity of carbonic anhydrase
   C. increased number of tubulovesicles
   D. increased ATP production by mitochondria
   E. increased area devoted to intracellular canaliculus

48. According to the two-component hypothesis, the Na^+ concentration in gastric secretion decreases with the rate of secretion because:
   A. the concentration of H^+ being secreted from the parietal cells increases
   B. the nonoxyntic component of secretion is stimulated
   C. the volume of the oxyntic component increases
   D. the secretion of Na^+ is inhibited
   E. the Na^+ is exchanged for K^+

49. Acidification of the gastric antrum to pH 1.0:
   A. stimulates secretin release
   B. inhibits acid secretion by releasing enterogastrones
   C. inhibits acid secretion via a vagovagal reflex
   D. inhibits gastrin release by releasing bombesin
   E. inhibits gastrin release by releasing somatostatin

50. Between meals, when the stomach is empty of food:
   A. it contains a large volume of juice with an approximate pH of 5
   B. gastrin release is inhibited by a strongly acidic solution
   C. it contains a small volume of gastric juice with a pH near neutrality
   D. bombesin acts on the parietal cells to inhibit secretion
   E. it secretes large volumes of weakly acidic juice

51. During the cephalic phase:
   A. secretin stimulates pepsin secretion
   B. CCK stimulates pancreatic enzyme secretion
   C. ACh stimulates the G cells to release gastrin
   D. bombesin stimulates parietal cell secretion
   E. ACh stimulates pancreatic enzyme secretion

52. Acidification of the duodenal mucosa to pH <4.0:
   A. stimulates pancreatic bicarbonate secretion
   B. inhibits pepsinogen secretion
   C. stimulates G cells to release gastric acid
   D. inhibits bile production
   E. stimulates gastric emptying

53. **Maximal rates of pancreatic bicarbonate secretion in response to a meal in humans are due to:**
    A. the effects of small amounts of secretin being potentiated by ACh and CCK
    B. large amounts of secretin released from the duodenal mucosa
    C. VIP acting on the ductule cells
    D. potentiation between CCK and ACh released from vagovagal reflexes
    E. potentiation between small amounts of secretin and gastrin

54. **In the absence of enterokinase, one would also expect a decrease in the activity of:**
    A. pepsin
    B. lipase
    C. chymotrypsin
    D. amylase
    E. sucrase

55. **Conjugation of cholic acid to glycine:**
    A. makes it less soluble in water
    B. increases its secretion from the liver
    C. ensures that it will be reabsorbed from the gut
    D. lowers its pK
    E. converts it to a secondary bile acid

56. **Ileal resection:**
    A. decreases the proportion of primary bile acids in bile
    B. increases the synthesis of bile acids by the liver
    C. increases the volume (production) of bile
    D. will not affect the absorption of dietary fat
    E. decreases the fecal excretion of bile salts

57. **Which of the following is water soluble?**
    A. oleic acid (C18)
    B. vitamin A
    C. cholesterol
    D. cholic acid
    E. bilirubin glucuronide

58. **Gallbladder contraction is stimulated by:**
    A. fat digestion products in the duodenum
    B. bile acids returning to the liver in the portal circulation
    C. secretin
    D. glucose in the duodenum
    E. osmotic concentration of the solutes within the gallbladder

59. **Exhaustive digestion of starch by pancreatic amylase produces:**
    A. glucose alone
    B. maltose and glucose
    C. maltose, maltotriose, and α-limit dextrins
    D. maltose, maltotriose, and galactose
    E. sucrose alone

60. **Colipase:**
    A. digests triglycerides
    B. converts prolipase to active lipase
    C. is a brush border enzyme
    D. prevents the inactivation of lipase by bile salts
    E. binds to absorbed fatty acids, transporting them to the smooth endoplasmic reticulum for resynthesis into triglycerides

61. **In the small intestine, Na^+ is absorbed by each of the following processes EXCEPT:**
    A. by diffusion
    B. by being coupled to amino acid absorption
    C. by being coupled to galactose absorption
    D. by being coupled to the transport of H^+ in the opposite direction
    E. by being coupled to the absorption of HCO_3-

62. **Diarrhea might be expected to result in each of the following EXCEPT:**
    A. dehydration
    B. metabolic acidosis
    C. decreased frequency of respiration
    D. hypokalemia
    E. decreased mean circulatory filling pressure

63. **Of the 8–10 liters of water that enters the GI tract each day:**
    A. the majority comes from food and drink in the diet
    B. most is absorbed in the small intestine
    C. most is absorbed in the large intestine
    D. approximately 4 liters enters the large intestine
    E. most is absorbed by an active transport mechanism

64. **A patient with a total absence of gastric parietal cells would have:**
    A. lower than normal serum gastrin
    B. normal digestion and absorption of dietary protein
    C. impaired digestion of starch
    D. normal absorption of vitamin B_{12}
    E. normal levels of pepsin activity

65. **Patients with a congenital absence of one of the amino acid carriers do not become deficient in that amino acid due to the fact that:**
    A. the amino acid is absorbed by passive diffusion
    B. the amino acid can make use of other carriers
    C. the amino acid is absorbed by facilitated diffusion
    D. peptides containing the amino acid are absorbed by different carriers
    E. the amino acid is an essential amino acid

66. **Following a thorough examination of a patient with chronic (several days) severe diarrhea, you would expect to find:**
   A. increased serum pH
   B. decreased mean systemic (circulatory) filling pressure
   C. hyperkalemia
   D. decreased frequency of breathing
   E. decreased heart rate

67. **Each of the following is true about active glucose absorption by enterocytes EXCEPT:**
   A. it is dependent on cotransport with Na^+
   B. it is dependent on the activity of the Na^+/K^+ ATPase in the basolateral cell membrane
   C. it is inhibited by hypoxia
   D. it will decrease the transepithelial electrical potential difference
   E. it will be inhibited by galactose

Questions 68–70. Gastric emptying of three solutions was measured under three different conditions. These solutions were added to the empty stomach without any salivary contamination.

Solutions	*Conditions*
1. isotonic saline	1. normal—control
2. isotonic starch	2. pancreatic secretion inhibited
3. hypertonic glucose	3. surgical bypass of the proximal 50% of the small intestine with anastomosis of the pylorus to the proximal ileum

For each of the following statements, answer A if it is true, B if it is false.

68. **In condition 1, solutions 1 and 3 will empty from the stomach at the same rate.**

69. **In condition 2, solutions 1 and 2 will empty from the stomach at the same rate.**

70. **In condition 3, all three solutions will empty at the same rate.**

71. **Administration of a drug that blocks the H^+/K^+ ATPase of the parietal cells of a secreting stomach will:**
   A. have no effect on the volume of secretion
   B. increase the concentration of H^+ in the secretion
   C. decrease the concentration of Na^+ in the secretion
   D. decrease the pH of the gastric venous blood
   E. decrease the potential difference across the stomach

72. **Each of the following might be expected to be found in micelles EXCEPT:**
   A. bilirubin glucuronide
   B. cholesterol
   C. taurolithocholic acid
   D. lecithin
   E. vitamin A

73. **Gallbladder:**
   A. contraction is physiologically stimulated by secretin
   B. bile has a lower Na^+ concentration than hepatic bile
   C. bile has a lower concentration of cholesterol than hepatic bile
   D. contraction is stimulated by bile acids returning to the liver
   E. bile has the same concentration of water as hepatic bile

74. **From the following list, the enzyme most essential to protein digestion is:**
   A. elastase
   B. enterokinase
   C. α-dextrinase
   D. pepsin
   E. trehalase

75. **Micelles are necessary for the normal absorption of all of the following EXCEPT:**
   A. vitamin K
   B. medium-chain fatty acids
   C. long-chain fatty acids
   D. long-chain monoglycerides
   E. dietary cholesterol

76. **The ileocecal sphincter:**
   A. relaxes when the ileum is distended
   B. relaxes when the proximal colon is distended
   C. response to ileal distention is mediated by a vagovagal reflex
   D. pressure is under hormonal control
   E. constricts when the pressure in the ileum increases

77. **Receptive relaxation of the stomach:**
   A. is abolished by vagotomy
   B. is triggered by relaxation of the lower esophageal sphincter (LES)
   C. occurs primarily in the antrum
   D. results in large increases in intragastric pressure following a meal
   E. depends entirely on the enteric nervous system

78. **The main function of the colon is to absorb:**
   A. vitamins
   B. water
   C. fats
   D. carbohydrates
   E. electrolytes

79. The most likely place to find an increase in somatostatin levels following acidification of the stomach would be:

A. small veins of the stomach
B. gastric artery
C. gastric lumen
D. hepatic portal vein
E. a pancreatic vein

80. Gastric slow waves are different from intestinal slow waves in that they:

A. occur at a higher frequency
B. can cause muscle contractions
C. increase or decrease in frequency depending on the digestive state
D. disappear during fasting
E. may be associated with spike potentials

ENDOCRINE PHYSIOLOGY

1. **A 46-year-old man has lost innervation to both his adrenal glands; otherwise, his nervous system is intact and functioning normally, and his adrenals have adequate circulation. Late one afternoon, he receives a telephone message that one of his children has been seriously injured. Which of the following hormones will fairly quickly increase in his plasma?**
   A. ACTH, cortisol, epinephrine, and norepinephrine
   B. ACTH, epinephrine, and norepinephrine
   C. ACTH, cortisol, and norepinephrine
   D. only ACTH and norepinephrine
   E. only ACTH

2. **During an oral GTT (glucose tolerance test) given in the late afternoon, which of the following hepatic enzymes is stimulated by elevated concentrations of glucagon?**
   A. hexokinase
   B. acetyl Co-A carboxylase
   C. phosphofructosekinase
   D. fructose 1,6-bisphosphatase
   E. pyruvate dehydrogenase

3. **In males, testosterone (or DHT) stimulates all the following *EXCEPT:***
   A. pubertal growth of the penis, which will be permanent
   B. thelarche
   C. lowering of pitch of the voice, which will be permanent
   D. hair growth on chest and face
   E. hair growth up the midline of the abdomen (linea alba)

4. **In females, estrogen directly produces all of the following *EXCEPT:***
   A. secretion by uterine endometrial glands
   B. pituitary hypertrophy
   C. increased contractility of uterine and oviduct muscles
   D. mammary gland growth
   E. stimulation of a thin, watery secretion by cervical glands

5. **MIS (MRF; anti-Müllerian factor) causes the:**
   A. Wolffian ducts to develop into male internal structures
   B. Müllerian ducts to develop into female internal structures
   C. Müllerian ducts to disappear, leaving Wolffian ducts intact
   D. gonadal ridges to develop into testes instead of ovaries
   E. testes to secrete testosterone in early fetal life, inducing Wolffian ducts to develop into male external structures

6. **The plasma concentration of hCG:**
   A. increases steadily throughout pregnancy
   B. increases beginning about 2 months after fertilization
   C. increases beginning less than 2 weeks after fertilization
   D. peaks 4–6 months after fertilization
   E. Both C and D are correct.

7. **Erection can occur when:**
   A. penile blood flow increases about 25-fold
   B. parasympathetic input to penile arterioles causes them to relax
   C. sympathetic input to penile arterioles is blocked by stimulation of an inhibitory interneuron
   D. some appropriate stimulus (such as tactile, visual, or psychological) reaches the erection center in the lower spinal cord
   E. all of the above are correct

8. **ADH secretion would be increased by all of the following *EXCEPT:***
   A. increased plasma osmolality
   B. decreased fluid intake
   C. excessive fluid loss
   D. increased water ingestion
   E. decreased ECF volume

9. **An assay of serum samples from a normal woman with a history of regular 28-day cycles indicates that, during the last 12 h, there has been a peak in the serum concentration of estradiol -17β in the absence of any detectable progesterone. Which of the following can be expected to occur within 3 days?**
   A. cessation of menstruation
   B. decreased basal body temperature
   C. onset of menstruation
   D. ovulation
   E. regression of the corpus luteum

10. **All of the following are true about growth hormone in humans *EXCEPT:***
    A. somatostatin withdrawal is sufficient to induce GH secretion
    B. much of our daily GH secretion occurs when we first enter deep sleep
    C. integrated daily GH secretion is highest during the pubertal growth spurt
    D. only human-derived GH is clinically useful
    E. thyroid hormones increase pituitary GH synthesis

11. **In humans, the stimulus that initiates parturition is:**
    A. increased fetal cortisol
    B. increased ratio of free progesterone to free estrogen in fetal blood
    C. increased ratio of free progesterone to free estrogen in maternal blood
    D. maternal oxytocin secretion
    E. still unknown

12. **PTH:**
   A. secretion increases when plasma ionized calcium ($P_{Ca^{2+}}$) increases
   B. directly stimulates osteoclasts to prevent bone resorption
   C. acts on kidney and bone to raise $P_{Ca^{2+}}$
   D. secretion is stimulated after excessive vitamin D intake
   E. acts directly on intestinal mucosa to increase Ca absorption

13. **All of the following are true about vitamin D EX-CEPT:**
   A. Vitamin D is formed in three steps: first in the skin, then the liver, and then the kidney.
   B. In severe renal failure, 1,25-dihydroxy vitamin D accumulates in plasma because it cannot be excreted in the urine.
   C. PTH enhances formation of calcitriol, the most active form of vitamin D.
   D. Vitamin D facilitates movement of Ca into and out of bone.
   E. Vitamin D facilitates intestinal Ca absorption.

14. **ACTH:**
   A. is a dimer of alpha and beta subunits
   B. has a beta subunit that contains all the ACTH-like biological activity
   C. has an alpha subunit that can produce its antigenic activity
   D. All of the above are correct.
   E. None of the above is correct.

15. **All of the triplets listed below are correct EXCEPT:**

Pituitary Hormone	Hypothal-amic Hormone	Action of Hypothalamic Hormone
A. somatotropin	SS	decreases GH secretion
B. prolactin	DA	decreases PRL secretion
C. follicle-stimulating hormone	GnIH	increases FSH secretion
D. thyrotropin	TRH	increases TSH secretion
E. luteinizing hormone	GnRH increases	LH secretion

16. **In humans, the major circulating steroids that produce the three main types of adrenal steroid actions are:**

Glucocorticoid	Mineralocor-ticoid	Adrenal Androgen
A. cortisol	aldosterone	DHEA*
B. cortisone	DOC**	androstenedione
C. ACTH	cortisol	testosterone
D. cortisol	DOC	androstenedione
E. corticosterone	aldosterone	testosterone

*DHEA = dehydroepiandrosterone ($\pm$ sulfate).
**DOC = deoxycorticosterone.

17. **Which of the following situations will result in stimulation of glucagon secretion?**
   A. decreased plasma amino acid concentration
   B. increased somatostatin secretion within the islets
   C. increased plasma glucose, especially above 70 mg/dl
   D. decreased plasma insulin when peripheral insulin resistance occurs
   E. high levels of plasma insulin in the absence of insulin resistance

18. **To evaluate whether the pancreas has recovered some beta cell secretory capability in an insulin-requiring type-2 diabetic (adult-onset diabetes), which of the following plasma measurements would be most useful?**
   A. insulin in a GTT
   B. C-peptide in a GTT
   C. proinsulin after injecting epinephrine
   D. insulin after stimulation with amino acids
   E. glucagon after inducing mild hypoglycemia

19. **As plasma glucose concentrations fall from normal toward those that could produce a coma, all the following can be considered beneficial (counter-regulatory) responses EXCEPT:**
   A. decreased cognitive function
   B. decreased insulin secretion
   C. increased epinephrine secretion (SNS activation)
   D. increased glucagon secretion
   E. increased GH, ACTH, and cortisol secretion

20. **All of the following are important actions of insulin EXCEPT:**
   A. increased synthesis of lipoprotein lipase, which facilitates FA removal from circulating VLDL and chylomicrons
   B. increased synthesis of muscle protein
   C. increased synthesis of glycogen
   D. inhibition of hormone-sensitive lipase, reducing TAG (triacylglycerol) breakdown
   E. stimulation of intestinal glucose absorption

21. **When taken orally, all the following hormones should have biological effects on their usual target tissues EXCEPT:**
   A. progesterone
   B. parathyroid hormone
   C. estrogen
   D. T_3
   E. thyroxin

22. **Excessive secretion of GH before fusion of the epiphyseal growth plates causes:**
   A. giantism
   B. acromegaly
   C. Cushing's syndrome
   D. Addison's disease
   E. dwarfism

23. In males, inhibin reduces:
    A. libido, by directly inhibiting adrenal androgen secretion
    B. testosterone synthesis, by a direct action on Leydig cells
    C. FSH secretion and, hence, spermatogenesis
    D. LH secretion and, hence, testosterone secretion
    E. All of the above are correct.

24. Which of the following hormones is anabolic on muscle protein at physiologic concentrations, but is catabolic at very high levels?
    A. insulin
    B. GH
    C. testosterone
    D. thyroid hormone
    E. none of the above

25. Figure 6-1 depicts the response to an increased dose of a hormone.

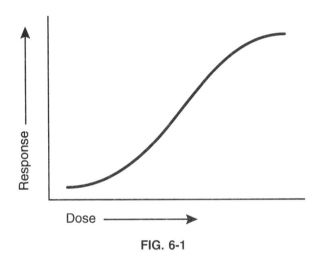

FIG. 6-1

The addition of an inhibitor that competes for the receptor to the hormone would:
    A. lower the maximal response and shift the curve to the right
    B. shift the curve to the left
    C. lower the maximal response
    D. shift the curve to the right
    E. lower the maximal response and shift the curve to the left

26. Prolonged administration of metyrapone is likely to increase all the following *EXCEPT*:
    A. CRH secretion
    B. plasma glucocorticoid activity
    C. ACTH secretion
    D. plasma deoxycorticosterone (DOC) concentration
    E. potassium excretion

27. As its plasma concentration progressively increases, which hormone's feedback regulation can change from negative to positive and back to negative?
    A. GH
    B. FSH
    C. progesterone
    D. estradiol
    E. testosterone

28. In boys, the first anatomical event signaling the onset of puberty usually is:
    A. the appearance of some pubic hair
    B. testicular enlargement
    C. the beginning of a growth spurt
    D. the appearance of some axillary hair
    E. the presence of mature sperm in a semen analysis

29. After delivery of her fourth child, a 40-year-old woman had severe hemorrhage and hypotension. She then developed Sheehan's syndrome (from postpartum necrosis of the anterior pituitary gland). She lost all normal anterior pituitary function. She does not want any more children, but does desire to avoid bone loss, reduce her risk of atherosclerosis, and have a satisfactory sex life (e.g., example adequate lubrication by vaginal mucus glands). She does not want to nurse her latest baby. To induce relatively normal physiologic function of important target tissues, you would likely treat her with all of the following *EXCEPT*:
    A. gonadotropins
    B. a glucocorticoid, given orally
    C. an estrogen
    D. oral thyroid hormone, e.g., T_4/T_3
    E. progesterone

30. A 35-year-old woman desperately wants a child, but has isolated hypogonadotropic hypogonadism of hypothalamic origin; i.e., all pituitary hormones and her ovaries and reproductive tract are normal, but FSH and LH secretion are minimal. With which one of the following could you treat her to induce a normal ovulation and pregnancy?
    A. estrogen alone, given so it peaks twice each month
    B. progesterone alone, given so it peaks once each month
    C. estrogen, and perhaps progesterone, taken on a regular monthly schedule (two peaks of estrogen, one of progesterone)
    D. daily shots of equal amounts of both FSH and LH every day each month
    E. pulses of GnRH, administered every 1 to 2 h by subcutaneous pump

31. **After the woman in question 30 has had her baby and nursed it until weaning, you probably would initiate long-term treatment with:**
  A. daily estrogen alone, given continuously until she is 50 years old
  B. daily progesterone alone, given continuously until she is 50 years old
  C. estrogen, and perhaps progesterone, taken on a regular monthly schedule, as in combination or sequential birth control pills
  D. daily shots of a gonadotropin every 28 days: FSH for 14 days, LH for 10 days, nothing for 4 days
  E. pulses of GnRH, administered every 1 to 2 h by subcutaneous pump

32. **After estrogen is increased for several weeks, such as in pregnancy or from taking birth control pills, what are the new steady-state plasma levels of CBG, cortisol, and ACTH, compared to before?**

	Total CBG	Cortisol	Free Cortisol	ACTH
A.	↑	↑	↑	↑
B.	↑	↑	≈ same*	≈ same*
C.	≈ same*	≈ same*	↓	↑
D.	≈ same	≈ same	≈ same	≈ same
E.	↓	↓	≈ same	≈ same

  *about the same, i.e., no change from pretreatment

33. **During absorption of a normal meal, how do plasma insulin and glucagon concentrations change, and what effects does this have on nutrient stores, i.e., protein, glycogen, and fat?**

	Plasma Insulin Concentration	Plasma Glucagon Concentration	Synthesis of Nutrient Stores	Breakdown of Nutrient Stores
A.	↓	↑	↑	↓
B.	≈ same*	↓	≈ same*	↓
C.	↑	≈ same*	↑	≈ same*
D.	↑	≈ same*	↑	↓
E.	↑	↓	↑	≈ same*

  *about the same concentration or rate as before eating and absorbing a meal.

34. **During nursing, oxytocin is secreted from the X but it had earlier been synthesized in the X.**

	X	Y
A.	mammary myoepithelial cells	mammary alveolar cells
B.	anterior lobe of pituitary	posterior lobe of pituitary
C.	posterior lobe of pituitary	hypothalamus
D.	intermediate lobe of pituitary	hypothalamic suckling center
E.	anterior lobe of pituitary	median eminence of hypothalamus

35. **Of the thyroxine produced by the thyroid:**
  A. more than 90% is converted to biologically active triiodothyronine (T_3)
  B. at least 30% is converted to biologically inactive reverse triiodothyronine (rT_3).
  C. most is deiodinated before being secreted by the thyroid gland
  D. 230more than 90% is transported into the body cells as thyroxine and, as such, it binds to DNA and regulates metabolism

36. **When concentrations of thyroid hormones have been abnormally high for 2 or 3 months due to an overdose with T_4, then the circulating TSH concentration will:**

  A. increase
  B. be subnormal but increase after a single TRH injection
  C. be subnormal and not increase after a single TRH injection
  D. remain normal and not increase after a single TRH injection
  E. remain normal and increase after a single TRH injection

37. **Thyroperoxidase functions in:**
  A. iodination of thyroglobulin
  B. thyroxine's action on body cells
  C. hydrolysis of thyroglobulin
  D. release of thyroxine from thyroglobulin
  E. conversion of T_4 to T_3

38. **For a diabetic patient (type 1) who is being successfully treated for ketoacidosis by the administration of insulin, a potassium salt also might be administered because:**
  A. insulin directly stimulates the excretion of potassium by the kidney
  B. a rapid (minutes) return of plasma pH and glucose to normal will lower the total body potassium content
  C. a rapid (minutes) return of plasma pH and glucose to normal will cause potassium to shift into the cells
  D. a rapid (minutes) return of plasma glucose to normal will cause a decrease in plasma volume

39. **The following are characteristic of steroid hormones EXCEPT:**
  A. they have a relatively long half-life
  B. most are bound to protein in the blood
  C. they bind to cytoplasmic receptor
  D. they are synthesized for the most part continuously
  E. their early action is on mRNA synthesis

40. **In a patient with untreated diabetic ketoacidosis, you would expect an increased urinary excretion of all the following EXCEPT:**
  A. glucose
  B. keto-acids
  C. NH_4^+
  D. bicarbonate
  E. titratable acids

41. **Excessive secretion of growth hormone (GH) in pre-pubertal individuals can cause which of the following abnormal states?**
    A. giantism
    B. acromegaly
    C. hyperglycemia
    D. both A and C
    E. both A and B

42. **Either decreased blood volume or increased plasma osmolality would be expected to increase plasma levels of:**
    A. ADH
    B. renin
    C. aldosterone
    D. both A and C
    E. none of the above

43. **Cutting the preganglionic sympathetic nerves to the adrenal gland would cause:**
    A. hyponatremia, dehydration, and death
    B. increased plasma levels of angiotensin II
    C. hyperkalemia
    D. all of the above
    E. none of the above

44. **Which of the following physiologic abnormalities would you expect to cause dilutional hyponatremia?**
    A. hyposecretion of aldosterone
    B. inability to form angiotensin II
    C. hypersecretion of vasopressin
    D. all of the above
    E. both A and B

45. **Gonadectomy of a female fetus (XX genotype) during the ''critical phase'' of uterine life would result in the birth of an infant having:**
    A. masculinized external genitalia
    B. masculinized internal genitalia
    C. no uterus
    D. all of the above
    E. none of the above

46. **Following hypophysectomy, an individual's responsiveness to a fixed dose of insulin increases because of:**
    A. decreased growth hormone secretion
    B. decreased FSH secretion
    C. decreased cortisol secretion
    D. both A and C
    E. none of the above; the opening statement is false

47. **In human females, menopause is thought to be due to:**
    A. failure of the hypothalamus to secrete GnRH
    B. failure of the anterior pituitary to secrete gonadotrophins
    C. failure of the ovaries to secrete estrogen and progesterone
    D. failure of peripheral tissues to respond to female sex hormones
    E. none of the above

48. **A pituitary acidophilic adenoma would most likely be associated with:**
    A. an elevated metabolic rate
    B. acromegaly
    C. hirsutism in females
    D. osteoporosis
    E. hyperpigmentation

49. **The 24-h urinary excretion of 19-carbon androgenic steroids would be lowest in:**
    A. castrated males
    B. castrated females
    C. adrenalectomized males
    D. adrenalectomized females
    E. intact females

50. **Consider a 21-year-old female patient presenting with the following**
    1. hyperpigmentation
    2. blood pressure 165/105
    3. acne
    4. hypokalemia
    5. hypernatremia
    6. amenorrhea
    7. low fasting blood glucose level
    8. physical and mental fatigue
    9. enlarged clitoris
    10. chromatin positive buccal smear

    Identify the only endocrine disorder in the list below that could account for all of these symptoms and laboratory findings.
    A. an ACTH-secreting tumor
    B. 11β-hydroxylase deficiency
    C. absence of androgen receptors
    D. 21-hydroxylase deficiency
    E. primary hypercortisolism

51. **During normal development, adult sexual characteristics do not appear before puberty. The best explanation for this is that prior to puberty in normal development:**
    A. the juvenile gonads lack the mechanism(s) required to secrete sex hormones
    B. the juvenile pituitary lacks the mechanism(s) required to respond to GnRH
    C. juvenile sex accessory structures lack the mechanism(s) required to respond to sex hormones
    D. the juvenile hypothalamus lacks the mechanism(s) required to release GnRH appropriately
    E. none of the above is best; they all are equally responsible

52. **Daily injections of testosterone into an adult male in amounts that would raise serum level above normal for 10 days would be expected to increase:**
    A. the size of the prostate
    B. the rate of spermatogenesis
    C. the mass of the testes
    D. all of the above
    E. none of the above

53. **Fertility in hypophysectomized adult males could be restored by appropriate administration of:**
    A. follicle-stimulating hormone
    B. luteinizing hormone or testosterone
    C. prolactin
    D. combinations of A and B
    E. none of the above

54. **Shortly after birth, a patient is found to have the following:**
    Karyotype: XX
    Internal genital structure:
       Müllerian: normally developed
       Wolffian: regressed
    External genitalia: feminine
    Fasting blood sugar: low
    Plasma volume: expanded
    This patient has:
    A. 17α-hydroxylase deficiency
    B. 11β-hydroxylase deficiency
    C. 21-hydroxylase deficiency
    D. androgen insensitivity
    E. gonadotropin deficiency

55. **The most important reason we can survive not eating for at least 48 h is that:**
    A. GH, thyroid hormones, catecholamines, and cortisol act in concert to promote muscle breakdown, providing more amino acids for gluconeogenesis
    B. there is increased secretion of GH, a rapidly acting, potent inhibitor of glucose utilization
    C. insulin secretion increases as plasma glucose rises on the second day
    D. once-daily secretion of cortisol stimulates synthesis of sufficient amounts of key enzymes in the liver to allow redistribution of carbon from stores to glucose
    E. once-daily secretion of glucagon stimulates muscle breakdown, providing amino acids for gluconeogenesis

56. **Which of the following groups consists of only those hormones that regulate body metabolism primarily on a minute-by-minute basis, rather than on a long-term basis (hours/days)?**
    A. glucagon, insulin, epinephrine
    B. glucocorticoids, GH, thyroid hormones
    C. GH, glucocorticoids, glucagon
    D. TSH, catecholamines, insulin
    E. none of the above

57. **Weakness from loss of muscle mass in prolonged hyperthyroidism occurs because high levels of thyroid hormone:**
    A. inhibit muscle protein synthesis
    B. decrease nutrient uptake from the GI tract (because they greatly increase GI motility)
    C. stimulate muscle protein degradation
    D. directly and strongly activate hepatic gluconeogenesis, drawing amino acids out of muscle
    E. decrease TSH

58. **Glucagon increases blood glucose concentration mainly because it:**
    A. inhibits insulin secretion
    B. enhances muscle protein degradation
    C. stimulates glycogen synthetase in the liver
    D. stimulates hepatic glycogenolysis and gluconeogenesis
    E. stimulates lipolysis in adipose tissue; the resulting increased FFA inhibits glucose utilization

59. **Normally, the major fraction of triiodothyronine in the body is:**
    A. produced in the thyroid gland
    B. produced in the nonthyroid tissues of the body
    C. bound to TBG
    D. activated by iodination of di-iodothyronine
    E. formed from reverse T_3

60. A patient with diabetic ketoacidosis hyperventilates because:
   A. elevated blood glucose stimulates central thirst and respiratory centers
   B. increased formation of CO_2 stimulates peripheral chemoreceptors
   C. elevated plasma H^+ ion concentration stimulates central respiratory centers
   D. the decrease in extracellular volume enhances bicarbonate reabsorption
   E. insulin directly inhibits the respiratory center

61. A high plasma Ca^{2+} level in the normal adult is likely to cause:
   A. bone decalcification (resorption)
   B. increased formation of $1,25(OH)_2D_3$
   C. increased formation of $24,25(OH)_2D_3$
   D. decreased secretion of calcitonin
   E. decreased urinary calcium excretion

62. An adult with a parathyroid gland tumor has a very elevated plasma PTH level. This person's urinary phosphate excretion is expected to X, whereas the plasma phosphate level is likely to Y.

	X	Y
A.	increase	increase
B.	increase	decrease or show no change
C.	decrease	increase or show no change
D.	decrease	decrease
E.	show no change	show no change

63. Which of the following factors is the most important in regulating the secretory rate of cortisol in normal humans?
   A. potassium
   B. angiotensin II
   C. cortisol
   D. sodium
   E. ionized calcium

64. Patients with a pancreatic β-cell adenoma (a tumor that hypersecretes the hormone[s] of its cell type) would tend to have:
   A. hyperglycemia
   B. elevated growth hormone and ACTH levels
   C. glycosuria
   D. all of the above
   E. none of the above

65. Marked increases in cortisol secretion can occur within minutes after exposure to stress. The physiological mechanism involved depends upon:
   A. increased use of cortisol by peripheral tissues, leading to decreased plasma cortisol concentration
   B. increased impulses in nerve fibers from the median eminence of the hypothalamus to corticotrophin cells in the anterior pituitary
   C. increased impulses in nerve fibers from the hypothalamus to the adrenal
   D. increased release of corticotrophin-releasing hormone (CRH) from the hypothalamus
   E. none of the above

66. The single most important hormone regulating the rate of milk production (synthesis) in lactating females is:
   A. oxytocin
   B. estradiol-17β
   C. FSH
   D. progesterone
   E. prolactin

For questions 67–71, refer to the information below.

You are presented with a 27-year-old patient manifesting the following symptoms:
   1. polyuria
   2. polydipsia
   3. elevated urine osmolality
   4. history of increased bone fragility
   5. hyperpigmentation
   6. easy bruisability

On the basis of these observations, you requested the laboratory tests that are listed below with their results.

   Thyroxine: Normal
   Fasting insulin: 50% higher than expected for normal individuals

67. In light of all other data (1–6, above), the laboratory report for insulin is probably:
   A. correct
   B. incorrect

68. The most reasonable diagnosis for this patient is a primary disorder of the:
   A. pancreatic β cells
   B. neurohypophysis (posterior pituitary)
   C. adenohypophysis (anterior pituitary)
   D. thyroid
   E. adrenal cortex

69. The gland having the primary malfunction in this case is secreting non-normal levels of its hormone
   A. insulin
   B. ADH
   C. ACTH
   D. thyroxine
   E. cortisol

70. **During your early differential diagnosis, an alternative diagnostic hypothesis might have been a primary hypersecreting lesion of the:**
    A. pancreatic β cells
    B. neurohypophysis
    C. adenohypophysis
    D. thyroid
    E. adrenal cortex

71. **However, you ruled out this alternative diagnostic hypothesis because of the:**
    A. polyuria
    B. polydipsia
    C. elevated urine osmolality
    D. history of increased bone fragility
    E. hyperpigmentation

72. **You obtain the following data for a patient: plasma $[T_4]$ is slightly elevated, plasma [TSH] is low, and thyroid gland size is below normal. Which of the following would best explain this set of observations?**
    A. a lesion in the anterior pituitary gland is preventing the secretion of TSH
    B. the patient is taking a drug that blocks the ability of the thyroid gland to synthesize thyroid hormone
    C. the patient is taking thyroid extract
    D. plasma levels of the thyroid hormone carrier protein are elevated
    E. a lesion in the hypothalamus is preventing the secretion of TRH

73. **A sudden increase in the plasma concentration of a hormone-binding protein would**
    A. decrease the response to the hormone
    B. increase the response to the hormone
    C. have no effect on the response to the hormone
    D. increase the amount of hormone free in the plasma
    E. decrease the release of the hormone from the endocrine gland

74. **All of the following are consistent with a diagnosis of hypopituitarism EXCEPT:**
    A. decreased cortisol response to an ACTH stimulation test
    B. frankly elevated FSH and LH with hypogonadism
    C. decreased ACTH response to CRH
    D. low TSH with very low free and total thyroxine levels
    E. very low IGF-1 levels

75. **All of the following are true about a typical adult patient with acromegaly EXCEPT:**
    A. the patient is usually at least 1 foot taller than predicted
    B. the patient usually has a pituitary tumor
    C. the patient usually has elevated IGF-1 levels
    D. the patient often has insulin insensitivity
    E. the patient often has organomegaly

76. **The pubertal growth spurt usually starts at a younger age in females. The most logical explanation is that:**
    A. males have higher levels of growth hormone at puberty
    B. pubertal increase in gonadal function occurs at a younger age in females
    C. the pubertal increase in testosterone is greater in males compared to the pubertal increase in progesterone in females
    D. the GHRH nuclei in the hypothalamus of males are less sensitive to glucocorticoid negative feedback
    E. epiphyseal fusion occurs earlier in males

77. **A patient has been taking health food pills containing ten times the normal dose of T_3. All of the following findings are likely to occur in this patient EXCEPT:**
    A. increased oxygen consumption
    B. increased body temperature
    C. suppressed TSH
    D. increased appetite
    E. elevated plasma T_4

78. **Compared to a 25-year-old woman, a 75-year-old woman would be expected to have:**
    A. lower urinary excretion of estrogen, progesterone, and gonadotropins
    B. higher plasma progesterone, but lower plasma estrogen concentrations
    C. lower plasma progesterone, but higher plasma estrogen concentrations
    D. lower plasma gonadotropins, estrogen, and progesterone concentrations
    E. higher plasma gonadotropins, but lower plasma estrogen and progesterone

79. **If both adrenal glands of a person are severely damaged by tuberculosis, which of the following hormones will increase in the blood?**
    A. aldosterone
    B. ACTH
    C. corticosterone
    D. cortisol
    E. all of the above

80. **The plasma concentration of which of the following hormones will increase following successful transplantation of the pituitary underneath the kidney capsule?**
    A. growth hormone
    B. somatostatin
    C. prolactin
    D. TSH
    E. ACTH

81. **Rational initial treatment of newly diagnosed panhypopituitarism in an 8-year-old boy would likely include all of the following EXCEPT:**
    A. GH
    B. testosterone
    C. a glucocorticoid
    D. T_4
    E. ADH

82. Increased secretion from the adrenal medulla will cause all the following *EXCEPT:*
   A. constriction of airways in the lungs
   B. decreased insulin secretion
   C. increased metabolic rate
   D. increased muscle tension
   E. increased lipolysis

83. Excessive secretion of DOC or aldosterone will promote all the following *EXCEPT:*
   A. Na retention, but only for about two weeks
   B. K excretion
   C. blood pressure elevation
   D. production of adrenal androgens
   E. weight gain

84. Which of the following would be a reasonable treatment for a person from whom Chvostek's and Trousseau's signs can be elicited after provocation by a thorough physician?
   A. tablets containing thyroid hormone
   B. increased dietary iodide
   C. PTU and beta-blocking drugs
   D. parathyroidectomy (avoiding thyroidectomy)
   E. greatly increased dietary vitamin D and Ca

85. An absolute or relative increase in which of the following hormones contributes to the hyperglycemia of diabetes?
   A. cortisol
   B. glucagon
   C. epinephrine
   D. All of the above are correct.
   E. Only A and C are correct.

86. All the following help reduce testicular temperature *EXCEPT:*
   A. contraction of cremasteric muscle during sexual arousal
   B. countercurrent heat exchange in the pampiniform plexus
   C. sweat glands in the scrotum
   D. lowering of scrotum and testes in hot environments
   E. numerous folds in the scrotum

87. Sertoli cells perform all the following *EXCEPT:*
   A. synthesize testosterone when stimulated by LH
   B. nourish developing spermatozoa
   C. synthesize androgen binding protein (ABP)
   D. provide the physical "blood-testis barrier" at their tight junctions
   E. produce fluid that pushes mature sperm toward the epididymis

88. Removal of the right testis at age 5 weeks in a 46-XY fetus will lead to:
   A. sterility in adulthood
   B. bilateral cryptorchidism
   C. bilateral failure of the Wolffian ducts to develop into male internal structures
   D. failure of the Müllerian ducts to regress on the right side only
   E. failure to develop masculine external genitalia during gestation

89. Progesterone does all of the following *EXCEPT:*
   A. increase basal body temperature
   B. synergize with estradiol to inhibit LH secretion
   C. convert the endometrium to a secretory state
   D. make cervical mucus thin and watery
   E. decrease myometrial contractility

90. Variation in the length of a menstrual cycle is determined primarily by variation in the:
   A. length of the luteal phase
   B. time between the mid-cycle FSH surge and ovulation
   C. frequency that a woman has (protected) sexual intercourse
   D. length of menstruation
   E. length of the follicular phase

91. Three hours after nursing, a mother hears her baby cry. This is likely to elicit which of the following?
   A. secretion of oxytocin
   B. secretion of prolactin
   C. milk ejection ("let-down")
   D. All of the above are correct.
   E. Only A and C are correct.

92. The predominant type of biological activity of hMG is that of:
   A. progesterone
   B. estrogen
   C. LH
   D. FSH
   E. none of the above

93. The initial increase in estrogen in a 10-year-old female produces:
   A. menarche
   B. the first ovulation
   C. thelarche
   D. adrenarche
   E. epiphyseal closure

94. If plasma calcium suddenly falls from 11.0 to 8.0 mg/dl in an otherwise normal child, all the following will occur *EXCEPT:*
   A. increased plasma PTH, which increases renal tubular calcium reabsorption
   B. increased plasma PTH, which stimulates conversion of cholecalciferol to $24,25\text{-}(OH)_2$-vitamin D_3 in the liver
   C. increased plasma PTH, which stimulates bone resorption
   D. increased plasma PTH, which decreases renal tubular phosphate reabsorption
   E. decreased plasma CT, which reduces the previous inhibition of bone resorption by CT

95. The maximum effect of a single oral dose of thyroid hormone on the human body is produced:
    A. between 15 min and 2 h after ingestion
    B. between 2 and 10 h after ingestion
    C. on the fourth day after ingestion
    D. during the second month after ingestion
    E. never, because it is ineffective orally

96. In a patient with diabetes mellitus who has ketoacidosis, you would probably find all of the following EXCEPT:
    A. increased plasma renin
    B. increased plasma aldosterone
    C. contracted intracellular volume
    D. expanded extracellular volume
    E. hyperpnea

97. In a patient who is being treated for diabetic ketoacidosis, a calcium salt might be administered because:

    A. insulin directly stimulates renal calcium excretion
    B. a rapid return of plasma pH to normal will lower total plasma calcium concentration
    C. a rapid return of plasma pH to normal will lower the plasma ionized calcium concentration
    D. a rapid return of plasma glucose concentration will cause a decrease in plasma volume
    E. insulin directly inhibits the entry of calcium into fat cells

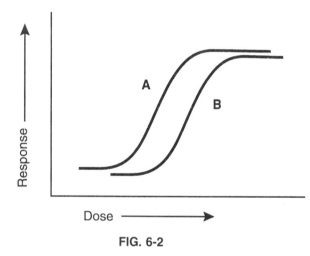

FIG. 6-2

98. In the above figure, the change from curve A to curve B in the responses to increasing doses of a hormone could have been caused by:
    A. an increase in the number of hormone receptors on the target cells
    B. a decrease in the number of the hormone receptors on the target cells
    C. an increase in the number of target cells
    D. a decrease in the number of target cells
    E. the presence of a noncompetitive inhibitor of the hormone

For questions 99–104, refer to the following data.

You are confronted with a 19-year-old patient with a positive (sex chromatin) buccal smear and manifesting the following physical findings:
A. delayed puberty, primary amenorrhea, absence of pubic and axillary hair, and failure of breast development
B. dark complexion
C. fasting hypoglycemia
D. decreased basal metabolic rate
E. juvenile, but otherwise apparently normal, female external genitalia

99. The observation that is least likely to be related to the basic problem in this patient is:
    A. delayed puberty, primary amenorrhea, absence of pubic and axillary hair, and failure of breast development
    B. dark complexion
    C. fasting hypoglycemia
    D. decreased basal metabolic rate
    E. juvenile, but otherwise apparently normal, female external genitalia

100. The remaining observations are most completely explained by a primary malfunction of the:
    A. adrenal cortex
    B. ovary
    C. testis
    D. anterior pituitary
    E. thyroid

101. An exploratory laparotomy performed in this patient would reveal the presence of:
    A. testis and male internal genital structures
    B. testis and female internal genital structures
    C. ovaries and male internal genital structures
    D. ovaries and female internal genital structures
    E. none of the above

102. The fasting hypoglycemia noted in this patient would best be explained by a lesion that has directly impaired the cells that secrete the hormone(s):
    A. ACTH
    B. cortisol
    C. growth hormone
    D. A and C are correct.
    E. A, B, and C are all correct.

103. To correct only the low basal metabolic rate, the most reasonable therapy would be oral administration of replacement doses of:
    A. TSH
    B. cortisol
    C. thyroid hormone
    D. ACTH
    E. estradiol

104. In order to induce the phenotypic morphological changes of puberty in this patient, the most reasonable therapy would be administration of:
    A. TSH
    B. testosterone
    C. estradiol-17β
    D. progesterone
    E. FSH

105. All the following patients would have normal or elevated C-peptide levels *EXCEPT*:
    A. a patient with early Type II diabetes
    B. a normal subject in the fed state
    C. a normal subject after an oral glucose load
    D. a patient with Type I diabetes receiving recombinant human insulin injections
    E. a patient with severe Cushing's syndrome

106. A female patient can produce androgens from the ovaries. However, she is unable to synthesize estradiol within the ovary. The most likely explanation is that:

    A. the patient has panhypopituitarism
    B. theca cell function is abnormally low
    C. granulosa cell function is abnormally low
    D. the patient has an adrenal tumor secreting cortisol
    E. the patient has a pituitary tumor overproducing the α-subunit of FSH

Questions 107–110. Match the phrases below to the situations in questions 107–110. Note that a phrase set may be selected once, more than once, or not at all.
    A. conversion of cholesterol to pregnenolone
    B. conversion of progesterone to 17-OH pregnenolone
    C. conversion of progesterone to 17-OH progesterone
    D. conversion of pregnenolone to progesterone
    E. conversion of 11-deoxycorticosterone to aldosterone

107. Occurs only in the zona fasciculata/reticularis:

108. Occurs only in the zona glomerulosa:

109. Catalyzed by 3β-hydroxysteroid dehydrogenase:

110. Rate-limiting first step of steroidogenesis:

Questions 111–114. Match the phrases below with the situations given in questions 111–114. Use each answer (phrase) only once.
    A. conversion of 7-dehydrocholesterol to cholecalciferol (Vitamin D_3)
    B. conversion of 25-hydroxycholecalciferol to 24,25(OH)$_2$ D_3
    C. conversion of 25-hydroxycholecalciferol to 1,25(OH)$_2$ D_3
    D. conversion of cholecalciferol to 25-hydroxycholecalciferol

111. Increased by UV light:

112. Stimulated by 1,25(OH)$_2$ D_3

113. Stimulated by PTH:

114. Occurs primarily in the liver:

Questions 115–118. Match the phrases below with the situations given in questions 115–118. Use each answer (phrase) only once.
    A. primary hyperparathyroidism
    B. secondary hyperparathyroidism
    C. primary hypoparathyroidism
    D. vitamin D intoxication

115. Characterized by elevated plasma PTH and low plasma calcium:

116. Characterized by elevated plasma PTH and elevated plasma calcium:

117. Characterized by low plasma PTH and elevated plasma calcium:

118. Characterized by low plasma PTH and low plasma calcium:

Questions 119–121. Match the words below to the situations given in questions 119–121.
    A. increased
    B. decreased
    C. unchanged

119. Plasma LH concentration at day 10 of the menstrual cycle as compared to day 6:

120. Plasma progesterone in mid-luteal phase as compared to mid-follicular phase:

121. Plasma estradiol at day 1 of the menstrual cycle as compared to mid-luteal phase:

Questions 122–125. Match the phrases below to the situations given in questions 122–125. A phrase may be used once or not at all.
    A. elevated plasma ACTH; decreased plasma cortisol
    B. low plasma ACTH; elevated urine free cortisol
    C. high normal plasma ACTH; elevated plasma cortisol; augmented petrosal sinus ACTH gradient after CRH injection
    D. very high plasma ACTH and cortisol; no petrosal sinus gradient for ACTH
    E. low plasma ACTH and subnormal cortisol response to ACTH

122. Ectopic ACTH syndrome:

123. Hypopituitarism:

124. Primary adrenal insufficiency:

125. ACTH-independent Cushing's syndrome (adrenal tumor):

126. A pharmacological dose of dexamethasone (8 mg/day), a potent glucocorticoid, was administered to a patient with Cushing's syndrome (elevated circulating cortisol and ACTH levels). Dexamethasone did not alter the patient's circulating cortisol level. From your knowledge of pituitary-adrenal function, this observation is consistent with:
   A. normal adrenal function
   B. a tumor of the adenohypophysis
   C. a cortisol-secreting tumor of the adrenal cortex
   D. an extrasellar tumor that produces a substance with ACTH activity(ectopic ACTH)
   E. None of the above choices is correct.

127. Prolactin plays an important role in the endocrine regulation of lactation. Despite increased prolactin secretion during pregnancy, little milk production occurs until after parturition because:
   A. plasma cortisol levels are suppressed
   B. secretion of oxytocin does not occur
   C. the neuroendocrine reflex brought about by suckling has not yet occurred
   D. there are high circulating levels of estrogen
   E. there are high circulating levels of placental lactogen

128. Which of the following acts as a prohormone?
   A. vasopressin
   B. aldosterone
   C. luteinizing hormone
   D. testosterone
   E. triiodothyronine (T_3)

Questions 129–132. Match the phrases below with the situations given in questions 129–132.
   A. increase in ACTH in a normal subject
   B. decrease in ACTH in a normal subject

129. Administration of metyrapone, an inhibitor of 11β-hydroxylase:

130. Administration of a competitive antagonist of the CRH receptor:

131. Administration of a potent glucocorticoid agonist:

132. Administration of the glucocorticoid receptor antagonist RU486:

133. Directly or indirectly, increased cortisol secretion in the late stages of diabetic ketoacidosis (DKA) reduces:
   A. the metabolic acidosis
   B. insulin's effectiveness
   C. the impaired insulin secretion
   D. gluconeogenesis
   E. mobilization of depot fat

134. The hypothalamus releases factors that directly do all the following EXCEPT:
   A. increase the production of milk
   B. increase the secretion of parathyroid hormone
   C. facilitate ovulation
   D. increase cortisol secretion
   E. facilitate the growth of long bones

135. In the adolescent girl, progesterone in the absence of estrogen causes:
   A. growth and development of the uterus
   B. growth and development of the breasts
   C. closure of the epiphyses of long bones
   D. deposition of subcutaneous fat to hips and thighs
   E. none of the above changes

136. In a healthy 30-year-old woman with a menstrual cycle of 26 days:
   A. injection of estrogen will increase the size of the ovaries
   B. the proliferative phase of the uterus is caused by estrogen derived from the Graafian follicle
   C. menstruation is caused by progesterone from the corpus luteum
   D. estradiol concentration begins to fall prior to ovulation and continues to decrease until menstruation
   E. the highest plasma levels of FSH are associated with the start of menstruation

137. After implantation has occurred, the first missed period in a healthy female is caused by the fact that:
   A. the corpus luteum degenerates
   B. a trophoblast is formed that secretes estrogen and progesterone
   C. a trophoblast is formed that secretes gonadotropins
   D. the ovaries decrease their production of estrogen and progesterone
   E. the placenta releases enough estrogen and progesterone to prevent menstruation

CENTRAL NERVOUS SYSTEM PHYSIOLOGY

1. **The peripheral receptive field is defined as the spatial area on the receptor surface:**
   A. that increases first-order afferent nerve activity when stimulated with an adequate stimulus
   B. comprising the excitatory "on-center" area
   C. with the lowest absolute threshold to the adequate stimulus
   D. that evokes any change in neural activity when stimulated with an adequate stimulus
   E. containing all the receptors of the branches of a first-order afferent

2. **The "pattern" code of sensory information:**
   A. compares the relative action potential frequency evoked from the center and the surround portions of a receptive field
   B. proposes that the sensation evoked by afferent stimulation depends primarily upon the specific nerves stimulated
   C. depends upon the relative activation of several afferents with different response sensitivities
   D. contributes to the coding of stimulus intensity
   E. is based upon the law of specific nerve energies

3. **Phasic (rapidly adapting) receptors:**
   A. generally respond best to changes in stimulus strength
   B. discharge continuously with stimulation of constant intensity
   C. primarily encode the intensity of a stimulus
   D. encode both rate of change and stimulus magnitude
   E. encode information regarding pain and joint position

4. **The law of specific nerve energies states that:**
   A. a perceived sensation depends upon the type of energy stimulating the afferent receptor
   B. perceived sensation depends solely upon the afferent nerve stimulated
   C. a sensation is perceived to originate in a specific location regardless of where in the afferent chain the stimulus is applied
   D. magnitude is encoded by action potential frequency in afferent nerves
   E. all afferent nerves of a given modality terminate in the same cortical region

5. **The anterior spinothalamic and lateral spinothalamic tracts carry information about:**
   A. fine touch and pressure
   B. vibration
   C. joint position
   D. slight skin movement
   E. pain

6. **Each of the following contributes to the adaptation characteristics of rapidly adapting, somatic pressure receptors EXCEPT:**
   A. presence or absence of a tissue capsule
   B. elasticity of the tissue surrounding the receptor
   C. physical characteristics of capsule enclosing the receptor
   D. the threshold of receptor membrane tissue distortion needed for depolarization

7. **The visual abnormality resulting from uneven curvature of the cornea in different planes is called:**
   A. astigmatism
   B. myopia
   C. hyperopia
   D. emmetropia
   E. presbyopia

8. **Glaucoma results from:**
   A. decreased intraocular pressure
   B. vascular hypertrophy in the retina
   C. intraocular hemorrhage
   D. blockade of the canal of Schlemm
   E. accumulation of denatured proteins on the lens

9. **Substances that stimulate peripheral chemoreceptors that encode pain sensation include all of the following EXCEPT:**
   A. serotonin
   B. histamine
   C. potassium
   D. enkephalin
   E. proteolytic enzymes

10. **Sensations of sharp, pricking pain are mediated via:**
    A. most sensory receptors subjected to sudden, intense stimulation
    B. specialized free nerve endings of A-delta nerve fibers
    C. specialized encapsulated nerve endings of "C" fibers
    D. specialized free nerve endings of "C" fibers
    E. specialized encapsulated nerve endings of A-delta fibers

11. **Precise topographic representation of fine touch/pressure information is:**
    A. present throughout the spinothalamic system
    B. present for visceral sensation
    C. lost in the somatosensory cortex
    D. present throughout the dorsal column system
    E. not present in the medulla, but regained in the cortex

12. **The anterolateral system in the spinal cord:**
    A. carries pain information originating on the contralateral side of the body
    B. decussates in the medial lemniscus so that second-order afferents terminate in the contralateral thalamus
    C. has first-order afferents that synapse in the ipsilateral medulla
    D. carries fine touch/pressure information originating on the ipsilateral side of the body
    E. has first-order afferents that do not synapse until they reach the thalamus

13. **The most likely site of direct interaction between afferent and efferent sensory systems that modulate pain sensation is the:**
    A. sensory nerve endings transducing pain
    B. anterior commissure of the spinal cord
    C. substantia gelatinosa
    D. periaqueductal grey region
    E. thalamus

14. **Nerve fibers that carry information that is perceived consciously as visceral pain enter the spinal cord with the:**
    A. sympathetic nerves
    B. parasympathetic nerves
    C. cutaneous nerves
    D. cranial nerves

15. **A positive lens with a refractive power of 10 diopters focuses parallel light rays _____ behind the center of the lens:**
    A. 0.1 cm
    B. 1 cm
    C. 10 cm
    D. 100 cm
    E. 1,000 cm

16. **Which portion of the eye provides the greatest amount of light refraction?**
    A. the anterior surface of the cornea
    B. the posterior surface of the cornea
    C. the anterior surface of the crystalline lens
    D. the posterior surface of the crystalline lens
    E. the aqueous humor

17. **Presbyopia results from:**
    A. insufficient refraction by the anterior cornea
    B. insufficient refractive capability of the lens
    C. maintenance of the lens in an oval shape
    D. fatigue of the zonule fibers (suspensory ligaments)
    E. development of cataracts

18. **The correct lens combination for an individual with myopia and presbyopia would be bifocals with a:**
    A. combination lens on top and a negative lens on the bottom
    B. combination lens on top and a positive lens on the bottom
    C. positive lens on top and a negative lens on the bottom
    D. negative lens on top and a negative lens on the bottom
    E. negative lens on top and a positive lens on the bottom

19. **The outer layer of the retina, including the outer segments of the rods and cones, obtains nutrition primarily from:**
    A. blood vessels coursing through the retina
    B. the cornea
    C. the schlera
    D. the choroid
    E. the pigmented layer

20. **11-cis retinal:**
    A. exists only in the light
    B. is found only in rods
    C. converts to all-trans retinal in the dark
    D. spontaneously binds to both scotopsin and photopsin
    E. does not bind with scotopsin

21. **When light strikes the outer segment of a rod:**
    A. the receptor cell depolarizes
    B. action potentials are generated in the first and second-order afferents
    C. 11-cis retinal isomerizes to all-trans retinal
    D. diffusion of sodium ions out of the inner segment of the receptor increases
    E. binding of retinal to photopsin increases

22. **When a visual stimulus is continually focused on a specific population of receptor cells:**
    A. the perceived stimulus intensity increases
    B. there is adaptation mediated by the lateral geniculate body
    C. ganglion cells become facilitated
    D. the amount of lateral inhibition increases in the inhibitory surround
    E. the perceived image will fade and disappear

23. **Color vision is coded by:**
    A. rods
    B. activation of color-specific receptor cells that are responsive to wavelengths representing each color perceived
    C. differential responses in ganglion cells that depend upon the wavelength of the stimulus
    D. differential spectral sensitivity of receptors mediating ''scotopic'' and ''photopic'' vision
    E. the concentration of rhodopsin present in the cones

24. **A point of light from the right visual field will stimulate receptors:**
    A. on the nasal side of the left eye
    B. on the temporal side of the right eye
    C. in the right eye that have terminal projections in the contralateral visual cortex
    D. in the right eye that have terminal projections in the ipsilateral visual cortex
    E. in the right and left eyes that have terminal projections in the ipsilateral visual cortex

25. **The impedance mismatch between sound pressure waves traveling through air and through the cochlear fluid is compensated for by:**
    A. a decrease in the force of the pressure stimulus resulting from the leverage exerted during vibration of the tympanic membrane
    B. an increase in the force of the pressure stimulus resulting from the configuration of the ossicles
    C. an increase in the amplitude of the pressure stimulus due to contraction of the tensor tympanic muscle
    D. a decrease in the amplitude of the pressure stimulus due to the relative sizes of the tympanic membrane and the oval window
    E. concentration of the sound pressure stimulus by the pinna

26. **Stimulation of the tensor tympanis and the stapedius muscles:**
    A. diminishes the amplitude of sound pressure stimuli entering the cochlea
    B. occurs during auditory stimulation with low-amplitude stimuli
    C. compensates for the impedance mismatch between air and cochlear fluid
    D. increases the amplitude of the basilar membrane wave envelope
    D. is initiated by bone conduction

27. **A sound pressure stimulus of 60 dB is _____ times larger than a sound pressure stimulus of 30 dB.**
    A. 2
    B. 10
    C. 20
    D. 100
    E. 1,000

28. **When the point of maximal displacement of the basilar membrane is close to the oval window, it indicates that the:**
    A. stimulating frequency is high
    B. stimulating frequency is low
    C. stimulus is very loud
    D. stimulus is near the detection threshold for audition
    E. stimulus was transferred to the cochlea by bone conduction

29. **The endocochlear potential is:**
    A. generated in the endolymph by stimulation of the auditory receptor cells
    B. an electrical potential difference between the scala tympani and scala vestibuli
    C. maintained by the tectorial membrane
    D. created by the initiation of a traveling wave along the basilar membrane
    E. an electrical potential difference between the perilymph and the endolymph

30. **Gustatory receptor cells are different from olfactory receptor cells because they:**
    A. hyperpolarize when stimulated
    B. are rapidly adapting chemoreceptors
    C. have chemical binding sites on their cell bodies
    D. are depolarized by stimuli representing a single primary taste
    E. are separate receptor cells that make synaptic contact with the first-order afferent nerve fibers

31. **Directional sensitivity of single receptor cells in the vestibular system:**
    A. is present because the receptor cells have a high degree of spontaneous activity
    B. accounts for the similarity of first-order afferent responses from contralateral semicircular canals during rotational acceleration
    C. is present only in receptor cells located on the ampular crest
    D. is independent of reflex activation of efferent inhibitory neurons
    E. is independent of CNS integration of afferent activity originating in the semicircular canals and otolith organs

32. **The rate of change of length of intrafusal muscle fibers is detected by X afferent fibers from nuclear Y fibers and can be modified by efferent activity in gamma Z nerve fibers.**

	X	Y	Z
A.	primary	chain	dynamic
B.	primary	bag	dynamic
C.	secondary	chain	static
D.	secondary	bag	dynamic
E.	primary	chain	static

33. **During a normal voluntary muscle movement, the:**
    A. gamma motor system is not activated
    B. extrafusal muscle fibers shorten, while the intrafusal fibers do not
    C. intrafusal fibers provide the main contractile force for movement of the joint
    D. intrafusal and extrafusal fibers both shorten
    E. contraction of the intrafusal fibers inhibits the stretch reflex

34. **Increased tension on Golgi tendon organs:**
    A. produces inhibition of the gamma motor system
    B. produces adaptation of the stretch reflex
    C. enhances the strength of the stretch receptor response
    D. excites spinal interneurons that inhibit extrafusal muscle fiber activity
    E. sensitizes the "load reflex" (ie, enhanced gamma motor neuron activity as a muscle contracts against a load).

35. **Parkinson's disease is characterized by:**
    A. decreased dopamine in the putamen and caudate nucleus
    B. lesions of the pyramidal decussation
    C. lesions located in the motor cortex
    D. lesions of the cerebellum
    E. excitation of the basal ganglia

36. **All of the following are characteristics of the blood–brain barrier EXCEPT:**
    A. tight junctions of endothelial cells
    B. glial foot processes
    C. increased mitochondria in capillary endothelial cells
    D. reduced permeability of high-molecular-weight substances
    E. reduced permeability of lipid soluble substances

37. **Cerebrospinal fluid is absorbed from the brain through the:**
    A. choroid plexus
    B. arachnoid villi
    C. Foramen of Monro
    D. fenestrae in cerebral capillaries
    E. cerebral aqueduct

38. **Activation of the cross-extensor reflex:**
    A. stimulates the ipsilateral extensor
    B. inhibits the ipsilateral flexor
    C. stimulates the contralateral flexor
    D. inhibits the contralateral extensor
    E. stimulates the contralateral extensor

39. **Each of the following is important in encoding constant stimulus magnitude EXCEPT:**
    A. the size of the receptive field of the stimulated afferent
    B. the size of the receptor potential generated by stimulation
    C. the number of afferents activated by the stimulus
    D. the thresholds of the activated afferents
    E. the adaptation characteristic (i.e., phasic or tonic) of the stimulated afferents

40. **The receptive field of a first-order cutaneous afferent is characterized by:**
    A. constant threshold for stimulation across the receptive field
    B. innervation by multiple sensory units of the same type
    C. evoking both excitatory and inhibitory responses in the afferent nerve
    D. modality specificity
    E. encoding of several cutaneous sensations

41. **All cutaneous receptors are characterized by:**
    A. histological specificity of stimulus encoding
    B. physiological specificity of stimulus encoding
    C. ability to encode multiple cutaneous sensations
    D. rapid adaptation
    E. encapsulated nerve endings

42. **The tissue lamina surrounding the nerve ending of a Pacinian corpuscle:**
    A. dampens receptor membrane distortion during stimulus onset
    B. changes the response pattern of the receptor from phasic–tonic to phasic
    C. is necessary for generation of the receptor potential
    D. prevents afferent activation during removal of the stimulus
    E. is necessary for encoding constant stimulus magnitude

43. **According to the gate control theory of pain, enkephalin, an endogenous opioid, inhibits pain sensation by:**
    A. facilitation of second-order touch-pressure afferent nerves
    B. postsynaptic inhibition of third-order afferent pain nerves
    C. presynaptic inhibition at first-order afferent pain nerve terminals
    D. inhibition of enkephalin interneurons in the substantia gelatinosa
    E. competing for receptor sites on the peripheral pain receptor

44. **First-order afferent nerve fibers from visceral pain receptors:**
    A. do not synapse in the substantia gelatinosa
    B. travel with cutaneous afferent nerves originating in the same dermatomal segments as the organ of innervation
    C. have cell bodies in sympathetic ganglia
    D. are topographically organized
    E. densely innervate visceral organs

45. **When the axial length of the eyeball is shorter than the focal length of the optical apparatus:**
    A. the eye is myopic
    B. the eye is presbyopic
    C. the eye is emmetropic
    D. vision can be corrected by a negative lens
    E. parallel light rays are focused posterior to the retina

46. **When you are viewing a near object:**
    A. parasympathetic activity to the ocular apparatus increases
    B. the tension of ocular zonular fibers increases
    C. sympathetic activity to iris musculature increases
    D. the crystalline lens flattens
    E. the ciliary muscles relax

47. **Hyperopia results from:**
    A. parallel light rays being focused anterior to the retina
    B. maintenance of the lens in its most oval shape
    C. the axial length of the eye exceeding the focal length
    D. insufficient refractive capability of the optical apparatus
    E. excess curvature of the cornea

48. **The X luminosity curve represents Y cell function derived from the Z eye.**

	X	Y	Z
A.	photopic	rod	light-adapted
B.	scotopic	rod	dark-adapted
C.	scotopic	cone	light-adapted
D.	photopic	cone	dark-adapted
E.	scotopic	cone	dark-adapted

49. **Neural convergence is the principal mechanism for:**
    A. color weakness
    B. foveal resolution
    C. monocular detection of depth
    D. visual feature detection
    E. the ''photopic'' luminosity curve

50. **Auditory pitch is encoded by the:**
    A. frequency of basilar membrane oscillation at high frequencies (>1,000 Hz)
    B. point of maximal displacement of the basilar membrane at low frequencies (<100 Hz)
    C. frequency of oscillation of basilar membrane at low frequencies (<100 Hz)
    D. frequency of action potentials in the auditory nerve at all frequencies
    E. pattern of neural activity in a population of nerves at all frequencies

51. **Outer hair cells of the cochlea do each of the following** *EXCEPT:*
    A. provide 95% of afferent neurons in the auditory portion of the VIIIth cranial nerve
    B. contract
    C. modify basilar membrane movement
    D. modify inner hair cell response
    E. outnumber inner hair cells

52. **Rotation of the head to the left in the horizontal plane:**
    A. increases activity in the vestibular portion of the left VIIIth nerve
    B. increases activity in the vestibular portion of the right VIIIth nerve
    C. bends the kinocilia in the right horizontal canal away from the stereocilia
    D. bends the kinocilia in the left horizontal canal toward the stereocilia
    E. has no effect on the neural activity in the right VIIIth nerve

53. **Olfactory and gustatory receptor cells:**
    A. are the sites for complete adaptation of taste and smell sensation
    B. are narrowly tuned and respond only to stimuli that represent one or two basic odors and tastes
    C. are depolarized by specific chemicals binding to protein receptors located on their cell bodies
    D. are both bipolar neurons
    E. are slowly adapting, phasic–tonic receptors

54. **When gamma-motor neuron discharge increases simultaneously with alpha-motor neuron discharge, the:**
    A. activity of primary spindle afferents is inhibited
    B. contraction of the muscle is prolonged
    C. activity of secondary spindle afferents is inhibited
    D. activity of primary spindle afferents is less than that observed with alpha-motor neuron stimulation alone
    E. activity of primary spindle afferents is greater than that observed with alpha-motor neuron stimulation alone

55. **Increasing tension in innervated skeletal muscle eventually causes relaxation of the extrafusal muscle fibers because of:**
    A. alpha-motor neuron fatigue
    B. inhibition of afferent input from primary muscle spindle receptors
    C. stimulation of afferent input from secondary muscle spindle receptors
    D. stimulation of afferent activity from Golgi tendon organs
    E. inhibition of afferent activity from Golgi tendon organs

56. **For a person with both astigmatism and presbyopia, the lens combination yielding the best vision would be:**
    A. a positive lens for far vision and a positive lens for near vision
    B. a combination lens for far vision and a positive lens for near vision
    C. a negative (nonrefracting) lens for far vision and a positive lens for near vision
    D. a combination lens for far vision and a negative lens for near vision
    E. a positive lens for far vision and a negative lens for near vision

57. The following events occur when rods are stimulated by light. Select the proper sequence.
1. production of phosphodiesterase
2. isomerization of retinal
3. decreased intracellular cGMP
4. receptor hyperpolarization
5. closure of sodium channels in the outer segment
   A. 3, 4, 5, 2, 1
   B. 2, 3, 1, 4, 5
   C. 1, 3, 2, 5, 4
   D. 1, 2, 3, 5, 4
   E. 2, 1, 3, 5, 4

58. Mechanisms of visual accommodation include:
   A. increased tension on suspensory ligaments of the lens
   B. a decrease in the curvature of the lens
   C. pupillary dilation
   D. contraction of the ciliary muscle
   E. activation of sympathetic nerve fibers to the iris

59. All of the following are adaptations of the fovea *EXCEPT*:
   A. increased rhodopsin concentration
   B. increased cone density
   C. increased melanin concentration in the pigmented layer
   D. the presence of cylindrically shaped cones
   E. the fibers of the receptor cells are splayed radially

60. Activation of the parasympathetic nervous system innervating the optical apparatus:
   A. induces accommodation
   B. causes pupillary dilation
   C. causes ciliary muscle relaxation
   D. flattens the lens
   E. decreases refraction of the optical apparatus

61. Opposite responses in visual ganglion cells to specific pairs of wavelengths demonstrate:
   A. the Purkinje shift
   B. feature detection
   C. the difference between scotopic and photopic vision
   D. the presence of three distinct populations of cones
   E. opponent processing of color sensation

62. Receptors located on the temporal side of the left eye are activated by stimuli in the X visual field and project to the Y side of the brain.

	X	Y
A.	right	contralateral
B.	left	ipsilateral
C.	right	ipsilateral
D.	left	contralateral
E.	right	ipsilateral and contralateral

63. The sacculus and the utricle:
   A. have hair cells arranged with kinocilia oriented toward the striola
   B. are stimulated by fluid forces bending the ampullary crest
   C. have hair cells embedded in the cupula
   D. respond to rotational acceleration
   E. do not contain otoliths

64. Adaptation of gustatory sensation occurs because:
   A. stimulant molecules transiently depolarize receptor cells
   B. gustatory receptors are phasic receptors
   C. of lateral inhibitory connections between receptor cells
   D. of central nervous system interactions
   E. of concurrent activation of tactile afferents from the tongue

65. Stimulation of the gamma X fibers contracts the Y muscle fibers, which enhances the Z response to muscle stretch.

	X	Y	Z
A.	dynamic	bag	phasic
B.	dynamic	chain	phasic
C.	static	bag	tonic
D.	dynamic	chain	tonic
E.	static	bag	phasic

66. Activation of Golgi tendon organs:
   A. stimulates alpha-motor neurons
   B. excites inhibitory interneurons in the spinal cord
   C. enhances the strength of the stretch reflex
   D. decreases muscle stretch
   E. induces reflex muscle contraction

67. Activation of the basal ganglia:
   A. induces rigidity
   B. excites the reticular formation
   C. decreases muscle tone throughout the body
   D. increases intention tremor
   E. produces symptoms characteristic of Parkinson's disease

68. Cerebrospinal fluid is produced by the:
   A. choroid plexus
   B. arachnoid villi
   C. brain capillary endothelium
   D. fenestrae of cerebral capillaries
   E. circumventricular organs

69. **Adaptation to a sensory stimulus is defined as:**
   A. inhibition of sensation when another stimulus is applied to an adjacent area on the receptive field
   B. diminished sensation when a stimulus is repeatedly administered
   C. a diminished sensation when a stimulus is continually administered
   D. failure to perceive a stimulus when attention is directed to another matter
   E. increased sensitivity to stimulation during continued application of a stimulus

70. **First-order A-delta afferents from free nerve endings primarily:**
   A. ascend the spinal cord and synapse in the nucleus gracilis or nucleus cuneatus
   B. synapse on second-order afferents that ascend the ipsilateral side of the spinal cord
   C. synapse on second-order nerve fibers that cross to the contralateral side of the brain in the medial lemniscus
   D. are the longest neurons in the human nervous system
   E. synapse in the spinal cord on second-order afferents that cross to the contralateral side of the cord

71. **Removal of the tissue capsule surrounding the nerve ending of a Pacinian corpuscle:**
   A. eliminates the amplifying effect of the capsule on weak pressure stimuli
   B. enhances the magnitude of the receptor potential
   C. changes the receptor response pattern from purely phasic to phasic–tonic
   D. decreases action potential frequency in the first-order afferent to a given pressure stimulus
   E. blocks generation of the receptor potential

72. **Sensations of dull, aching pain are mediated via:**
   A. most receptors during continuous, high-intensity stimulation
   B. encapsulated nerve endings of A-delta fibers
   C. free nerve endings of C-type fibers
   D. encapsulated nerve endings of C-type fibers
   E. free nerve endings of both C- and A-delta fibers

73. **The decrease in sensation resulting from continuous presentation of a sensory stimulus is termed:**
   A. adaptation
   B. deprivation
   C. facilitation
   D. habituation
   E. accommodation

74. **Axons in the fasciculus cuneatus:**
   A. contain second-order afferents from temperature receptors of the lower limbs
   B. decussate in the medial lemniscus
   C. carry touch/pressure sensation from the upper limbs
   D. synapse in the contralateral nucleus cuneatus
   E. carry somatic information from receptors in the face

75. **All axons of the lateral corticospinal tract:**
   A. represent the "final common pathway" of skeletal motor movement
   B. mediate reflex, involuntary movements
   C. descend ipsilaterally from the brain to the spinal cord
   D. originate exclusively from the pyramidal cells of Betz of the precentral gyrus
   E. form the pyramidal decussation

76. **Unilateral lesion of the internal capsule would result in:**
   A. chronic spastic paralysis on the contralateral side of the body
   B. chronic flaccid paralysis on the contralateral side of the body
   C. flaccid paralysis on the ipsilateral side of the body
   D. loss of spinally mediated reflexes such as the patellar tendon reflex
   E. loss of the Babinski reflex

77. **All of the following are characteristic of cerebellar damage EXCEPT:**
   A. improper muscle coordination
   B. increased muscle tone
   C. intention tremor
   D. cannot rapidly alternate pronation and supination
   E. failure to estimate distance in motor movement

78. **Parkinson's disease is characterized by:**
   A. intention tremor
   B. decreased muscle tone
   C. decreased ability to initiate movement
   D. damage to the internal capsule
   E. hypersecretion of dopamine

79. **The gamma motor neurons:**
   A. innervate the extrafusal muscle fibers
   B. innervate the intrafusal muscle fibers
   C. directly cause muscle shortening
   D. are not activated during alpha-motor neuron stimulation
   E. do not affect the stretch reflex

80. **The Renshaw cells of the spinal cord:**
   A. inhibit the stretch reflex responses
   B. are excitatory interneurons
   C. connect alpha-motor neurons in adjacent segments of the spinal cord
   D. integrate sensory input with alpha-motor neurons activation
   E. are responsible for recurrent inhibition

81. **When the receptor portion of a muscle spindle is stretched slowly:**
    A. the impulse frequency in both primary and secondary afferent stretch receptors increases
    B. the impulse frequency in only the primary stretch receptor afferents increases
    C. the impulse frequency in only the secondary stretch receptor afferents increases
    D. the response frequency in the primary afferents decreases after the muscle length stops changing
    E. the continued activation of stretch receptor afferents after the muscle has stopped changing is due to stretch of the nuclear bag intrafusal fibers

82. **The dynamic portion of the muscle stretch reflex:**
    A. inhibits antagonistic muscles
    B. is polysynaptic
    C. is initiated primarily by activity of the type Ia stretch receptors
    D. inhibits gamma motor neuron activity
    E. is abolished when the muscle is partially contracted

83. **Golgi tendon organs:**
    A. are in parallel with intrafusal muscle fibers
    B. are in series with extrafusal muscle fibers
    C. typically excite alpha-motor neurons when stimulated
    D. are rapidly adapting receptors
    E. sense muscle length

84. **Following decerebration, animals are characterized by:**
    A. spinal shock
    B. peripheral hypotonia
    C. enhanced stretch reflexes
    D. activation of extensor muscles
    E. intention tremor

85. **The primary afferent input into the basal ganglia comes from the:**
    A. associative cortex
    B. cerebellum
    C. motor cortex
    D. muscle spindles
    E. thalamus

86. **Normal movement requires the cerebral cortex to have afferent input from all the following structures EXCEPT the:**
    A. basal ganglia
    B. cerebellum
    C. thalamus
    D. cortical premotor area
    E. red nucleus

87. **The principal neurotransmitter released at the terminals of nerves originating in the caudate nucleus, globus pallidus, and putamen is:**
    A. dopamine
    B. enkephalin
    C. substance P
    D. acetylcholine
    E. gamma-aminobutyric acid

88. **The brain structure that controls the "long loop" muscle stretch reflex is the:**
    A. precentral gyrus
    B. globus pallidus
    C. red nucleus
    D. ventral posterolateral nucleus of the thalamus
    E. anterior lobe of the cerebellum

89. **The "two-point threshold" for cutaneous sensation is least on the:**
    A. lips
    B. lower back
    C. thighs
    D. palms of the hands
    E. forehead

90. **A lens brings parallel light rays to focus 50 mm behind the lens. This lens has a refractive power of:**
    A. 1 diopter
    B. 5 diopters
    C. 10 diopters
    D. 20 diopters
    E. 50 diopters

91. **The second-order afferent nerve cells in the visual system:**
    A. produce action potentials when receptor cells are stimulated with light
    B. exhibit only depolarization during visual stimulation
    C. are primarily responsible for lateral inhibition
    D. can disinhibit ganglion cells during stimulation
    E. project into the brain

92. **The Y of a sinusoidal pressure stimulus is the physical characteristic that produces the psychological perception of Z.**

	Y	Z
A.	frequency	pitch
B.	phase	loudness
C.	amplitude	pitch
D.	frequency	loudness
E.	phase	pitch

93. **A sound stimulus transmitted by bone conduction:**
    A. initiates a traveling wave at the helicotrema end of the basilar membrane
    B. stimulates the tympanic membrane
    C. initiates a traveling wave at the oval window end of the basilar membrane
    D. is transmitted through the ossicles
    E. directly stimulates the outer hair cells

94. **The basilar membrane is:**
    A. more flexible at the helicotrema end than at the oval window end
    B. thicker at the helicotrema end than at the oval window end
    C. composed of a series of independent resonators
    D. under constant tension, similar to stretched rubber

95. **Otoliths:**
    A. are present on the ampular crest
    B. are embedded in the cupula
    C. are located in the semicircular canals
    D. are present in the macula
    E. anchor the cilia of vestibular hair cells

96. **The mechanism that makes the greatest contribution to dark adaptation is:**
    A. pupillary dilation
    B. neural facilitation
    C. increased photopigment in cones
    D. increased rhodopsin concentration in rods
    E. accommodation

97. **The receptor cells for audition are contained in the:**
    A. organ of Corti
    B. scala vestibuli
    C. scala tympani
    D. helicotrema
    E. perilymph

98. **Endolymph:**
    A. is contained in the scala vestibuli and tympani
    B. surrounds the cell bodies of the auditory receptor cells
    C. has a higher sodium concentration than perilymph
    D. has a higher potassium concentration than perilymph
    E. has a potassium concentration equal to that of extra-cellular fluid

99. **In a relaxed human adult, at rest with eyes closed, and not concentrating, the most prominent wave pattern of the electroencephalogram would be:**
    A. alpha rhythm
    B. beta rhythm
    C. theta rhythm
    D. delta rhythm
    E. asynchronous, nonrhythmic

100. **During REM (rapid eye movement) sleep, the electro-encephalogram is characterized by:**
    A. high-amplitude alpha waves
    B. low-amplitude, high-frequency beta waves
    C. slow-frequency theta waves
    D. slow-frequency delta waves
    E. low-amplitude, high-frequency waves characteristic of the awake state

101. **The brain structure that is most responsible for arousal is the:**
    A. neostriatum
    B. cerebellum
    C. motor cortex
    D. sensory cortex
    E. reticular formation

102. **Periods of dreaming are associated with all the following EXCEPT:**
    A. increased motor tone
    B. rapid eye movement
    C. desynchronization of the EEG
    D. increased brain metabolism
    E. the person is less easily aroused than during non-dreaming sleep

103. **Mental concentration is associated with:**
    A. a predominance of alpha rhythms in the EEG
    B. a predominance of theta rhythms in the EEG
    C. an asynchronized EEG
    D. a synchronized EEG
    E. high-amplitude slow waves in the EEG

104. **Sleep induction is associated with decreased release of:**
    A. serotonin
    B. acetylcholine
    C. dopamine
    D. gamma-amino butyric acid
    E. glutamate

105. **Axons comprising the corticospinal and corticobulbar motor pathways have cell bodies located in the:**
    A. motor cortex of the precentral gyrus
    B. parietal cortex
    C. premotor cortex
    D. somatic sensory area I on the post-central gyrus
    E. all of the above

106. **Alzheimer's disease is characterized by a loss of CNS neurons that are:**
    A. cholinergic
    B. adrenergic
    C. dopaminergic
    D. serotonergic
    E. noradrenergic

107. **The phenomenon of sensory stimulation perceived to occur at the receptor, regardless of where the stimulus is applied in the afferent circuit, demonstrates:**
    A. the law of specific nerve energies
    B. the law of projection
    C. the pattern coding of sensory information
    D. adaptation
    E. feature detection

108. **Stretch receptors and Golgi tendon organs are examples of:**
    A. exteroceptors
    B. interoceptors
    C. proprioceptors
    D. nociceptors
    E. chemoceptors

109. **Most fibers that transmit information about fine touch and to the CNS are classified as:**
    - A. A-alpha axons
    - B. A-beta axons
    - C. A-delta axons
    - D. A-gamma axons
    - E. C-fibers

110. **The anterolateral system of the spinal cord:**
    - A. transmits information faster than in the dorsal column system
    - B. is highly topographically organized
    - C. responds to rapidly changing stimulation with great fidelity
    - D. can respond to small changes in stimulus intensity
    - E. carries crude touch information

111. **All the following mechanisms contribute to referred pain *EXCEPT*:**
    - A. convergence of visceral and cutaneous afferents on second-order pain afferents of the somatic structure
    - B. facilitation of second-order pain afferents originating in the somatic structure by activation of first-order afferents originating in the viscera
    - C. the Law of Specific Nerve Energies
    - D. the Law of Projection
    - E. gating of pain transmission in the substantia gelatinosa

112. **The area of the body that has the largest representation in the somatosensory cortex is the:**
    - A. feet
    - B. thighs
    - C. lips
    - D. forehead
    - E. palms

113. **In the touch-pressure system, sensory units with large receptive fields:**
    - A. have large cortical representation
    - B. permit precise localization of the site of stimulation
    - C. are found in body regions with small two-point thresholds
    - D. are not topographically organized
    - E. innervate areas of low receptor density

114. **Sensory systems can respond to an exceptionally wide range of stimulus intensities because:**
    - A. the receptor potential represents a log transformation of the stimulus intensity
    - B. the receptor potential increases linearly with stimulus intensity
    - C. lateral inhibition decreases afferent input from adjacent sensory units
    - D. action potential frequency is a log transformation of the receptor potential
    - E. action potential amplitude increases with stimulus intensity

115. **The second-order afferent nerve fibers from the touch-pressure (dorsal column) system synapse in the:**
    - A. nucleus gracilis and nucleus cuneatus
    - B. medial lemniscus
    - C. ventral lateral posterior nucleus of the thalamus
    - D. anterior nucleus of the thalamus
    - E. somatosensory cortex

116. **When someone is viewing an object 50 cm from the eye, the:**
    - A. parasympathetic innervation of the eye is stimulated
    - B. ciliary muscles relax
    - C. tension on the suspensory fibers surrounding the lens increases
    - D. lens flattens
    - E. light refraction decreases

117. **The heavily pigmented epithelial layer underlying the retina does all the following *EXCEPT*:**
    - A. absorb stray light rays
    - B. contain large quantities of vitamin A
    - C. phagocytize discarded segments of the receptor cells
    - D. produce aqueous humor

118. **The outer segments of photoreceptors in the vertebrate retina:**
    - A. are pointed away from the pupil
    - B. produce photopigment
    - C. actively extrude sodium ions
    - D. contain the cell nucleus
    - E. synapse with bipolar cells

119. **The four photopigments present in the vertebrate retina have the same:**
    - A. spectral sensitivity
    - B. luminosity function
    - C. opsin protein
    - D. chromophore, retinal
    - E. distribution across the retina

120. **Maximal dark adaptation in the visual system:**
    - A. is greatest in the fovea
    - B. occurs more quickly in rods than in cones
    - C. is due predominantly to increased sensitivity of the rods
    - D. is due predominantly to changes in pupil diameter
    - E. is due predominantly to increased sensitivity of the cones

121. **Light-induced hyperpolarization of visual receptor cells results from:**
    - A. decreased permeability of sodium ions in the outer segment
    - B. increased extrusion of sodium ions from the inner segment
    - C. decreased concentration of phosphodiesterase in the outer segment
    - D. increased concentration of guanosine monophosphate (cGMP) in the outer segment
    - E. closing of sodium channels in the inner segment

122. **Which of the following colors is a principal contributor to the opponent responses characteristic of color-sensitive ganglion cells, but is not a principal stimulus for any population of cones?**
   A. blue
   B. yellow
   C. green
   D. orange
   E. red

123. **Glaucoma results in blindness because it:**
   A. produces intraocular hemorrhage
   B. decreases intraocular pressure, leading to retinal detachment
   C. destroys the axons of the ganglion cells
   D. induces hypertrophy of the retinal arterioles
   E. induces clouding of the crystalline lens

124. **In humans, the primary visual cortex is located in the:**
   A. frontal lobe
   B. postcentral gyrus
   C. insular cortex
   D. calcarine fissure area
   E. parietal lobe

125. **The best visual acuity in the dark-adapted eye, i.e., rod vision only, is in the:**
   A. optic disc
   B. fovea
   C. peripheral retina
   D. macula
   E. parafoveal region

126. **Efferent nerve fibers from the brain to the cochlea:**
   A. innervate only the inner hair cells
   B. innervate the tensor tympani
   C. depolarize auditory receptor cells
   D. inhibit hair cells in the cochlea
   E. increase the amplitude of vibration of the basilar membrane

127. **All the following are associated with the utricle and/ or saccule *EXCEPT*:**
   A. ampulla
   B. otoconia
   C. calcium carbonate crystals
   D. striola
   E. linear acceleration

128. **The semicircular canals:**
   A. each contain a striola
   B. are connected to the saccule
   C. respond to linear acceleration
   D. each contain a cupula
   E. are not innervated by efferent nerves

129. **Auditory receptor cells are different from vestibular hair cells because they:**
   A. lack kinocilia
   B. lack efferent innervation
   C. are not mechanoreceptors
   D. are depolarized by activation of efferent nerves
   E. have stereocilia bathed in perilymph

130. **The most important factor correcting the impedance mismatch between sound waves in air and sound waves in the cochlear fluid is:**
   A. contraction of the tensor tympani to increase tension on the tympanic membrane
   B. the size difference between the tympanic membrane and the stapes
   C. the flexibility of the round window
   D. ossicular amplification of tympanic membrane movement
   E. contraction of the stapedius muscle

131. **The perilymph contained in the cochlea:**
   A. is in the scala media
   B. has a high potassium concentration
   C. has a low sodium concentration
   D. is in the scala vestibuli
   E. is formed by the stria vascularis

132. **The ionic concentration difference between the endolymph and perilymph is maintained by:**
   A. Reissner's membrane
   B. the tectoral membrane
   C. the basilar membrane
   D. the helicotrema
   E. the organ of Corti

133. **The cilia of vestibular receptor cells:**
   A. are bathed in endolymph
   B. are oriented parallel to the ampular crest in the semicircular canals
   C. are similar to cochlear hair cells
   D. consist of a single kinocilia circled by stereocilia
   E. always depolarize the receptor cell when bent

134. **High-frequency stimuli excite hair cells that are located:**
   A. close to the helicotrema
   B. close to the oval window
   C. throughout the length of the basilar membrane
   D. at the distal end of the basilar membrane
   E. far from the oval window

135. **The pressure threshold for evoking auditory sensation in young adults is lowest at:**
   A. 30 Hz
   B. 100 Hz
   C. 3,000 Hz
   D. 10,000 Hz
   E. 30,000 Hz

136. **Gustatory and olfactory receptor cells:**
    A. adapt completely during continued presentation of a stimulus
    B. have binding sites located on their cell bodies
    C. respond only to chemicals representing single tastes or smells
    D. increase their sensitivity during continued stimulation
    E. are phasic–tonic receptors that maintain depolarization for long periods of stimulation

137. **It is postulated that complete adaptation of olfactory sensation involves all the following *EXCEPT*:**
    A. receptor cell fatigue
    B. stimulation of centrifugal nerve fibers to the olfactory bulb
    C. stimulation of granule cells
    D. inhibition of transmission from olfactory cell to mitral cell
    E. feedback inhibition from the CNS

138. **Efferent fibers from the cortex of the cerebellum are composed entirely of:**
    A. climbing fibers
    B. mossy fibers
    C. Betz cells
    D. granule cells
    E. Purkinje cells

139. **Stimulation of a Golgi tendon organ (GTO):**
    A. activates alpha-motor neurons of the contralateral antagonistic muscle
    B. activates the alpha-motor neurons of the muscle attached to the tendon innervated by the GTO
    C. results in inhibition of the alpha-motor neuron attached to the tendon innervated by the GTO
    D. results in inhibition of the antagonistic muscle
    E. stimulates excitatory interneurons on the spinal cord

140. **Group II (secondary afferent) nerve fibers from muscle spindles:**
    A. innervate both nuclear bag and nuclear chain nerve fibers
    B. innervate only nuclear bag nerve fibers
    C. respond to both rate of muscle stretch and length of muscle stretch
    D. do not respond directly to rate of stretch
    E. respond to tension on the muscle

141. **The patellar tendon reflex (knee jerk) involves all of the following *EXCEPT*:**
    A. stretch of nuclear bag intrafusal muscle fibers
    B. group 1a (primary) afferent receptors from the muscle spindle
    C. spinal cord interneurons
    D. alpha-motor neurons
    E. extrafusal muscle fibers

142. **Stimulation of gamma dynamic efferent nerve fibers:**
    A. contracts nuclear chain and nuclear bag intrafusal muscle fibers
    B. can stimulate type 1a (primary) afferent nerve fibers
    C. increases the response of type II (secondary) nerve fibers to a constant muscle stretch
    D. results in relaxation of extrafusal muscle fibers
    E. does not occur during contraction of extrafusal muscle fibers against a load

143. **During contraction of extrafusal muscle fibers against a heavy load**
    A. gamma-motor neuron stimulation is inhibited
    B. the stretch reflex is attenuated
    C. extrafusal muscle fibers shorten more than intrafusal muscle fibers
    D. there is reflex inhibition of alpha-motor neuron activity
    E. stretch receptors increase extrafusal muscle fiber excitation

144. **The ''clasp knife'' reflex, i.e., muscle relaxation, which occurs during increases in muscle tension, involves all the following *EXCEPT*:**
    A. stimulation of Golgi tendon organs (GTO)
    B. stimulation of type 1a sensory afferents from the muscle spindle
    C. stimulation of inhibitory interneurons in the spinal cord
    D. inhibition of alpha-motor neuron activity
    E. facilitation of antagonistic extrafusal muscle fibers

145. **Nerve fibers from the cerebellar cortex:**
    A. have an effect on deep cerebellar nuclei that is opposite to the effect of climbing fibers
    B. terminate directly on alpha-motor neurons in the spinal cord
    C. excite the neurons of the deep cerebellar nuclei
    D. project directly to the motor cortex
    E. join with fibers from the motor cortex in the pyramidal tracts

146. **Degeneration of gamma-amino butyric acid-containing neurons in the caudate nucleus and putamen results in:**
    A. Parkinson's disease
    B. paralysis agitans
    C. Huntington's chorea
    D. dementia
    E. Alzheimer's disease

147. **All of the following can be characteristic of cerebellar dysfunction *EXCEPT*:**
    A. uncoordinated movements
    B. failure of progression
    C. intention tremor
    D. loss of the long loop component of the stretch reflex
    E. increased peripheral muscle tone

148. **Inability to form new declarative (verbal or symbolic) memories results from damage to the:**
    A. hippocampus
    B. medulla
    C. hypothalamus
    D. limbic system
    E. cerebellum

149. **During sleep in normal adults, the percentage of time in:**
    A. REM sleep decreases with age
    B. REM sleep increases with age
    C. stage 4 slow-wave sleep decreases with age
    D. stage 3 slow-wave sleep increases with age
    E. stage 4 sleep increases with age

150. **All the following structures are part of the basal ganglia *EXCEPT*:**
    A. putamen
    B. caudate nucleus
    C. striatum
    D. substantia nigra
    E. reticular formation

151. **Decerebration, i.e., transecting the neuroaxis so that the forebrain is isolated from the hindbrain and spinal cord:**
    A. results in spinal shock
    B. decreases alpha-motor neuron excitability
    C. unloads the muscle–spindle stretch receptors
    D. activates the gamma-motor neuron system
    E. inhibits the antigravity muscles

152. **The heat transfer mechanism that accounts for the existence of the thermal boundary layer is:**
    A. conduction
    B. convection
    C. evaporation
    D. long-wave radiation
    E. short-wave radiation

153. **The major heat source for a febrile reaction in a nude, 65-kg person in an environment of 29°C is the:**
    A. brain
    B. brown adipose tissue
    C. liver
    D. skeletal muscle
    E. white adipose tissue

154. **A thermoregulatory response of man controlled by cholinergic sympathetics is:**
    A. brown adipose tissue thermogenesis
    B. hand vasomotion
    C. shivering thermogenesis
    D. sweat secretion
    E. thermoregulatory behavior

155. **Which of the following most faithfully reflects changes in human core temperature caused by immersion in a warm water bath?**
    A. oral temperature
    B. rectal temperature
    C. axillary temperature
    D. esophageal temperature at the cardia
    E. tympanic temperature

156. **Which of the following structures is likely to have the highest skin temperature in a comfortably dressed individual standing upright, at rest in the shade, in a still (windless) environment at 20°C?**
    A. forehead
    B. trunk
    C. finger
    D. toe
    E. all will be equal

157. **All of the following are correct for human neonates *EXCEPT*:**
    A. cold-exposed neonates never shiver
    B. the mean skin temperature of neonates is lower than that of adults
    C. the cutaneous circulation of humans is not well organized at birth
    D. they possess relatively little subcutaneous fat at birth
    E. the thermal conductivity of neonatal skin is higher than that of adult skin

158. **In a man passively warmed such that his mean skin temperature reaches 40.5°C, which of the following circulatory responses will occur?**
    A. increased cardiac output, decreased splanchnic blood flow
    B. increased cardiac output, increased muscle blood flow
    C. unchanged cardiac output, decreased right atrial pressure
    D. unchanged cardiac output, decreased renal blood flow
    E. decreased stroke volume, increased finger blood flow

159. **At the beginning of the rising phase of fever:**
    A. sweat secretion is stimulated
    B. mean skin temperature is below normal
    C. muscle blood flow is decreased
    D. behavioral thermoregulatory responses are inhibited
    E. warm-sensitive neurons in the preoptic–anterior hypothalamus are excited

160. **The most characteristic endocrinological feature of cold acclimatization is an increased responsiveness to the metabolic effects of:**
    A. growth hormone
    B. thyroglobulin
    C. norepinephrine
    D. cortisol
    E. insulin

161. **Which of the following is currently believed to ultimately account for the febrile response that is the hallmark of infection?**
    A. the invading pathogenic organisms *per se*
    B. products released by the pathogenic organisms during their encounter with the host's immune system
    C. mediators released by the host's immune cells during their encounter with the invading microorganisms
    D. prostaglandins released in the host's brain
    E. none of the above

162. **A feature that essentially differentiates a febrile from a hyperthermic patient is that a febrile patient:**
    A. typically has a core temperature in excess of 39.5°C
    B. generally seeks a cool environment
    C. generally has a warm, wet skin
    D. is often thirsty
    E. generally has a dry, cool skin over most of the body

163. **The principal physical mechanism that accounts for the transfer of heat within the body is:**
    A. conduction
    B. convection
    C. radiation
    D. evaporation
    E. none of the above

164. **When a euhydrated 70-kg man at rest is exposed for 30 min to a dry 3o°C environment, the expected order of his thermoregulatory responses will normally be:**
    A. behavioral changes, sweating, cutaneous vasodilation
    B. behavioral changes, cutaneous vasodilation, sweating
    C. cutaneous vasodilation, sweating, behavioral changes
    D. sweating, behavioral changes, cutaneous vasodilation
    E. none of the above; these responses generally occur simultaneously

165. **All of the following are characteristics of our shell or insulating layer *EXCEPT*:**
    A. in the cold, the subcutaneous fat layer contributes significantly to the insulation of the shell
    B. in the heat, the subcutaneous fat layer contributes significantly to the insulation of the shell
    C. in the cold, most of the heat transfer through the shell occurs by conduction
    D. in the heat, most of the heat transfer through the shell occurs by circulatory convection
    E. the insulation value of the shell is determined by its thickness, which varies with the environmental temperature

166. **Naked human neonates exposed for 1 h to a dry environment of 26°C do not adequately maintain their body temperature because:**
    A. they are unable to produce heat in an amount and duration sufficient to compensate for their body heat loss
    B. they possess insufficient subcutaneous fat to adequately insulate them
    C. their surface area-to-body mass ratio is unfavorable for heat conservation
    D. their cutaneous circulation is poorly organized and poorly innervated
    E. all of the above

167. **Long-term adaptation to tropical climates involves:**
    A. increased thyroxine production
    B. decreased maximal sweating rate
    C. increased catecholamine release
    D. increased aldosterone release
    E. all of the above

168. **When environmental temperature increases, blood flow to the skin:**
    A. decreases to stop the transport of heat from the skin surface to deeper tissues
    B. decreases because the local thermoreceptors in the skin sense an increase in body temperature
    C. decreases because the sweat glands release vasoconstrictor kinins, which increases skin blood flow resistance
    D. increases as part of the body temperature regulatory mechanism
    E. increases as the metabolic needs of the skin tissue increase

SECTION II: QUESTIONS AND ANSWERS

The following measurements were made in an adult human. (Note: some or all of these data will be used for the next three questions).

total body water	42 liters
plasma volume	3 liters
hematocrit	0.40
extracellular fluid volume	14 liters
plasma osmolarity	300 mOsm/liter

1. **The interstitial fluid volume in liters is:**
    A.   10.0
    B.   10.4
    C.   11.0
    D.   14.0
    E.   28.0

    Answer = C.   The extracellular fluid volume is made up of the interstitial fluid volume and the plasma volume.

2. **The cell volume in liters is:**
    A.   10.0
    B.   10.4
    C.   11.0
    D.   14.0
    E.   28.0

    Answer = E.   The cell volume is the difference between total body water and the extracellular volume.

3. **The blood volume in liters is:**
    A.   3.0
    B.   4.0
    C.   5.0
    D.   7.5
    E.   12.0

    Answer = C.   Blood volume can be estimated from the relationship:
    plasma volume/(1 − Hct) or 3 liters/(1 − 0.4) = 5 liters.

4. **The subject above ingests 3 liters of water. Assuming no water loss from the body, the plasma osmolarity in mOsm/liter after steady state has been attained will be:**
    A.   260
    B.   265
    C.   270
    D.   275
    E.   280

    Answer = E.   Water distributes throughout all of the fluid compartments and will dilute the osmolarity of all of the fluid compartments. Since the subject had 42 liters of total body water before ingesting the 3 liters of water, the subject now has 45 liters of water. The total number of osmotic particles in the body did not change. Hence, you can estimate the change in plasma osmolarity by dividing (42 liters × 300 mOsm/liter = 12,600 mOsmoles, the total number of osmotic particles) by 45 liters = **280** mOsm/liter.

5. Which of the following substance(s) would you need to inject into a patient to obtain a measure of intracellular volume?
    A. deuterium oxide (D_2O) and ^{131}I-albumin
    B. tritiated H_2O and inulin
    C. inulin
    D. inulin and ^{131}I-albumin
    E. deuterium oxide (D_2O)

    Answer = B.   The intracellular fluid volume cannot be directly determined, but we can calculate the intracellular volume by measuring total body water with either deuterium oxide (D_2O) or tritiated H_2O and then subtracting from that value the extracellular volume. Extracellular volume can be measured (estimated) with inulin or some other substance that distributes within the extracellular compartment.

6. Which of the following infusions would cause the greatest increase in extracellular fluid volume? (Assume that these infusions have equilibrated, but have not been excreted.)
    A. 1 liter of H_2O
    B. 1 liter of isotonic saline
    C. 1 liter of plasma
    D. 1 liter of iso-osmotic urea
    E. 1 liter of hypertonic sodium chloride

    Answer = E.   All of the infusions will increase total body water by 1 liter. The infusion of a hypertonic sodium chloride solution, however, will raise extracellular osmolarity, causing additional water to be drawn out of the intracellular compartment. Thus, extracellular volume will increase by 1 liter plus the amount of water that is drawn from the cells. H_2O and iso-osmotic urea will cause less than a liter increase in extracellular volume because both solutions are hypotonic; some of the 1-liter solution will diffuse into the intracellular compartment (not **A** or **D**). Isotonic saline and plasma are both isotonic, so the entire 1 liter will remain in the extracellular compartment; water will not be drawn out of the intracellular compartment (not **B** or **C**).

7. The following data were obtained in a normal human subject:
    Inulin: 3 g injected intravenously; extrapolated zero-time plasma concentration = 0.2 mg/ml.
    Evan's blue dye: 50 mg injected intravenously; extrapolated zero-time plasma concentration = 0.01 mg/ml.
    The measured plasma volume in liters is:
    A. 42
    B. 15
    C. 10
    D. 5
    E. 2

    Answer = D.   Only the volume of distribution of Evan's Blue is needed to determine the plasma volume. 50 mg/(0.01 mg/ml) = 5 liters (the injected amount/the plasma concentration at time zero). The inulin data would allow you to determine the size of the extracellular fluid compartment.

8. Approximately how much Na would you have to give to a 70-kg patient to increase plasma Na concentration from 140 to 160 mM?
    A. 60 mMol of Na
    B. 280 mMol of Na
    C. 420 mMol of Na
    D. 560 mMol of Na
    E. 840 mMol of Na

    Answer = E.   Although sodium remains almost entirely within the extracellular fluid compartment, the increase in osmolarity causes osmosis of water out of the intracellular compartment until the osmolarities of the intracellular and extracellular fluid compartments equilibrate. Therefore, you have to add enough Na to raise the osmolarity (increase the [K] inside the cells by approximately 20 mM) of all of the fluid compartments. To raise the Na concentration by 20 mM, you estimate the total body water content (60% of body weight = 42 liters) and multiply by 20 mM (the change in [Na] you want to produce). 42 liters × 20 mM = 840 mMoles of Na. Choice **A** (60 mM) is the amount of Na you would need to add to a beaker that contained 3 liters (approximate plasma volume). Choice **B** (280 mM) is the amount of Na you would need to add to a beaker that contained 14 liters (approximate extracellular fluid volume).

9. When a red blood cell is placed in a hypertonic environment, initially its volume will *(X)* because of the movement of *(Y)*.

	X	Y
A.	increase	water into the cell
B.	increase	electrolytes into the cell
C.	decrease	water out of the cell
D.	decrease	electrolytes out of the cell
E.	decrease	water and electrolytes out of the cell

Answer = C. A hypertonic solution will cause water to move out of the cell until the intracellular tonicity (osmolarity) equals the extracellular tonicity (osmolarity). Hence, the volume of the cell will decrease because water moves out. The decrease in volume is not due to the movement of ions.

The next two questions (10 and 11) are based on Fig. 1-1.:

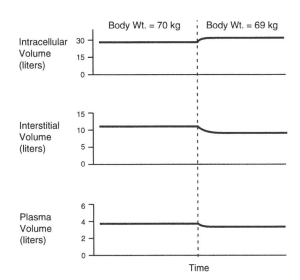

FIG. 1-1

10. What happened to plasma osmolarity (tonicity) in this individual?
    A. increased
    B. no change
    C. decreased

Answer = C. First consider what happened to this subject. Body weight decreased rapidly after the event line while intracellular volume increased, but both interstitial fluid and plasma volume decreased. There was a shift of water into the cells, but overall there was a loss of fluid (rapid decreases in body weight reflect fluid loss). Since water moves into and out of cells by osmosis, there must have been a decrease in extracellular osmolarity that caused water to diffuse from the extracellular into the intracellular compartment.

11. Which of the following situations could account for the above results?
    A. a loss of hypertonic urine
    B. a loss of isotonic urine
    C. an infusion of hypertonic saline
    D. an infusion of hypotonic saline
    E. an infusion of hyperoncotic albumin

Answer = A. A loss of hypertonic urine is the only choice given that will produce the results. Choices **C**, **D**, and **E** will cause a gain in body weight. Choice **B** will cause a loss of body weight; but since plasma osmolarity does not change, intracellular fluid volume will not change.

Questions 12–14. The diagrams in solid lines represent the volumes and osmolarities of the extracellular (EC) and intracellular (IC) fluid compartments of a normal adult. For each situation, select the diagram with a dotted line that best reflects the change that will occur.

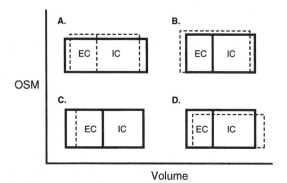

FIG. 1-2

12. **Loss of isotonic salt (NaCl) solution**

    Answer = C. With a loss of an isotonic salt solution, EC compartment volume decreases without a change in osmolality. Osmolality did not change, so no change in cell volume will occur.

13. **Water deprivation**

    Answer = A. Because osmolality increased and there was a proportional decrease in the volume within both the EC and IC compartments, a loss of water occurred. If a salt gain had caused the increase in osmolality, the EC compartment volume would increase while the IC compartment volume would decrease in size as water left the cell by osmosis to reestablish osmotic equilibrium.

14. **Intravenous infusion of hypertonic saline**

    Answer = B. Because osmolality and the volume of the EC compartment increased whereas the volume of the IC compartment decreased, a net gain in the amount of osmotic particles (NaCl) occurred. Water left the IC compartment to reestablish osmotic equilibrium with the EC compartment. If a water loss had caused the increase in osmolality, both the EC and IC compartment volumes would decrease.

15. **Over a short period of time, a patient loses 3 liters of isotonic fluid (NaCl/HCO$_3$) due to diarrhea and then ingests 3 liters of water. All of the following are true EXCEPT:**
    A. body weight decreases
    B. extracellular fluid volume decreases
    C. plasma volume decreases
    D. plasma osmolarity decreases
    E. intracellular volume increases

    Answer = A. *Remember; you are looking for the exception.* The patient lost the same volume of fluid that was ingested, so no change in body weight occurred (not **A**). Short-term changes in body weight are an excellent measure of short-term changes in total body water. The patient did lose osmotic particles, primarily from the extracellular compartment. This would cause the plasma osmolarity to decrease (**D**) and water to leave the extracellular compartment (decreased EC and plasma volume; **B** and **C**) and enter the intracellular compartment (**E**).

16. **Approximately 30 min following the infusion of 1 liter of isotonic saline (0.9% NaCl) or 1 liter of isotonic glucose (5% dextrose) in an anephric adult, you would expect these infusions to cause:**
    A. similar decreases in plasma osmolality
    B. similar increases in extracellular volume
    C. no change in cell volume in either group following either infusion
    D. a similar increase in total body water
    E. no change in plasma osmolality following either infusion

Answer = D. We know that none of the infused fluid would be excreted or lost from the body of an anephric person. Hence, total body water would increase by the same amount (1 liter) that was infused. Because glucose is taken up by the cells and stored as glycogen, the osmotic particle (glucose) is lost, leaving 1 liter of water to dilute the osmolality of the body fluids. Isotonic saline by definition will have no effect on the extracellular osmolality (not **A** or **E**). As the osmolality decreases (glucose uptake), water diffuses by osmosis into the cell; this causes an increase in cell volume and, hence, a shift of water from the extracellular to the intracellular compartment. In contrast, all of the saline will remain in the extracellular compartment (not **B** or **C**).

17. **When the concentration of extracellular alanine increases and the flux of alanine into a cell increases, the flux of leucine into the cell is found to decrease. How might this be explained?**
    A.   increased activity of the Na/K ATPase
    B.   diffusion
    C.   restricted diffusion
    D.   decreased activity of the Na/Ca exchanger
    E.   competition for a carrier protein

    Answer = E. Amino acids often share a common transporter (membrane protein carriers) that allows them to enter the cells. Hence, amino acids compete with one another, and an increase in the concentration of one decreases the flux of the other. An increase in Na/K ATPase activity (**A**) tends to increase the flux when the carrier is a sodium/amino acid cotransporter. A characteristic of simple diffusion is that no competition between similar molecules occurs (**B**). Restricted diffusion is diffusion through channels (i.e., a restricted pathway) and does not show competition between similar molecules (**C**). Choice **D** is a nonsense issue for considering amino acid transport.

18. **Following a feast of wild mushrooms, an individual arrives in the emergency room. The mushrooms were of the species *Inocybe*, which has a very high muscarine content. One probable symptom is:**
    A.   an overresponsive, or exaggerated, patellar tendon reflex
    B.   increased blood glucose levels
    C.   fast heart rate
    D.   muscle contractions or spasms
    E.   constricted pupils

    Answer = E. You would expect the activation of muscarinic receptor-mediated responses, such as pupillary constriction and slowed heart rate (not **C**). The nicotinic responses associated with the neuromuscular junction (not **A** or **D**) and those mediated by activation of the adrenal medulla (not **B**) would not be affected.

19. **What is the approximate osmolarity of a solution containing only 10 mM NaCl, 120 mM KCl, and 1 mM $CaCl_2$?**
    A.   120 mOsm/l
    B.   131 mOsm/l
    C.   243 mOsm/l
    D.   263 mOsm/l
    E.   295 mOsm/l

    Answer = D. Osmolarity is a chemical property of a solution, and it depends on the number of molecules (mM) per liter of solution. Since NaCl and KCl both dissociate in solution into a cation and an anion, they contribute 240 mOsm/l (NaCl) + 20 mOsm/l (KCl). $CaCl_2$ disassociates into one cation and two anions, yielding 3 mOsm/l; hence, the total osmolarity of the solution is 263 mOsm/l.

20. **For a neuron, which of the following could account for a decrease in temporal summation?**
    A.   an increase in the duration of EPSPs occurring postsynaptically
    B.   a decrease in the postsynaptic space constant
    C.   a decrease in the duration of IPSPs occurring postsynaptically
    D.   an increase in spatial summation of EPSPs
    E.   a decrease in the interval between presynaptic action potentials

    Answer = B. Any factor that tends to cause the postsynaptic potential to spread less far—such as a decrease in the space constant—to occur less frequently (not **E**), or to become shorter in duration (not **A, C,** or **D**) will decrease the amount of temporal summation.

21. **A lipophilic substance is likely to:**
    A. have a low permeability coefficient
    B. be a charged particle
    C. have a high partition coefficient
    D. be more concentrated in the extracellular fluid than in the cell membrane
    E. be a substrate for the Na^+/K^+ pump

Answer = C. Lipophilic substances tend to be nonpolar (not **B**) and have a high solubility in the cell membrane. Hence, they have a high partition coefficient and permeability coefficient (not **A** or **D**) and are not ions, which are the substrates for the Na^+/K^+ pump (not **E**).

22. **The receptor potential created due to an environmental stimulus:**
    A. sums spatially, not temporally
    B. decays as a function of the space constant
    C. is self-propagating
    D. is not caused by changes in membrane permeability to ions
    E. is fixed in amplitude regardless of stimulus intensity

Answer = B. Receptor potentials are nonpropagating (not **C**) changes in ionic permeability (not **D**) that summate both spatially and temporally (not **A**), and the rate of decay of these potentials is determined by both the space and time constants. A receptor's potential magnitude is dependent on the stimulus intensity (not **E**).

23. **The antagonistic nature of sympathetic and parasympathetic innervation leads to:**
    A. finer autonomic control of organs
    B. tonic activation of the autonomic nervous system
    C. increased activity of organs
    D. decreased activity of organs
    E. activation of both α- and β-adrenergic receptors

Answer = A. By having the ability to either increase or decrease a variable, such as heart rate or GI motility, the organ gains the ability to have fine control over that variable. Even though there is tonic activity in the autonomic nervous system, it is not the result of the antagonism (not **B**). The antagonism does not in itself lead to an increase (not **C**) or decrease (not **D**) in the activity of organs, nor does it have anything to do with which type of receptor is involved (not **E**).

24. **As the threshold for the generation of a nerve action potential is reached:**
    A. Na^+ influx exceeds K^+ efflux
    B. Na^+ efflux and K^+ influx are equal
    C. Na^+ channels are time-inactivated
    D. Na^+ efflux begins
    E. K^+ efflux begins

Answer = A. Threshold occurs when there is enough depolarization to cause the voltage-gated sodium channels to open, allowing for an influx (not **B** or **D**) of sodium sufficiently larger than the efflux of potassium. Although the sodium channels are time-inactivated, this occurs after they have been activated—not at threshold (not **C**). The change in potassium permeability occurs after the opening of the sodium channels (not **E**).

25. **Typically, normal nerves at rest have a net electrochemical driving force on K^+, causing a continual leakage of K^+ out of the cell. Because of this, we can say that:**
    A. K^+ is not in a steady state
    B. K^+ is not passively distributed
    C. K^+ is continually pumped out of the cell
    D. there is a net passive influx of K^+
    E. intracellular $[K^+]$ continually decreases

Answer = B. At rest, the normal cell is in a steady state (not **A**), not in equilibrium; hence, potassium is not passively distributed. Potassium is constantly leaking out of the cell, while the Na/K ATPase is actively pumping K back into the cell (not **C** or **D**) at the same rate that maintains the intracellular potassium content constant (not **E**).

26. **Drug X has a molecular weight of 500 g/M, while Drug Y has a molecular weight of 50 g/M. The net flux of Drug X across the lipid bilayer will be:**
    A. greater than the net flux of Drug Y if both drugs are lipophilic
    B. inversely proportional to the concentration gradient of Drug X
    C. independent of Drug X's partition coefficient
    D. directly related to Drug X's permeability coefficient
    E. independent of the thickness of the lipid bilayer

    Answer = D. The permeability coefficient is proportional to the net flux of the drug. The size of the molecule (Drug X is less than Drug Y; not **A**) and the thickness of the membrane (not **E**) inversely affect the flux. The partition coefficient plays an important role in determining the flux of any drug across a lipid bilayer (not **C**).

27. **The net electrochemical driving force on a permeable ion:**
    A. is independent of the concentration gradient of the ion
    B. is dependent on the ion's equilibrium potential and independent of the cell membrane potential
    C. can lead to a violation of the law of electroneutrality
    D. will determine the direction of net flux of an ion
    E. is independent of the ion's net charge

    Answer = D. The direction of the net flux of an ion is determined by the electrochemical driving force. It is determined in part by the ratio of the concentration of the ion inside and outside the cell (not **A**), the membrane potential (not **B**), and the electrical charge of the ion (not **E**). The law of electroneutrality cannot be violated (not **C**).

28. **Plasma membrane proteins:**
    A. are present in equimolar concentrations with phospholipids
    B. are found exclusively on the outer or inner surface of the membrane
    C. determine the transmembrane movement of hydrophobic substances
    D. may span the membrane and move laterally within the membrane
    E. are all ion channels

    Answer = D. Although protein molecules may span (not **B**) and move within the lipid bilayer, they make up a small portion of the membrane (not **A**). These proteins serve as channels, receptors, and carriers (not just **E**) for hydrophilic (not **C**) molecules and ions.

29. **The "all or none" principle for nerve conduction means that under a given set of conditions:**
    A. the number of nerves excited by a stimulus is independent of the stimulus intensity
    B. the electrical potential above threshold can be transmitted long distances
    C. all nerves are refractory for the same duration of time after a stimulus
    D. all EPSPs and IPSPs will summate
    E. all nerves conduct action potentials at the same velocity

    Answer = B. A more classical statement of the "all or none" principle is that an action potential with a similar level of depolarization is induced once threshold is reached. Hence, the action potential will be transmitted for very long distances.

30. **Immediately after a bullet transects (cuts) the spinal cord, all sensation and voluntary movement of the legs are lost. Weeks later, the legs become spastic (involuntary contractions), and the drug baclofen is prescribed. One way in which baclofen may decrease leg spasms is to:**
    A. decrease the number of IPSPs on the motor efferent
    B. decrease the magnitude of IPSPs on the motor efferent
    C. decrease the action potential threshold of the motor efferent from -50 mV to -55 mV
    D. decrease the relative refractory period of the motor efferent
    E. increase presynaptic inhibition on the afferent nerve

    Answer = E. Since spinal level afferent activity excites the motor neuron, an effect is needed that will decrease the number of synaptic vesicles released by the afferent. Actions **A–D** would all tend to increase the number of action potentials. **A** and **B** would ultimately produce less hyperpolarization at the neuromotor junction, while **C** and **D** would make it more likely that afferent input would generate an action potential in the motor neuron.

31. **The duration of the after-hyperpolarization of a nerve action potential:**
    A.   determines the absolute refractory period
    B.   can be influenced by a decrease in K^+ permeability
    C.   is not significantly influenced by TEA
    D.   is the period immediately after an IPSP
    E.   would increase if Na^+ channels were open

    Answer = B.   The after-hyperpolarization, which immediately follows the peak of the nerve action potential (not **D**), is due to a high potassium permeability, causing the membrane potential to approach the K equilibrium potential. Hence, a decrease in potassium permeability induced, e.g., by TEA (not **C**) would definitely affect its duration. The absolute refractory period is caused by the inactivation of voltage-gated sodium channels (not **A**). Any increase in the number of open Na^+ channels would shorten the duration of the after-hyperpolarization by depolarizing the membrane potential (not **E**).

32. **Neurotransmitter X opens Channel Y on the postsynaptic membrane. The reversal potential for ions flowing through Channel Y is equal to +102 mV. Which ion is probably flowing through Channel Y? (Assume extracellular ions: Na^+ = 140 mM, K^+ = 4 mM, Ca^{2+} = 2.5 mM, Cl^- = 110 mM, HCO_3^- = 2 0 mM and intracellular ions: Na^+ = 14 mM, K^+ = 120 mM, Ca^{2+} = 0.001 mM, Cl^- = 11 mM, HCO_3^- = 10 mM.)**
    A. Na^+
    B. K^+
    C. Ca^{2+}
    D. Cl^-
    E. HCO_3^-

    Answer = C.   Since the K^+, Cl^-, and HCO_3^- would produce a negative reversal potential, apply the Nernst equation to Na^+ and Ca^{2+}. Since calcium is a divalent ion, you must divide the Nernst constant, 60, by 2; i.e., $(2.500/0.0001 = 2,500) = \log 2,500 = 33.398 * 60/2 = +102$ mV.

33. **Tricyclic antidepressants are used to treat major depression. This class of drugs acts at synapses by blocking the reuptake of biogenic amines into the nerve terminals. Tricyclic antidepressants act as a:**
    A.   GABA antagonist
    B.   facilitator of GABA
    C.   neurotransmitter
    D.   neuromodulator
    E.   neuroactive peptide

    Answer = D.   By affecting the activity of a neurotransmitter after it has been released, the tricyclic antidepressants are acting as a neuromodulator. They are not acting as a transmitter (not **C**); without the release of the biogenic amines, tricyclic antidepressants would have no action (not **E**). GABA is a neurotransmitter and has been assigned neither an antagonist nor a facilitatory role (not **A** or **B**).

For questions 34–36, refer to Fig. 1-3.

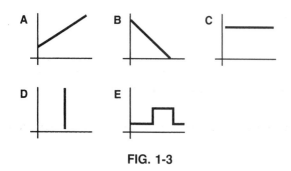

FIG. 1-3

34. **Which figure best illustrates the relationship of acetylcholine concentration in the synaptic cleft (Y-axis) as a function of extracellular $[Ca^{2+}]$ (X-axis)?**

    Answer = A.   As the amount of calcium that influxes into the presynaptic terminal increases, the amount of ACh that is released increases.

35. **Which figure best illustrates the relationship of the amplitude of a muscle action potential (Y-axis) as a function of acetylcholine concentration in the synaptic cleft (X-axis)?**

Answer = C. Once the level of ACh exceeds that necessary to generate a threshold level of depolarization on the postsynaptic membrane, an action potential occurs. Further increases in ACh will not affect the magnitude of the action potential.

36. **Which figure best illustrates the relationship of frequency of action potentials along an autonomic nerve (Y-axis) as a function of potassium channel relative permeability (X-axis)?**

Answer = B. As the potassium channel activity increases, the membrane potential will become more hyperpolarized; consequently, it will be more difficult for threshold to be reached. Hence, the frequency of the action potential will decrease with an increase in K permeability.

37. **In cell membranes:**
    A.   hydrophobic phospholipid heads associate to form a bilayer
    B.   solutes with a low partition coefficient move more readily across the lipid bilayer than solutes with a high partition coefficient
    C.   membrane proteins have no known function but are necessary for life
    D.   membrane proteins can increase the speed of solute transport
    E.   when a lipid-soluble solute is in equilibrium across the membrane, there is a net flux of that solute from an area of high concentration to one of low concentration

Answer = D. Because the lipid bilayer is very impermeable to hydrophilic molecules, membrane proteins (channels, carriers, cotransporters, etc.) (not **C**) have evolved to facilitate the movement of hydrophilic molecules across the cell membrane. The hydrophilic (not **A**) phospholipid heads are part of that bilayer. The partition coefficient is directly proportional to the solubility of the molecule in the membrane; hence, substances with a high partition coefficient move more readily (not **B**). At equilibrium there is no net flux (not **E**).

38. **During an action potential, the direction of net flux of K^+ during repolarization and of Na^+ during depolarization are (respectively):**
    A.   inward, inward
    B.   outward, outward
    C.   inward, outward
    D.   outward, inward
    E.   no net flux, outward

Answer = D. The electrochemical gradient for K^+ during the repolarization phase is outward; during the depolarization phase, the electrochemical gradient for Na^+ is inward.

39. **Typically, postganglionic neurons of the parasympathetic system release:**
    A.   acetylcholine, which binds to muscarinic receptors
    B.   acetylcholine, which binds to nicotinic receptors
    C.   norepinephrine, which binds to α-adrenergic receptors
    D.   epinephrine, which binds to β-adrenergic receptors
    E.   norepinephrine, which binds to β-adrenergic receptors

Answer = A. Although the preganglionic fibers release ACh that acts on postganglionic nicotinic receptors, the postganglionic parasympathetic fibers release ACh that tends to act on muscarinic receptors.

40. **At the neuromuscular junction, the influx of sodium ions that partially determines the endplate potential is due to:**

    A.   hyperpolarization of the postsynaptic membrane
    B.   a net outward driving force for sodium
    C.   potassium efflux
    D.   high intracellular Na concentrations in the endplate region
    E.   a ligand-activated process

Answer = E. The opening of ACh-gated ionic channels allows sodium to flow down its electrochemical gradient, depolarizing the endplate.

PART 1: GENERAL PHYSIOLOGY

41. **Sympathetic stimulation of the adrenal medulla:**
   A. decreases dopamine concentration in the blood
   B. increases acetylcholine concentration in the blood
   C. increases epinephrine concentration in the blood
   D. would occur through stimulation of somatic nerves
   E. would occur through stimulation of cell bodies in the sacral segment of the spinal cord

   Answer = C. When activated, the adrenal medullary cells primarily secrete epinephrine rather than norepinephrine or dopamine.

42. **For a cell with 120 mM K^+ protein$^-$ inside and 4 mM K^+ protein$^-$ outside, with proteins$^-$ impermeable and K^+ permeable to the membrane, which of the following statements is true *at equilibrium*?**
   A. The chemical potential driving K inward is equal in magnitude to the electrical potential driving potassium outward.
   B. Bulk movement of K out of the cell occurs due to the impermeable proteins$^-$.
   C. The net flux of potassium equals zero.
   D. There will be 62 mM K protein inside and 62 mM K protein outside the cell.
   E. The inside of this cell will be electrically positive with respect to the outside.

   Answer = C. At equilibrium, the inside of the cell is negative (not **E**) to the outside and there will be no net flux of K. At equilibrium, the chemical gradient driving K outward is equal to the electrical gradient driving K inward (not **A**). The magnitude of the flux of K out of the cell to reach equilibrium produces no detectable change in the K concentration inside or outside the cell (not **B** or **D**).

43. **Electrical synapses:**
   A. deliver the electrical signal to multicellular preparations more quickly than chemical synapses
   B. conduct an action potential in only one direction
   C. have a direct susceptibility to receptor antagonist drugs
   D. have longer synaptic delays than chemical synapses
   E. do not lead to the generation of an action potential in the postsynaptic neuron

   Answer = A. Electrical synapses have very little delay since they do not depend on the diffusion of a transmitter across a synaptic cleft but do allow for the rapid generation of an action potential in the connecting cell. Such synapses are bidirectional and are not susceptible to receptor antagonists.

44. **If an uncharged solute crosses the cell membrane by diffusion, then the flux of that solute will be:**
   A. inversely proportional to the concentration gradient of the solute across the cell membrane
   B. inversely proportional to the molecular weight of the solute
   C. directly proportional to the radius of the solute
   D. directly proportional to the thickness of the membrane
   E. inversely proportional to the partition coefficient of the solute

   Answer = B. The flux of a neutral molecule across the cell membrane will be inversely proportional to its molecular weight and directly proportional to the concentration gradient (not **A**) and the partition coefficient (not **E**), while being inversely proportional to the radius (not **C**) and the thickness of the membrane (not **D**).

45. **What would the approximate resting membrane potential be for a cell with intracellular concentrations of K = 120 mM and Na = 14 mM, extracellular concentrations of K = 4 mM and Na = 140 mM, and the following ion permeabilities: $P_{Na} = 0.09$, $P_K = 0.91$ (permeability for all other ions is zero)?**
   A. -50 mV
   B. -60 mV
   C. $+60$ mV
   D. 0 mV
   E. -30 mV

   Answer = A. Since more than one ion is permeable, the Goldman equation should be used. Thus, $60 \log (P_K[K]_o + P_{Na}[Na]_o)/(P_K[K]_i + P_{Na}[Na]_i) = -50$ mV.

46. A hypothetical cell contains 10 mM Na$^+$ and 10 mM proteins$^-$ and is immersed in a 10-mM NaCl solution. The cell membrane is permeable to water, Na$^+$, and Cl$^-$, but impermeable to proteins$^-$. Which of the following will occur?
   A. Osmolarity inside the cell will be less than osmolarity outside the cell.
   B. The [Na] inside the cell will be less than the [Na] outside the cell.
   C. Millimoles of Na outside the cell will not equal millimoles of Cl outside the cell.
   D. The impermeable proteins will cause an asymmetric distribution of ions.
   E. [Cl] inside the cell will be greater than [Cl] outside the cell.

   Answer = D. A Gibbs-Donnan distribution will occur. Cl will diffuse into the cell, making the cell interior negatively charged, and Na will follow. At equilibrium, the Na$_o$ times Cl$_o$ will equal Na$_i$ times Cl$_i$, but Na$_i$ will be greater (not **B**) than Na$_o$ and vice versa for Cl (not **E**). Outside the cell, the Na$_o$ = Cl$_o$ (not **C**) in order to maintain electroneutrality. This creates an osmotic pressure gradient, with the inside osmolarity being greater than the outside osmolarity (not **A**).

47. Which of the following statements is true regarding normal propagation of an action potential?
   A. When extracellular [Na] decreases, the peak of the action potential decreases.
   B. It requires opening of voltage-gated channels: first to potassium, then to sodium.
   C. The peak amplitude of the action potential decreases as the distance from the stimulus increases.
   D. Action potential propagation is typically bidirectional in nerves.
   E. Action potentials can summate spatially.

   Answer = A. Although the action potential is an all-or-none process (not **C**) caused by the initial opening of voltage-gated sodium channels (not **B**), the absolute magnitude of the peak is determined by the sodium equilibrium potential, which will decrease as the extracellular sodium concentration is reduced. Normally, an action potential is unidirectional from the cell body down the axon (not **D**). Action potentials do not summate (not **E**) since there is an absolute refractory period during which the cell cannot be driven to generate another action potential.

48. Which of the following statements is true regarding an uncharged solute X that enters a cell through facilitated diffusion?
   A. Inhibition of the carrier proteins that transport solute X would increase the net flux of solute X.
   B. For all increases in extracellular [X], a decrease in net flux would result.
   C. Oxygen would be a good example of solute X.
   D. Solute X would be transported from an area of low concentration to one of high concentration.
   E. When solute X is in equilibrium, the [X] outside the cell would equal the [X] inside the cell.

   Answer = E. Since facilitated diffusion is a passive process (not **D**) that involves a membrane carrier protein that assists (not **A**) the solute through the membrane, the inside and outside concentrations at equilibrium will be identical. Up until the carrier is saturated, there is an increase in the net flux as the concentration of X increases (not **B**). Oxygen is not a good example because it diffuses directly through the lipid bilayer unassisted by any carrier protein (not **C**).

49. Which of the following determines the distance that a graded potential will travel down an axon?
   A. increasing the axon diameter
   B. decreasing the axon's internal resistance
   C. decreasing the membrane resistance
   D. increasing the space constant
   E. increasing the amplitude of the graded potential

   Answer = C. The space constant determines how far down an axon a graded potential will travel. The space constant is proportional to [axon diameter × membrane resistance]/internal radius. Thus, the greater the space constant, the greater the distance a graded potential will travel. Although an increase in amplitude will cause the potential at a site at any distance from the origin to be greater, the absolute distance traveled will not be farther (not **E**).

50. Which of the following manipulations would decrease the endplate potential at the neuromuscular junction?
   A. increase the synaptic vesicle content of acetylcholine (assume no change in the number of vesicles released)
   B. increase the number of accessible acetylcholine binding sites in myasthenia gravis
   C. increase Ca entry at the presynaptic neuron terminal
   D. pharmacologically inactivate acetylcholinesterase
   E. apply a nicotinic antagonist to the postsynaptic membrane

Answer = E. The only one of the above that will decrease the endplate potential is the application of a nicotinic antagonist, which will block postsynaptic receptors and thus decrease the response. All of the other choices will increase the amplitude of the endplate potential.

51. Upon arrival of the action potential, acetylcholine released from a presynaptic nerve terminal results from:
     A. Cl^- entry
     B. acetylcholinesterase
     C. synapsin I phosphorylation
     D. opening of channels allowing Na/K to flow down their concentration gradients
     E. postsynaptic inhibition

Answer = C. As the presynaptic terminal is depolarized by the invading action potential, Ca^{2+} channels in the presynaptic terminal are opened and an influx of Ca^{2+} occurs. The increase in intracellular Ca^{2+} activates a kinase, which results in the phosphorylation of synapsin I, which is an essential step that causes the fusion of the synaptic vesicles with the presynaptic terminal cell membrane.

52. Reciprocal innervation is most accurately described as:
     A. inhibition of flexor muscles during activation of the extensor
     B. activation of contralateral extensors during activation of contralateral flexors
     C. reduction in Ia fiber activity during a contraction
     D. simultaneous stimulation of alpha motor neurons to flexor and extensor muscles
     E. Renshaw inhibition

Answer = A. Reciprocal inhibition refers to the ipsilateral inhibition of the antagonistic muscle group, which allows the muscle to cause an unopposed movement. Renshaw inhibition is an autoinhibition, not a reciprocal inhibition (not **E**).

53. Which of the following statements is true regarding a situation in which 500 presynaptic neurons synapse onto a single postsynaptic neuron?
     A. This is an example of divergence on the postsynaptic neuron.
     B. Temporal summation could not occur in the postsynaptic neuronal soma.
     C. If 250 of the synapses were excitatory and 250 were inhibitory, the postsynaptic neuron would never generate an action potential.
     D. The closer a synapse is to the axon hillock, the greater the influence on the frequency of action potentials generated.
     E. This scenario would never occur because postsynaptic neurons have only one presynaptic neuron.

Answer = D. Graded potentials generated by a synaptic ending close to the axon hillock have the shortest distance to travel and thus have the greatest influence on determining whether the axon hillock reaches threshold. This is an example of convergence (not **A**), and such an active synapse will display both spatial and temporal summation (not **B**). It is not the number of EPSPs and IPSPs but rather which one has the greatest influence on the membrane potential at the axon hillock (not **C**) that determines whether an action potential is generated. Such scenarios are the rule in the nervous system (not **E**).

54. The receptor potential of a given cell (receptor cell) that transduces environmental stimuli is:
     A. not affected by changes in the receptor cell space constant
     B. fixed in amplitude regardless of stimulus intensity
     C. self-propagating
     D. nonincremental
     E. due to a change in the receptor cell ion permeability

Answer = E. All receptor potentials are generated by some environmentally induced change in the membrane permeability that establishes a graded potential (not **C** or **D**) that is proportional (not **B**) to the magnitude of the environmental stimulus. The space constant of the cell will strongly influence how the graded potential spreads (not **A**).

55. A surgeon washes out a surgical wound from which a tumor has been removed with sterile distilled water (no ions) rather than sterile physiologic saline (similar to extracellular solution). She does this in order to cause any remaining tumor cells to:
   A.   depolarize and decrease action potential frequency
   B.   increase the activity of secondary active transport and destroy normal cell function
   C.   swell and burst
   D.   inhibit voltage-dependent K^+ channels and decrease the duration of action potentials
   E.   wash off any neurotransmitter and increase synaptic activity

   Answer = C.   The tumor cells will swell and burst because distilled water has an osmolarity of 0.

56. If the vagus nerve (preganglionic cell body in the brain stem) is severed, then:
   A.   the size of the pupils will decrease
   B.   heart rate will decrease
   C.   movement of food through the gut will decrease
   D.   airway resistance will increase (more difficult to breath)
   E.   skeletal muscle weakness will occur

   Answer = C.   The vagus nerve, part of the autonomic—not somatic (not **E**)—nervous system, supplies neuronal input that increases the motility of the GI tract; hence, cutting the vagus will decrease GI motility. The vagus nerve supplies the heart, and its removal will increase heart rate (not **B**). The vagus nerve does not supply the eye (not **A**); however, parasympathetic activity decreases the size of the pupils; so even if the vagus did innervate the eye, the pupils would tend to constrict. Removal of vagal tone will functionally enhance the activity of sympathetic nerves to the lungs, which will produce a bronchodilation (not **D**).

Use Fig. 1-4, which represents the intracellular concentration of phosphate with time, to answer question 57. Assume that the extracellular concentration of phosphate is 2 mM.

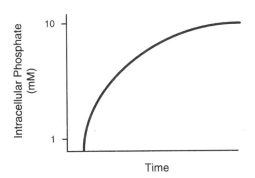

FIG. 1-4

57. Phosphate is transported through:
   A.   diffusion
   B.   facilitated diffusion
   C.   secondary active cotransport
   D.   osmosis

   Answer = C.   Since the intracellular concentration over time becomes greater than the extracellular concentration, some type of active process must be involved. Secondary active cotransport is the only possibility. All of the other processes cannot establish a concentration gradient.

58. Renshaw inhibition:
   A.   is an example of presynaptic inhibition
   B.   is an example of contralateral inhibition
   C.   is an example of positive feedback in the nervous system
   D.   involves an interneuron in its reflex arc
   E.   involves only EPSP generation

Answer = D. Renshaw cells are small interneurons that generate IPSPs (not **E**) on the postsynaptic terminal (not **A**). It is a type of negative feedback reflex (not **C**), and it is primarily an autoinhibition (not **B**).

59. A patient presents with a very slow and weak patellar tendon reflex. One cause of this may be:
    A. degradation of Schwann cells
    B. ingestion of an anti-acetylcholinesterase
    C. inhalation of nicotine
    D. decreased IPSPs on the motor efferent
    E. increased acetylcholine synthesis

Answer = A. When the myelin sheath is degraded, conduction velocity is slowed, the space constant (under the degraded Schwann cell) decreases to the point where the graded potentials may fall below threshold, and the ability to generate action potentials is lost (i.e., a weak response). Anything that tends to increase the release or action of ACh will tend to enhance or exaggerate the reflex (not **B**, **D**, or **E**). An increase in nicotine tends to activate postsynaptic receptors and cause an exaggerated reflex (not **C**).

60. Decongestants, which dilate airways, cause sympathetic postganglionic nerves to release their neurotransmitter. One symptom of a decongestant overdose might be:
    A. decreased heart rate
    B. contracted pupils
    C. decreased blood levels of norepinephrine and dopamine β-hydroxylase
    D. increased blood pressure due to constriction of blood vessels
    E. decreased blood levels of glucose

Answer = D. What would be activated by an increase in the circulating levels of norepinephrine (not **C**)? Norepinephrine is a powerful vasoconstrictor via its actions on the alpha-adrenergic receptors. It also causes the heart rate to increase (not **A**) and the pupils to dilate (not **B**). The activation of sympathetic postganglionic nerves causes the adrenal medulla to release epinephrine into the circulation, which increases the blood level of glucose (not **E**).

61. Drug-induced skeletal muscle relaxation is sometimes required when aligning fractured or dislocated bones. Which of the following causes skeletal muscle relaxation?
    A. an adrenergic antagonist
    B. a muscarinic agonist
    C. a dopaminergic antagonist
    D. a nicotinic antagonist
    E. an increase in $[K^+]$

Answer = D. Since the postsynaptic receptor at the neuromuscular junction is a nicotinic receptor (not **A**, **B** or **C**), the application of a nicotinic antagonist will relax skeletal muscles. An increase in the extracellular $[K^+]$ will depolarize the muscle cell and hence will tend to increase muscle tension by bringing the resting potential closer to the threshold potential.

62. Under normal conditions, a miniature endplate potential:
    A. is the smallest EPSP possible
    B. is due to the presynaptic release of a molecule of acetylcholine
    C. is equal in magnitude in the presence and absence of anti-acetylcholinesterase
    D. is equal in magnitude in the presence and absence of acetylcholinesterase
    E. causes an action potential postsynaptically

Answer = A. A miniature EPSP is caused by the release of a quantum of ACh (not **B**) that then diffuses over to the endplate and opens a number of postsynaptic channels that then produce a miniature potential; by itself, it is not capable of generating an action potential (not **E**). Anything that affects how much of the released ACh arrives at the endplate will affect the magnitude of the miniature endplate potential (not **C** or **D**).

63. The postsynaptic graded potential in neuron 3 during presynaptic inhibition is an *(first answer)*, while during postsynaptic inhibition it would be an *(second answer)*.

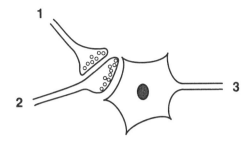

FIG. 1-5

A.   IPSP, IPSP
B.   IPSP, action potential
C.   EPSP, EPSP
D.   IPSP, EPSP
E.   EPSP, IPSP

Answer = E. Presynaptic inhibition reduces the amplitude of the EPSP in neuron 3 by causing a below-threshold EPSP in neuron 2, which inactivates Ca channels in neuron 2 and thus reduces the amount of neurotransmitter released by neuron 2. An IPSP produces presynaptic inhibition.

64.   **When two neurons synapse on a single postsynaptic neuron and cause EPSPs and IPSPs, then:**
A.   temporal summation cannot occur
B.   an action potential will never occur postsynaptically
C.   the presynaptic neuron ending farthest from the postsynaptic axon hillock will have a greater effect on the frequency of action potentials generated
D.   upon activation, the presynaptic nerves will have opposite effects on postsynaptic frequency of action potential generation
E.   spatial summation cannot occur

Answer = D. By having opposite effects on the postsynaptic endplate potentials, these two neurons will have opposite effects on the frequency of action potential generation. Presynaptic neurons closest to the axon hillock (not **C**) will have the greatest effect. The EPSPs and IPSPs will summate both temporally (not **A**) and spatially (not **E**). If the EPSPs are above threshold for an action potential after summating with an IPSP, then an action potential will occur (not **B**).

65.   **Ion X^- has equal intracellular and extracellular concentrations. When the cell membrane potential is -60 mV, ion X^- will (assume that no active transport pump exists for X^-):**
A.   have no net flux
B.   have a net outward flux
C.   have a net inward flux
D.   be in a steady state
E.   be in equilibrium

Answer = B. Since the chemical gradient acting on ion X^- is zero, the electrical potential determines both the magnitude and the direction of the flux. Since the intracellular potential is negative, there is a net outward flux of the negatively charged ions.

66.   **Removal of the Na^+ channel inactivation gate would result in:**
A.   a decrease in the duration of the action potential
B.   a resting membrane potential more negative than normal
C.   an action potential (if initiated) that would not propagate a distance greater than a few space (length) constants
D.   an increase in time the Na^+ channel would be open
E.   an inhibition of the opening of voltage-dependent potassium channels

Answer = D. The inactivation gates decrease Na permeability and allow for increased K permeability to repolarize the membrane during an action potential. If the inactivation gates were lost, the time that the sodium channels would be open would increase, as would the duration of the action potential (not **A**). An increase in P_{Na} due to removal of inactivation gates would tend to depolarize (not **B**) the resting membrane potentials. Action potentials would still be able to be conducted (not **C**). The voltage-dependent potassium channels would not be affected since they are activated by the depolarization (not **E**).

67. GABA opens Cl^- channels on a postsynaptic membrane in which resting membrane potential is -40 mV. Assume the extracellular Cl^- is 110 mM and intracellular Cl^- is 11 mM. GABA would lead to:
    A. an IPSP
    B. an EPSP
    C. no change in membrane potential since Cl^- is in equilibrium
    D. opening of voltage-dependent Na^+ channels
    E. net Cl^- efflux

Answer = A. The chemical force acts to drive Cl into the cell and has a magnitude of 60 mV. The electrical force acts to repel (push outward) the negative Cl ions and has a magnitude of 40 mV. The net electrochemical driving force is therefore inward at a magnitude of 20 mV. When Cl^- channels open, this produces an IPSP (not **B** or **C**) as Cl^- diffuses into the cell (not **E**) and tends to prevent sodium channels from opening (not **D**).

68. When a neurotransmitter opens a ligand-gated channel to an unknown ion^+ and no change in the membrane potential of -60 mV is observed, then the unknown ion^+ (assume that $[K^+]_{out} = 12$ mM, $[K^+]_{in} = 120$ mM, $[Na^+]_{out} = 140$ mM, and $[Na^+]_{in} = 14$ mM):
    A. has a greater electrical than chemical potential
    B. has a net outward flux
    C. is at equilibrium
    D. is in equal concentrations in and outside the nerve
    E. is at a greater concentration outside the nerve than inside it

Answer = C. Since a channel was opened and no change in membrane potential occurred, we know that there was no net flux of ions (not **B**); hence, the ionic species was at electrochemical equilibrium (not **A**). Since the membrane potential was -60 mV, its chemical gradient must be outward (not **D** or **E**).

69. During the absolute refractory period of a nerve action potential:
    A. Na^+ channels have a high resistance
    B. the Na/K ATPase is inactive
    C. the Na^+ equilibrium potential is negative
    D. the reflection coefficient for all solutes is 1.0
    E. K^+ channels are inactivated

Answer = A. The absolute refractory period is the period of time when the inactivation gates of the sodium channels are closed (i.e., high resistance). During this time, potassium channels are open (not **E**) to help return the membrane potential to the resting level so that the Na^+ activation gates can be reset. The absolute refractory period has nothing to do with choices **B**, **C**, or **D**.

70. Cobra venom directly inhibits endplate potentials. The venom from this snake contains:
    A. a nicotinic agonist
    B. a nicotinic antagonist
    C. a muscarinic agonist
    D. a muscarinic antagonist
    E. an acetylcholinesterase inhibitor

Answer = B. ACh released into the neuromuscular junction reacts with nicotinic receptors (not **C** or **D**); hence, a nicotinic antagonist (not **A**) will inhibit the endplate potential. Since acetylcholinesterase increases the rate of ACh metabolism, an inhibitor will tend to increase the endplate potential by indirectly inhibiting acetylcholinesterase (not **E**).

71. **The voltage-gated K$^+$ channels in nerves are:**
   A. necessary for facilitated diffusion
   B. activated by membrane depolarization
   C. inactivated by any change in membrane potential
   D. directly activated by neurotransmitter
   E. none of the above

   Answer = B. These channels, which allow potassium to diffuse (not **A**) down its electrochemical gradient, are slowly activated when the cell is depolarized (not by a direct action on ACh; not **D**) and recover in a time-dependent manner (not **C**).

72. **Within the autonomic nervous system:**
   A. all preganglionic parasympathetic neurons are adrenergic
   B. all preganglionic sympathetic neurons are cholinergic
   C. all postganglionic parasympathetic neurons are adrenergic
   D. all postganglionic sympathetic neurons are cholinergic
   E. All of the above answers are correct.

   Answer = B. All preganglionic neurons are cholinergic (not **A**). Postganglionic parasympathetic neurons are cholinergic (not **C**), while postganglionic sympathetic neurons are primarily adrenergic (not **D**).

73. **At the neuromuscular junction, the influx of sodium ions that partially determines the endplate potential is due to:**

   A. hyperpolarization of the postsynaptic membrane
   B. a net outward driving force for sodium
   C. potassium efflux
   D. high intracellular Na concentrations in the endplate region
   E. a ligand-activated process

   Answer = E. At the neuromuscular junction, the preganglionic release of ACh binds to postsynaptic nicotinic receptors on the skeletal muscle and opens ionic channels that are equally permeable to Na$^+$ and K$^+$, causing a depolarization called an endplate potential (EPP) (not **A**). The EPP is caused by the high extracellular concentration of sodium (not **D**) diffusing into the cell (not **B**), while the increase in potassium permeability dampens (not caused by **C**) the magnitude of the EPP by diffusing out of the cell as the intracellular potential depolarizes.

74. **On the postsynaptic membrane of a normal neuron, an increase in K permeability:**
   A. would depolarize the membrane potential
   B. would make the neuron less likely to generate an action potential
   C. would generate an excitatory postsynaptic potential
   D. leads to a potential that would not summate with other postsynaptic potentials
   E. leads to a potential that would not degrade with distance traveled

   Answer = B. An increase in K permeability would tend to hyperpolarize the membrane potential (not **A**), causing an IPSP (not **C**) and thus making the generation of an action potential much less likely. The IPSP would summate (not **D**) with other postsynaptic potentials as it electrotonically decayed (not **E**).

75. **Which of the following ion channels would produce the greatest amount of membrane depolarization when opened by a neurotransmitter (assume a typical cell with a membrane potential of -60 mV)?**
   A. channels permeable to Cl only
   B. channels permeable to K and Na
   C. channels permeable to K only
   D. channels permeable to Na only
   E. channels equally permeable to Na, K, and Cl

   Answer = D. Since the reversal potential for sodium is $+40$ mV, whereas the Na + K reversal potential is 0 mV, the Cl$^-$ reversal potential is usually near the resting membrane potential, and the Na, K, and Cl reversal potential would also be near 0 mV.

76. Athletes have been known to self-inject steroids. One side effect of this abusive behavior is a change in the number of postsynaptic neurotransmitter receptors for GABA (possibly accounting for the alterations in behavior observed with steroid use). Steroids in this case are acting as a:
   A. neurotransmitter
   B. neuromodulator
   C. neuroactive peptide
   D. biogenic amine
   E. paracrine hormone

   Answer = B.   By changing the number of receptors for GABA, steroids, not a peptide (not **C**) or a biogenic amine (not **D**), are acting as a neuromodulator, not as a primary transmitter (not **A**). Since the steroids are being injected, they cannot be considered, in this case, as a paracrine (not **E**).

77. In resting cells, intracellular concentrations of K^+ and Na^+ are in a steady state due to:
   A. the law of electroneutrality
   B. membranes being impermeable to K^+ and Na^+
   C. zero net electrochemical driving force on K^+ and Na^+
   D. Na/K ATPase counteracting leakage of K^+ and Na^+
   E. Gibbs-Donnan equilibrium

   Answer = D. K^+ and Na^+ are in a steady state because their rate of passive leakage (not **B**) down their electrochemical gradients (not **C**) is balanced by the activity of the Na/K ATPase. The law of electroneutrality and Gibbs-Donnan equilibrium are not the reasons for the steady state.

78. Farmer Brown arrives at the emergency room after inhaling insecticide that she was spraying on her fields. She has constricted pupils, wheezy breathing (constricted airway), and a slowed heart rate. An appropriate treatment would be:
   A. acetylcholine
   B. a muscarinic antagonist
   C. anti-acetylcholinesterase
   D. a β-receptor antagonist
   E. a sodium channel blocker

   Answer = B.   The symptoms are all typical of overactivity of the postganglionic parasympathetic system. Furthermore, all of the symptoms are associated with muscarinic activation; hence, a muscarinic antagonist would be beneficial. ACh and an anti-acetylcholinesterase would make these symptoms worse, not better (not **A** or **C**). A sodium channel blocker would stop many of these symptoms along with most other neuronal and muscular functions (not **E**). Inhibiting the sympathetic system with a β-receptor antagonist might make the patient worse (not **D**) because the reflex activation of the sympathetic system is probably helping the patient by counteracting the effects of the insecticide.

79. In a typical nerve, increasing the resting membrane potential from -60 mV to -65 mV will:
   A. increase the probability of generating an action potential
   B. have the same effect on nerve excitability as the relative refractory period
   C. not allow that cell to develop an IPSP
   D. not allow that cell to develop an EPSP
   E. cause sodium channels to open

   Answer = B.   Like the effect of the hyperpolarization associated with the relative refractory period, any hyperpolarization will tend to make it harder to reach threshold (not **A** or **E**). Although an IPSP might not be as large and an EPSP might be larger, they would still occur at the more hyperpolarized potential (not **C** or **D**).

80. If the chloride ion is at electrochemical equilibrium in a nerve, an increase in the number of open chloride channels will cause:
   A. a decrease in its membrane potential
   B. an increase in its chloride content
   C. a decrease in its chloride content
   D. an increase in the unidirectional flux of chloride from the inside to the outside of the nerve
   E. no change in the unidirectional flux of chloride from the outside to the inside of the nerve

Answer = D. Although there will be no net change in either membrane potential (not **A**) or chloride content (not **B** or **C**), opening of chloride channels will increase the conductance of the membrane to chloride; and, consequently, the unidirectional fluxes of chloride in both directions will increase (not **E**), but net flux will be zero.

81. **A substance with a partition coefficient that is greater than 1:**
    A.   is more water-soluble than lipid-soluble
    B.   has a lower permeability coefficient than that of a similar-size molecule with a partition coefficient less than 1
    C.   is more concentrated in the cell membrane than in the adjacent extracellular fluid
    D.   is more concentrated in the cell cytoplasm than in the cell membrane
    E.   is usually a charged particle

    Answer = C. If a substance has a partition coefficient greater than one, then it will be more concentrated in the lipid cell membrane (more soluble; not **A**) than in the adjacent extracellular or intracellular (not **D**) fluid. Such substances are usually not charged but are nonpolar (not **E**).

82. **All the following statements concerning the passive flux of an ion across a cell plasma membrane are true *EXCEPT*:**

    A.   Passive flux is directly proportional to the electrical potential gradient across the membrane.
    B.   Passive flux is directly proportional to the concentration gradient of the ion across the membrane.
    C.   An active transport system is required for the ion if passive flux is to be maintained at a constant level.
    D.   Passive flux is directly proportional to membrane permeability of the ion.
    E.   Passive flux of the ion occurs primarily through the lipid bilayer portion of the membrane.

    Answer = E. *Remember you are looking for the exception.* The passive flux of ions occurs through membrane channels and transporters, not directly through the lipid bilayer. The flux is proportional to the electrical (**A**) and chemical gradients (**B**) and to the permeability (**D**). If the passive flux is to be maintained, energy must be applied to maintain the chemical gradient (**C**).

83. **Voltage-dependent activation of which membrane ion channel will result in the efflux of positively charged ions from the cell?**
    A.   sodium channel
    B.   potassium channel
    C.   calcium channel
    D.   sodium/potassium cation channel
    E.   chloride channel

    Answer = B. It is the slow (compared to the sodium channel) activation of voltage-dependent potassium channels that allows the flux of potassium out of the cell and helps return the membrane potential back to its resting value.

84. **In order to function normally in vivo (i.e., within the body), the living mammalian cell:**
    A.   will always be in a state of thermodynamic equilibrium with its extracellular environment
    B.   must maintain a zero electrochemical potential difference between cytoplasm and extracellular fluid for each permeable molecule or ion
    C.   must maintain a high permeability across its plasmalemmal membrane for passive diffusion of each essential nutrient and metabolic waste product
    D.   must maintain a cytoplasmic Na^+ concentration approximately 10-fold higher than extracellular Na^+ concentration and vice versa for K^+
    E.   must be in a state of osmotic equilibrium with its extracellular environment

    Answer = E. Osmosis occurs across the plasmalemma whenever there is an osmotic gradient across the cell membrane; thus, a cell will be in osmotic equilibrium with its extracellular environment. The cell is constantly spending energy to maintain large concentration gradients (not **A**) and electrochemical gradients (not **B**). The plasmalemma is very impermeable to essential nutrients, requiring special transport processes that may not always allow the transport of the essential nutrient (not **C**). Choice **D** is the opposite of what most cells actually do (not **D**).

85. **The cell membrane permeability coefficient of an uncharged solute molecule is inversely proportional to:**
    A.   the length of the pathway taken by the solute particle in its passage through the membrane
    B.   the diffusion coefficient for the solute molecule and membrane
    C.   the partition coefficient for the solute and membrane
    D.   the solubility of the solute molecule within the membrane phase
    E.   the concentration gradient of the solute molecule across the membrane

Answer = A. The membrane permeability coefficient is inversely proportional to the thickness of the membrane, but directly proportional (not **B**, **C**, or **D**) to the other factors. The concentration gradient of the solute does not affect the permeability coefficient; rather, the concentration gradient times the permeability coefficient determines the rate of flux (not **E**).

86. **The electrical potential difference for a single permeable cation-anion pair moving across a cell plasmalemmal membrane:**
    A. requires no energy to maintain its value constant
    B. would be reduced to zero if the membrane diffusion coefficients of the cation and anion were made equal
    C. would be reduced to zero if the membrane diffusion coefficient for the cation were reduced to zero
    D. would be reduced to zero if the membrane diffusion coefficient for the anion were reduced to zero

    Answer = B. If the diffusion coefficient for both the cation and anion were the same, there would be no basis for establishing an electrical potential gradient. If there is a potential gradient established for such a pair of ions, it will require energy to maintain the concentration gradient (not **A**). If the diffusion coefficient of only one of the ionic pairs were reduced to zero, there would be a basis for an electrical potential (not **C** or **D**).

87. **At equilibrium what will be the relative change in volume of cells placed in each of the following solutions? (Assume cell osmolarity is 300 mOsm/l, Na^+ and Cl^- are impermeable, and urea is permeable.)**
    Solution 1: 150 mM NaCl, 100 mM urea
    Solution 2: 100 mM NaCl, 150 mM urea
    Solution 3: 300 mM NaCl, 100 mM urea
    Solution 4: 100 mM NaCl, 50 mM urea
    Solutions that would cause cells to:

	Swell	*No change in volume*	*Shrink*
A.			Solutions 1,2,3,4
B.	Solutions 3,4	Solution 1	Solution 2
C.	Solutions 1,4	Solution 3	Solution 2
D.	Solutions 2,4	Solution 1	Solution 3
E.	Solutions 1,3,4	Solution 2	

    Answer = D. Solutions 2 and 4 are hypotonic, low concentrations of impermeable ions—~200 mOsm/l of NaCl, which will cause the cells to swell. Solution 1 is isotonic—~300 mOsm/l of NaCl (urea, being permeable, has a reflection coefficient of 0), which will not affect cell volume. Solution 3 is hypertonic—~600 mOsm/l of NaCl, which will make the cells shrink.

88. **A patient presents with sensory loss and weakness. An electromyogram (EMG) shows an increase in compound action potential amplitude and a slowed conduction velocity. Which of the following is the most likely explanation?**
    A. neuropathy
    B. myopathy
    C. disease of the neuromuscular junction

    Answer = A. The patient has a sensory loss and slowed conduction velocity. Both of these conditions suggest a neuropathy.

89. **A drug that blocks the chloride channel leads to a slight depolarization of the resting membrane potential of certain neurons. In which direction is the net electrochemical driving force on chloride?**
    A. inward
    B. outward
    C. no net electrochemical driving force

    Answer = A. If by blocking the chloride channel a depolarization is produced, then chloride was hyperpolarizing the membrane potential. For chloride to hyperpolarize the membrane potential, it must be fluxing into the cell.

90. **Which of the following occurs during osmosis in a cell that is not permeable to all ions?**
    A. Water moves from a region of low to high solute concentration.
    B. Water is pumped by active transport into the cell.
    C. Water moves from a region of low to high water concentration.
    D. Volume on both sides of the membrane remains the same.
    E. Osmolarity on both sides of the membrane is unchanged.

Answer = A. Water passively diffuses (not **B**) from an area of high concentration, low solute concentration, to an area with a low water concentration (not **C**), high solute concentration. As the water diffuses, it will affect the volume of the compartments (not **D**) and the osmolarity of the fluid in the two compartments (not **E**).

91.   In two cases (1 and 2), the initial concentrations of solute X separated by a membrane permeable to X are:

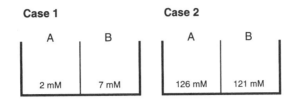

FIG. 1-6

Which one of the following statements is true?
A.   All other conditions being equal, Case 1 and 2 will reach equilibrium at the same rate.
B.   All other conditions being equal, Case 2 will reach equilibrium sooner than Case 1.
C.   Prior to equilibrium, net flux is directly proportional to the molecular weight of X.
D.   Prior to equilibrium, the direction of net flux (A to B) is the same in both cases.
E.   Prior to equilibrium, net flux does not depend on permeability.

Answer = A. Since the difference in concentration is the same for the two cases (not **B**), they will reach equilibrium at the same time. Prior to equilibrium, the net flux would be inversely proportional to the molecular weight of X (not **C**) and directly proportional to the permeability of the membrane to X (not **E**). Since the direction of the concentration gradient is different in the two cases, the direction of the net flux prior to equilibrium is also different (not **D**).

92.   Each of the following statements concerning the passive flux (leak) of an ion across the cell membrane is true *EXCEPT*:
A.   Passive flux is directly proportional to the electrical potential gradient across the membrane under conditions of a constant chemical gradient.
B.   Passive flux is directly proportional to the concentration gradient of the ion across the membrane under conditions of a constant electrical gradient.
C.   An active transport system is required for the ion if passive flux is to be maintained at a constant level.
D.   Passive flux increases as a function of the net electrochemical driving force on an ion.
E.   Passive flux of ions is independent of ion channel conductances.

Answer = E. *Remember you are looking for the exception.* The passive flux of ions is directly proportional to the conductances of the ion channels. All of the other statements are true.

93.   In an isolated unmyelinated nerve axon preparation, tetrodotoxin (TTX) is locally applied to a 2-mm segment on the axon that has a space constant of 20 mm. If an action potential is initiated proximal to the area of TTX, then an intracellular electrode placed 18 mm distal to the area of TTX would record:
A.   no action potential, but a normal resting membrane potential
B.   an action potential identical to the action potential at the proximal area
C.   an action potential reduced by 37% in amplitude as compared to the action potential at the proximal area
D.   an action potential of greater amplitude as compared to the action potential at the proximal area
E.   a longer-duration action potential with no after-hyperpolarization

Answer = B. Although TTX will block the voltage-gated sodium channels in the 2-mm segment, the 20-mm space constant means that there will be very little decrement of the electronic potential and that an action potential will develop on the other side of the TTX-blockade (not **A**); at the 18-mm site, a normal action potential (not **C**, **D**, or **E**) will be recorded.

94. **Assuming the typical concentration gradients of ions in nerves, an excitatory endplate potential could, in principle, be produced by:**
   A. a decreased permeability in K^+
   B. a decreased permeability in Na^+
   C. activation of voltage-dependent K^+ channels
   D. activation of the Na^+ channel inactivation gate
   E. inactivation of the calcium channel activation gate

   Answer = A. Since the membrane is permeable to some degree to ions other than K^+, a decrease in potassium permeability will depolarize the membrane potential. All of the other factors will result in a hyperpolarization of the membrane potential.

95. **Nerve A makes an excitatory synaptic contact with nerve B. Tetraethylammonium (TEA) is injected into the presynaptic terminal of nerve A. An action potential in nerve A would:**
   A. lead to an IPSP in nerve B
   B. lead to an action potential in nerve B of longer duration than a normal action potential
   C. decrease the duration the neurotransmitter is present in the synaptic cleft
   D. increase the neurotransmitter concentration in the synaptic cleft
   E. inhibit action potentials in nerve B

   Answer = D. TEA will block K^+ channels, leading to a prolongation of the action potential at the presynaptic terminal, increasing the influx of calcium and leading to a larger number of synaptic vesicles fusing with the membrane and releasing more neurotransmitter, which will cause a larger and longer-duration (not **C**) EPP (not **A**) that generates more normal action potentials (not **B** or **E**) in the postsynaptic nerve.

96. **All of the following are true of both the somatic and autonomic nervous systems _EXCEPT_:**
   A. presence of peripheral ganglia
   B. presence of afferent and efferent nerves
   C. use of acetylcholine as a neurotransmitter
   D. innervation of muscle
   E. presence of EPSPs

   Answer = A. _Remember you are looking for the exception._ The autonomic nervous system, unlike the somatic nervous system, has ganglia in the periphery. All of the other issues are true for both systems.

97. **What directly determines the value of the resting membrane potential?**
   A. the concentration gradient of uncharged molecules
   B. the concentration gradient of impermeable negatively charged proteins
   C. the concentration gradient of impermeable ions
   D. the relative conductances of ion channels
   E. the osmolarity of a cell

   Answer = D. The actual value for the resting membrane potential of any cell is determined by the relative conductances of the various ion channels in the cell membrane. The concentration gradient for the permeant (not **B** or **C**) ions (not **A**) is important. The osmolarity of a cell does not determine the resting membrane potential (not **E**).

98. **Which of the lines (A–E) in Fig. 1-7 represents the dependence of the resting membrane potential on extracellular K^+ concentration in a typical nerve? Assume intracellular K^+ concentration stays constant at 120 mM.**

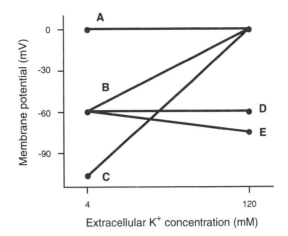

FIG. 1-7

Answer = C. In a normal nerve cell, at a K^+ concentration of 4 mM, the membrane potential is -60 mV, caused by the finite permeability of the resting membrane to sodium; ie, $P_K = 0.95$, while $P_{Na} = 0.05$. As the potassium concentration increases from 4 mM to 120 mM, you would expect a depolarization of the membrane potential from 60 mV to 0 mV.

99. **Myelin:**
   A. decreases the probability of graded potentials falling below threshold along an axon
   B. covers the axons of all nerves
   C. is formed from membranes of adjacent neurons
   D. shields the entire length of an axon from direct contact with extracellular fluid
   E. increases the internal resistance of an axon

Answer = A. The Schwann cells (not **C**) wrap around only the myelinated neurons (not **B**), leaving periodic (not **D**) nodes exposed to the extracellular fluid. Myelin has no effect on the internal resistance of an axon (not **E**), but it does reduce the membrane capacitance and thus increase the space constant, which ensures that there will be minimal electrotonic decrement in the internodal regions.

100. **In a cell, the resting membrane potential is -60 mV and the extracellular H^+ concentration is 39.8 nM (pH 7.4). If H^+ is in equilibrium across the plasma membrane, what is the pH inside the cell?**
   A. 0.398 nM (pH 9.4)
   B. 3.98 nM (pH 8.4)
   C. 39.8 nM (pH 7.4)
   D. 398 nM (pH 6.4)
   E. 3,980 nM (pH 5.4)

Answer = D. If H^+ is at equilibrium, then the concentration inside the cell is ten times greater than that outside the cell, i.e., 398 nM or a pH of 6.4. Normally, however, the cell has a pH of around 7.0 to 7.2, which means H^+ is not at equilibrium.

101. At a neuromuscular junction, the addition of a drug that blocks Ca^{2+} channels would be associated with a decrease in each of the following *EXCEPT*:
   A. postsynaptic duration of the EPP
   B. postsynaptic amplitude of the EPP
   C. postsynaptic amplitude of the MEPP
   D. presynaptic Ca^{2+} influx
   E. presynaptic release of neurotransmitter during an action potential

   Answer = C. *Remember you are looking for the exception.* The inhibition of the influx of calcium into the presynaptic terminal (**D**) will decrease the number of vesicles (**E**) that are released and thus decrease the amplitude (**B**) and duration (**A**) of the EPP. The amplitude of the miniature endplate potential will not be affected since the content of the vesicle will not be affected.

102. Counter-transporters:
   A. would increase their activity if the Na^+ concentration gradient increased
   B. cannot transport substances against their concentration gradient
   C. do not show saturation kinetics
   D. transport a cation and an anion in the same direction
   E. transport glucose in both directions across the membrane

   Answer = A. The counter-transport of cations (not **D**) using the inward electrochemical gradient for sodium is a common way to move cations out of the cell. Such a transport process can establish concentration gradients for the counter-transported ion (not **B**). The transporter shows saturation kinetics (not **C**). Glucose can be transported in both directions across the membrane by facilitated diffusion (not **E**).

103. In general, a specific neurotransmitter:
   A. binds to voltage-gated Na^+ channels responsible for nerve action potentials
   B. is involved in electrical synapses
   C. has effects that are independent of their rate of removal from the synaptic cleft
   D. is released from the postsynaptic terminals
   E. can be excitatory in some cells and inhibitory in others

   Answer = E. Neurotransmitters can be excitatory in some cells and inhibitory in others. They usually affect ligand-gated (not **A**) ion channels. Electrical synapses do not have a neurotransmitter (not **B**). The rate of their removal following release from the presynaptic terminal (not **D**) is critical for determining the duration and magnitude of the response (not **C**).

104. One factor that increases the propagation velocity of an action potential is:
   A. decreasing the length of the axon
   B. decreasing the membrane capacitance of the axon
   C. increasing the threshold of an action potential in the axon
   D. increasing the frequency of stimulation of the axon
   E. increasing the number of IPSPs occurring on the axon

   Answer = B. The propagation velocity is inversely proportional to the membrane capacitance. Decreasing the length of the axon (not **A**), increasing the frequency that it is stimulated (not **D**), or inhibiting the generation of action potentials (not **E**) will not affect velocity. Increasing the threshold will decrease the velocity since it will take longer for the neighboring section to reach threshold (not **C**).

105. What is one reason patients who suffer from severe and extensive burns develop tachycardia?
   A. Burns selectively stimulate the parasympathetic nervous system.
   B. Burns increase the activity of acetylcholinesterase at the skeletal neuromuscular junction.
   C. Burns hyperpolarize nerves within the sympathetic nervous system.
   D. Burns destroy many cells and cause a mass release of K^+ into the extracellular space.
   E. Burns inhibit adrenal medulla function.

   Answer = D. Damaged tissues release potassium into the extracellular space, which makes the membrane potential of the SA node cells become more depolarized and, hence, increases the heart rate. All of the other factors listed would tend to slow the heart rate.

Match the descriptions in questions 106–108 with the appropriate lettered point on this nerve action potential shown in Fig. 1-8.

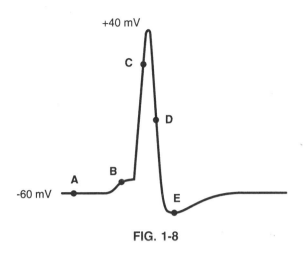

FIG. 1-8

106. The point at which Na^+ permeability is highest

   Answer = C. Virtually all sodium channels are open at point C; therefore, the Na^+ permeability is very high.

107. The point at which the net ion flux across the membrane is zero

   Answer = A. When the cell is at rest, it is also in a steady state, which, by definition, means that there is no net ion flux across the membrane.

108. The point at which the net electrochemical driving force on K^+ is greatest

   Answer = C. The electrical gradient favoring the efflux of K^+ is greatest at point C, while there is a large outward chemical gradient for K^+, which is the same at all points; hence, the greatest electrochemical driving force is at point C.

For questions 109–114, match the appropriate figure (A–E) with the situation that it most closely describes.

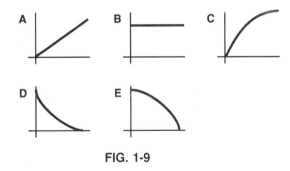

FIG. 1-9

109. The pressure (y-axis) necessary to prevent water flow as a function of solute concentration (x-axis) for a membrane bathed on one side by pure water and on the other side by a solution containing an impermeable solute.

   Answer = A. Osmotic pressure is a linear function of the solute concentration. As the osmotic pressure of the solution increases, there will be a linear increase in the pressure necessary to prevent a net flux of water.

110. The rate of urea diffusion (y-axis) across a membrane as a function of the concentration difference for urea (x-axis) across the membrane.

Answer = A. The rate of passive diffusion is a linear function of the urea concentration gradient. As the urea concentration gradient increases, there will be a linear increase in the rate of urea diffusion that does not show signs of saturation.

111. The relationship between the rate of d-glucose uptake across a red cell membrane (y-axis) as a function of the galactose concentration in the extracellular fluid (x-axis) if the glucose concentration in the extracellular fluid is kept constant and glucose and galactose *share* the same transporter.

Answer = D. Since galactose will compete with glucose for a limited number of transport molecules, increasing the galactose concentration will inhibit glucose uptake in a manner that can be described by Michaelis-Menten kinetics (ie, an exponential type of relationship).

112. The relationship between the rate of d-glucose uptake across a red cell membrane (y-axis) as a function of the galactose concentration in the extracellular fluid (x-axis) if the glucose concentration in the extracellular fluid is kept constant and glucose and galactose *do not share* a common transporter.

Answer = B. Since galactose *will not* compete with glucose, increasing the galactose concentration will not affect the rate of glucose uptake, which will remain constant.

113. The electrical potential difference across a membrane (y-axis) as function of the time (x-axis) if the membrane is bathed on one side with a solution of 10 mM NaCl and on the other side with a solution of 100 mM NaCl and if both Na and Cl can cross the membrane but the permeability to Na is greater than that to Cl.

Answer = D. Since the membrane is permeable to both ions, when the two sides of the membrane come into equilibrium, there will be no potential difference. Initially, however, with the membrane being more permeable to Na than to Cl, a transmembrane electrical potential difference will occur. The side with the 100 mM NaCl solution will become negatively charged until equilibrium is exponentially reached.

114. The relation between the rate of glucose transport across a red blood cell membrane (y-axis) and the concentration of d-glucose in the extracellular medium (x-axis).

Answer = C. Since glucose is transported across the red blood cell membrane by facilitated diffusion, glucose transport will be described by Michaelis-Menten kinetics, which will show saturation kinetics.

For questions 115–119, assume that a hypothetical cell contains 150 mM NaCl and that the cell membrane is impermeable to Na^+ and sucrose but permeable to Cl^- and urea.

115. If this cell were immersed in a solution containing 300 mM urea, the cell would:
   A. undergo no change in volume
   B. swell and ultimately burst
   C. double in volume
   D. shrink to one-third its original volume
   E. shrink to one-half its original volume
   F. initially shrink and then swell
   G. initially swell and then shrink

Answer = B. Since urea is permeable, it will not have the necessary osmotic activity across the membrane to prevent osmosis from causing the cell to swell and ultimately burst.

116. **If this cell were immersed in a solution containing 300 mM NaCl, the cell would:**
    A. undergo no change in volume
    B. swell and ultimately burst
    C. double in volume
    D. shrink to one-third its original volume
    E. shrink to one-half its original volume
    F. initially shrink and then swell
    G. initially swell and then shrink

    Answer = E. Since Na is impermeable, it will generate twice the osmotic pressure as the 150 mM NaCl that is inside the cell. At equilibrium, the inside of the cell will have lost half its water so that the NaCl concentration inside the cell will become 300 mM. Even though the Cl^- ion is permeable, there will be no net flux of Cl because it will be trapped by the electrical potential that will be generated.

117. **If this cell were immersed in a solution containing 300 mM sucrose, the cell would:**
    A. undergo no change in volume
    B. swell and ultimately burst
    C. double in volume
    D. shrink to one-third its original volume
    E. shrink to one-half its original volume
    F. initially shrink and then swell
    G. initially swell and then shrink

    Answer = A. Since a 300 mM sucrose solution will have the same osmolarity as a 150 mM NaCl solution, there will be no osmotic gradient and, hence, no change in cell volume.

118. **Assuming that the reflection coefficient of urea is 0.8, if this cell were immersed in a solution containing 500 mM urea, the cell would:**
    A. undergo no change in volume
    B. swell and ultimately burst
    C. double in volume
    D. shrink to one-third its original volume
    E. shrink to one-half its original volume
    F. initially shrink and then swell
    G. initially swell and then shrink

    Answer = F. Based on a reflection coefficient of 0.8, a 500 mM urea solution will initially have an osmotic activity of 400 mOsm/l; hence, the cell will initially shrink. Over time, however, the urea will gradually come into chemical equilibrium across the cell membrane, and the cell will ultimately burst.

119. **Assuming that the reflection coefficient of urea is 0.3, if this cell were immersed in a solution containing 500 mM urea, the cell would:**
    A. undergo no change in volume
    B. swell and ultimately burst
    C. double in volume
    D. shrink to one-third its original volume
    E. shrink to one-half its original volume
    F. initially shrink and then swell
    G. initially swell and then shrink

    Answer = B. Based on a reflection coefficient of 0.3, a 500 mM urea solution will initially have an osmotic activity of 150 mOsm/l; hence, the cell will swell and then burst.

120. **Exposure of red cells to ouabain will lead to all of the following *EXCEPT*:**
    A. a decrease in the electrical potential across the membrane
    B. cell swelling
    C. a decrease in cell Cl^-
    D. a loss of cell K^+
    E. a gain of cell Na^+

PART 1: GENERAL PHYSIOLOGY   115

Answer = C. *Remember you are looking for the exception.* Inhibiting the sodium/potassium pump will cause a loss of potassium (**D**) and a greater gain of sodium (**E**), which will 1) cause the cell to swell (**B**) and 2) cause the chemical gradient for potassium to disappear (**A**); thus, over time, the membrane potential will become 0. Since Cl ions distribute passively across the red blood cell membrane, the loss of the negatively charged interior will cause the chloride concentration to increase, not decrease.

121. **If an ion is passively distributed across a cell membrane:**
    A. transport across the membrane must be the result of simple diffusion
    B. a change in the permeability of the membrane to that ion will not change the distribution of that ion
    C. the distribution of that ion will not be affected by metabolic inhibitors
    D. the steady-state intracellular concentration of that ion will be halved if the volume of the cell doubles
    E. none of the above

Answer = B. By being passively distributed, the ion is at its electrochemical equilibrium; changing its permeability will not change its distribution, only the rate at which it will adjust to any change in the electrochemical gradient. Transport across the membrane may involve multiple channels, transporters, and exchangers (not **A**). Inhibitors that would affect the electrical gradient could readily affect the distribution of the ion (not **C**). If the cell volume alone was changed, there would be an influx of the ion until the concentration was appropriate for the electrical gradient (not **D**).

122. **Drug X, when applied to a nerve axon, results in both a gradual decrease in the amplitude of the individual action potentials and a slow (several hours) depolarization of the resting membrane potential. The drug is most likely:**
    A. blocking the voltage-gated sodium channels
    B. blocking the voltage-gated potassium channels
    C. blocking the Na/K pump
    D. blocking Na inactivation
    E. increasing the rate at which voltage-dependent changes in K^+ permeability occur

Answer = C. By affecting both the action potential magnitude and the resting membrane potential, the drug appears to be inhibiting the Na/K pump. The inhibition of the pump would decrease the chemical gradient for sodium and, hence, decrease the amplitude of the action potential. It would also decrease the chemical gradient for potassium, causing a gradual depolarization of the resting membrane potential. Blocking sodium channels would tend to decrease the amplitude of the action potential but not affect the resting membrane potential (not **A**). Blocking voltage-gated potassium channels will lengthen the duration of the action potential but not reduce the amplitude of the action potential or affect the resting membrane potential (not **B**). Blocking sodium inactivation would prevent the nerve from recovering from an action potential (not **D**). Increasing the rate at which voltage-dependent changes in K^+ permeability occur would have little effect on either the amplitude of the action potential or the resting membrane potential.

123. **For a motor neuron to initiate an action potential in a skeletal muscle, there must be:**
    A. release of norepinephrine
    B. temporal summation
    C. spatial summation
    D. release of acetylcholine
    E. none of the above is needed

Answer = D. When a motor neuron initiates an action potential, it releases acetylcholine, not norepinephrine (not **A**), from its presynaptic terminal. At the neuromuscular junction, neither temporal nor spatial summation (not **B** or **C**) is involved; these factors are involved in determining whether the motor neuron will generate an action potential.

124. **In hypertension, an adrenergic antagonist (blocker) is given to vasodilate blood vessels and reduce blood pressure. One common side effect of this antihypertensive medication is diarrhea (increased gastrointestinal motility). This is likely due to:**
    A. the adrenal medulla, located near the GI tract, increasing its activity
    B. decreased blood flow to the GI tract
    C. predominance of parasympathetic activity
    D. an overall increase in autonomic activity
    E. increased blood flow to the GI tract

Answer = C. When the adrenergic system is blocked, the parasympathetic system becomes more dominant because both systems are tonically active; and the parasympathetic system increases GI motility, which can cause diarrhea. Although the adrenal medulla may reflexly increase the amount of epinephrine released, it will not be very active since an adrenergic antagonist is present; and, in addition, epinephrine decreases GI motility (not **A**). An increase in blood flow is not a cause of diarrhea; but an increase in GI motility is, and it will be associated with an increase in GI blood flow (not **B** or **E**) not vice versa.

125. **Excessive vomiting in the short term can lead to hypokalemia with no change in intracellular $[K^+]$. One possible result of this is:**
    A. an increase in the Na/K ATPase activity
    B. a decreased probability of action potential generation
    C. a decrease in net K^+ efflux
    D. an increase in the number of IPSPs at the neuromuscular junction
    E. an increase in the number of EPSPs at the neuromuscular junction

    Answer = B. Hypokalemia with no change in intracellular $[K^+]$ implies that the ratio $K_o{:}K_i$ is increased, which will hyperpolarize the cell and make it harder for the membrane potential to reach the threshold level. The Na/K ATPase activity should decrease because it is sensitive to extracellular K and intracellular Na (not **A**). Since the concentration gradient for K increases, an increase in the net efflux of K should occur (not **C**). In general, a decrease in the number of action potentials will occur; hence, the number of EPSPs will decrease (not **D**). IPSPs do not occur at the neuromuscular junction (not **E**).

126. **A patient presents with a very strong patellar tendon reflex (i.e., a larger than normal reflex reaction). One cause of this might be:**
    A. degradation of Schwann cells
    B. ingestion of an anti-acetylcholinesterase
    C. long duration of presynaptic inhibition
    D. increased Renshaw inhibition of the motor efferent
    E. decreased number of Na^+/K^+ channels

    Answer = B. An anti-acetylcholinesterase will slow down the degradation of synaptically released ACh and cause an exaggerated response at ACh synapses such as the neural–muscular junction. Loss of Schwann cells would probably slow down conduction velocity in myelinated nerves and, if anything, decrease the postsynaptic response (not **A**). Presynaptic inhibition (not **C**) or Renshaw inhibition (not **D**) tends to decrease, not increase, responses. A decrease in the number of Na^+/K^+ channels such as those activated by ACh would decrease, not increase, the response (not **E**).

127. **Axon A has a longer time constant than Axon B. The action potentials:**
    A. have a slower conduction velocity in Axon A than in Axon B
    B. demonstrate differing degrees of temporal summation
    C. travel farther down Axon A than Axon B since the space constant is lower
    D. have a lower overshoot in Axon A
    E. in Axon B have a shorter after-hyperpolarization

    Answer = A. Recall that conduction velocity is inversely proportional to the time constant; hence, Axon A will have a slower conduction velocity than Axon B. Temporal summation is not directly affected by the time constant (not **B**). There is no decrement in the conduction of action potentials down a neuron regardless of the value of the time or space constant (not **C**). The magnitude of the overshoot and the duration of the after-hyperpolarization are determined more by the changes in membrane permeability to ions than by the time or space constants (not **D** or **E**).

128. **Action potential propagation velocity increases with an increase in an axon's:**
    A. capacitance
    B. partition coefficient
    C. myelination
    D. intracellular resistance
    E. time constant

Answer = C. Myelination greatly increases conduction velocity because it increases the space constant, which is directly proportional to the conduction velocity. An increase in membrane capacitance increases the time constant, while an increase in intracellular resistance decreases the space constant. An increase in the time constant or a decrease in the space constant would decrease velocity since velocity is proportional to the space constant/time constant (not **A, D** or **E**). The partition coefficient has to do with how soluble a molecule is in a lipid membrane, which has nothing directly to do with action potential conduction velocity (not **B**).

129. **TEA application to the presynaptic neuromuscular junction leads to an endplate potential that is:**
    A. greater than normal due to TEA's indirectly increasing Ca^{2+} influx
    B. less than normal due to TEA's indirectly decreasing Ca^{2+} influx
    C. less than normal due to TEA's directly blocking Na^+ channels
    D. greater than normal due to TEA's directly blocking Na^+ channels
    E. unchanged since TEA has no effect on presynaptic action potentials

    Answer = A. TEA blocks potassium channels (not **C** or **D**) and, hence, prolongs the action potential of the presynaptic neuron. When an action potential approaches the synaptic terminal, a larger than normal amount of Ca^{2+} enters the terminal (not **B**), causing the release of a greater number of synaptic vesicles (not **C** or **E**).

130. **A hypothetical cell contains 150 mM NaCl and is bathed in a solution of 500 mM urea. For this cell, the reflection coefficients are: $Na^+ = 1.0$, $Cl^- = 0$, urea $= 0.8$. This cell will:**
    A. have 75 mM Cl^- inside and outside at equilibrium
    B. initially swell and then shrink
    C. initially shrink and then swell
    D. shrink with no further change in volume
    E. undergo no change in volume

    Answer = C. Since the intracellular osmolality is 300 mOsm while the extracellular osmolality is 500 mOsm, the cell will initially shrink. However, because the reflection coefficient for urea is less than 1.0, urea will slowly diffuse into the cell. Sodium and chloride will not be able to leave (Cl^- will be trapped inside the cell due to Na being impermeable and the necessity of abiding by the law of electroneutrality). Since urea will continue to diffuse into the cell until the chemical gradient is dissipated and there will be no osmotic gradient due to a urea concentration gradient, water will enter the cell due to the osmotic gradient of the sodium and chloride; the cell will swell and eventually rupture.

131. **Which of the following statements is true for the compound action potential illustrated in Fig. 1-10?**
    A. Phase 4 is due to after-hyperpolarization.
    B. For a single action potential, the intracellular membrane potential is -2 mV.
    C. The resting intracellular membrane potential is 0 mV.
    D. The phase 2 peak is dependent on nerve and muscle mass.
    E. During phase 3, no action potentials are occurring.

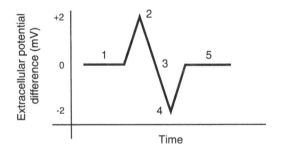

FIG. 1-10

Answer = D. The magnitudes of phases 2 and 4 are due to the mass of nerve and muscles being depolarized. The downward negative reflection of phase 4 is due to the depolarization wave passing by the downstream electrode and to how the electrodes are connected (not **A**). The magnitude of the extracellular recording is not a measure of the intracellular potential; it is affected by the distance of the electrode from the membrane and the conductance of the tissue between the electrode and the membrane (not **B**). The 0 potential shown in phases 1 and 5 reflects the fact that no action potential is traveling through the tissues at the recording electrodes and does not reflect the resting membrane potential of the cells (not **C**). During phase 3, the action potentials are between the sites of the two recording electrodes (not **E**).

132. **Facilitated diffusion of a substance:**
    A. moves it from an area of low concentration to an area of high concentration
    B. does not require a carrier protein
    C. is not saturable
    D. does not exhibit specificity
    E. is subject to competition

    Answer = E. Facilitated diffusion is a non-ATP-dependent (passive) carrier-mediated (not **A** or **B**) transport process that shows specificity (not **D**), competition, and saturability (not **C**).

133. **Many symptoms of cystic fibrosis are due to a genetic defect in which membrane ion channel?**
    A. sodium channel
    B. potassium channel
    C. calcium channel
    D. sodium/potassium cation channel
    E. chloride channel

    Answer = C. It is a defect in a chloride channel that is responsible.

134. **A 60-year-old man develops diplopia (double vision), difficulty in chewing and swallowing, and weakness of his limbs. All of these symptoms are made worse by exercise and occur more frequently late in the day. A drug that could potentially alleviate these symptoms is:**
    A. curare, a nicotinic antagonist
    B. atropine, a muscarinic antagonist
    C. neostigmine, an anti-acetylcholinesterase
    D. cocaine, to functionally increase the Na^+ channel threshold
    E. valium, to increase the number of IPSPs

    Answer = C. These symptoms are all associated with muscle weakness; hence, increasing the amount of ACh that acts on the postsynaptic membrane by inhibiting its metabolism would help reverse muscle weakness. All of the other factors would make matters worse since they all tend to decrease the ability of the body to generate action potentials.

135. **If the membrane potential is equal to the equilibrium potential for a given ion, then the net flux of the ion through the membrane will:**
    A. depend on the number of activated voltage-gated channels
    B. be zero
    C. be greater in the inward direction
    D. be greater in the outward direction
    E. be determined by the concentration (chemical) gradient alone

    Answer = B. When the membrane potential is equal to the equilibrium potential, there is no electrochemical gradient for the net movement of ions.

136. **With regard to osmosis:**
    A. osmotic pressure gradients are proportional to the concentration gradient of permeable ions
    B. osmosis is the net movement of water from an area of high osmolarity to one of low osmolarity
    C. osmotic pressure is increased by the Na/K ATPase
    D. water will usually flow against its concentration gradient
    E. the osmotic pressure gradient is zero when all molecules are permeable

    Answer = E. For osmosis to occur, there must be an impermeable molecule (not **A** or **E**) on one side or the other of the membrane to generate an osmotic pressure gradient. Recall that water, like all other molecules, moves from a high (low osmolality) to a low (high osmolality) concentration (not **D**). The osmolality of a solution is determined by the characteristics of the dissolved molecules alone (not **C**).

137. **Which group of substances constitutes the catecholamines?**
   A. norepinephrine, epinephrine, and acetylcholine
   B. norepinephrine, epinephrine, and serotonin
   C. norepinephrine, epinephrine, and dopamine
   D. norepinephrine, epinephrine, dopamine, and serotonin
   E. dopamine and serotonin

   Answer = C. Neither serotonin nor acetylcholine has the catechol-structure.

138. **The voltage-gated Na^+ channel of nerves:**
   A. can be influenced by extracellular $[Ca^{2+}]$
   B. possesses an inactivation mechanism that is faster than the process of activation
   C. is directly activated by neurotransmitters
   D. is identical to the voltage-gated K^+ channel
   E. is activated by any change in voltage in the cell

   Answer = A. A low extracellular calcium concentration causes the voltage-gated sodium channels to open at a lower (more negative) membrane potential, which increases the excitability of the nerve. The voltage-gated sodium channel inactivation gate closes more slowly than the activation gate opens (not **B**). It is the depolarization (not **E**) that directly opens the voltage-gated Na^+ channels, which are distinct from the voltage-gated K^+ channels (not **D**).

139. **In a cell that is in steady state, the chloride equilibrium potential (V_{Cl}) is -60 mV, and the resting membrane potential (V_m) is -80 mV. If the cell is permeable to chloride, which of the following is a true statement regarding this cell?**
   A. Chloride ions are at equilibrium; therefore, there is no need to postulate the existence of a chloride pump.
   B. There must be an active transport mechanism to pump chloride *out* in order to balance the net *inward* movement of chloride ions.
   C. There must be an active transport mechanism to pump chloride *in* in order to balance the net *outward* movement of chloride ions.
   D. There must be an active transport mechanism to pump chloride *out* in order to balance the net *outward* movement of chloride ions.
   E. There must be an active transport mechanism to pump chloride *in* in order to balance the net *inward* movement of chloride ions

   Answer = C. The electrical gradient driving Cl out of the cell is greater than the chemical gradient driving Cl into the cell, and a net outward flux of Cl would occur. Since there is a steady state, the net flux for Cl is zero; and, consequently, there must be an active pumping of chloride into the cell.

140. **Applying a single threshold stimulus to a somatic efferent neuron will cause:**
   A. a twitch contraction of a group of muscle fibers
   B. a twitch of a single muscle fiber
   C. a tetanic contraction of a group of muscle fibers
   D. a tetanic contraction of a single muscle fiber
   E. None of the above will occur.

   Answer = A. When a single action potential travels down a motor neuron, all of the muscle fibers (a group, not a single fiber; not **B**) innervated by that motor neuron will twitch (not generate a tetanic contraction; not **C** or **D**).

141. **All of the following are ways to physiologically increase active tension in muscle *EXCEPT*:**
   A. in cardiac muscle, increase contractility
   B. in smooth muscle, increase the number of cells recruited
   C. in skeletal muscle, increase length
   D. in cardiac muscle, increase length
   E. in skeletal muscle, increase the number of cells recruited

   Answer = C. *Remember you are looking for the exception.* Because skeletal muscle operates near the optimal sarcomere length, further increases in skeletal muscle length are not necessarily associated with increased tension development.

142. **Tetanic force in slow skeletal muscle will:**
   A. not increase further with increasing stimulation frequency
   B. increase with increasing extracellular calcium concentration
   C. decrease further with increasing stimulation frequency
   D. increase with increasing Golgi tendon organ afferent nerve activity
   E. not decrease with decreasing intracellular calcium concentration

   Answer = A. Once a tetanic contraction is established, no further increase in force is evoked by increasing the frequency of stimulation (but not **C** or **D**) . Skeletal muscle contraction is dependent on the release of calcium from the SR and very independent of acute changes in extracellular calcium (not **B** or **E**).

143. **All of the following statements are true about the role of Ca^{2+} in muscle contraction _EXCEPT_:**
   A. Ca^{2+} from outside the cell contributes to activation of contraction in both cardiac and smooth muscle.
   B. Ca^{2+} is conducted by specific membrane channels in smooth muscle.
   C. Ca^{2+} binds directly to troponin C in skeletal muscle.
   D. Ca^{2+} is stored in the sarcoplasmic reticulum in cardiac muscle.
   E. Ca^{2+} binds directly to myosin light-chain kinase in smooth muscle.

   Answer = E. _Remember you are looking for the exception._ Calcium binds first to calmodulin, and that complex binds to myosin light-chain kinase.

144. **Calcium channel blockers are widely prescribed to facilitate coronary vasodilation. A potential side effect could be:**

   A. decreased contractility of skeletal muscle
   B. increased blood pressure
   C. pupillary constriction
   D. increased gut peristalsis
   E. decreased contractility of cardiac muscle

   Answer = E. The contractility of cardiac muscle is determined by how much calcium is released during the action potential, which in turn is directly influenced by how much calcium enters the cell. Calcium channel blockers therefore tend to decrease the SR stores of calcium, leading to a decrease in cardiac contractility and relaxation of smooth muscle (not **B**, **C**, or **D**) in general. These drugs have little effect on skeletal muscle (not **A**).

145. **Which one of the following events will cause contraction of smooth muscle?**
   A. inhibition of the myosin light-chain kinase
   B. inhibition of the myosin light-chain phosphatase
   C. inhibition of calmodulin
   D. inhibition of calcium channels
   E. activation of troponin C

   Answer = B. When the activity of the myosin light-chain phosphatase is decreased, myosin tends to shift to the phosphorylated state and cause contraction. The events shown in **A**, **C**, and **D** will all cause relaxation, and troponin C is not a primary mediator of contraction in smooth muscle (**E**).

146. **All of the following events will lead to contraction of skeletal muscle _EXCEPT_:**
   A. depolarization of the T-tubules
   B. Ca^{2+} release from troponin C
   C. Ca^{2+} release by the sarcoplasmic reticulum
   D. cross-bridge formation between myosin and actin
   E. depolarization of the sarcolemma

   Answer = B. _Remember you are looking for the exception._ Calcium binding to troponin C allows the formation of cross-bridges that cause contraction (**D**). Membrane depolarization (**A** and **E**) is the first step in the process of releasing calcium from the SR (**C**).

147.   **Large motor units:**
    A.   are recruited first
    B.   produce tetanic tension at low stimulation frequencies
    C.   have fewer muscle fibers
    D.   produce more force than small motor units
    E.   use ATP less quickly

Answer = D. The larger motor units have more fibers (not **C**) that are fast and glycogenolytic; hence, they generate more force and use energy at a faster rate (not **E**). These units are recruited late (not **A**) and require a higher frequency to produce tetanic contractions (not **B**).

148.   **Which one of the following statements describes the motor units that are recruited to maintain posture?**
    A.   They contain small-diameter fibers.
    B.   They have primarily a glycogenolytic metabolism.
    C.   They produce large forces over a long period of time.
    D.   They use ATP quickly.
    E.   They produce large forces over a short period of time.

Answer = A. The postural muscles are small-diameter fibers that are slow and use oxidative phosphorylation (not **B**); they generate ATP at a slower rate than fast fibers (not **D**) and generate sustained forces over an extended period of time (not **C** or **E**).

149.   **The skeletal muscle α-motoneuron must:**
    A.   respond to excitatory Golgi tendon organ afferents but not to excitatory muscle spindle afferents
    B.   respond to inhibitory inputs but not to excitatory inputs
    C.   spatially sum postsynaptic potentials
    D.   respond to excitatory muscle spindle afferents but not to excitatory Golgi tendon organ afferents
    E.   temporally sum presynaptic potentials

Answer = C. Spatial and temporal summation of postsynaptic (not **E**) excitatory and inhibitory (not just **A, B,** and **D**) potentials is the primary integrative event that occurs on the α-motoneuron.

150.   **When more motor units are recruited to maintain a constant velocity of contraction against an increasing load, which of the following must be true?**
    A.   Fewer muscle fibers are active.
    B.   Greater force is generated by the newly recruited fibers.
    C.   The slower fibers are derecruited in favor of the faster fibers.
    D.   Increasing the frequency of firing increases velocity.
    E.   Less force is generated by the newly recruited fibers to increase velocity.

Answer = B. Since the newly recruited motor units are larger than the initially recruited units, they are able to generate more force (not **E**). As the load is increased, the added load has to be accelerated to reach the desired velocity; therefore, more units are recruited (not **A**). The initially recruited units are driven at a higher frequency (not **C**) and, hence, continue to contribute to the maintenance of the constant velocity. Increasing firing frequency does not affect velocity, as velocity is an intrinsic property of the motor unit at a given force (not **D**).

151.   **Which of the following must be true during successive recruitment of motor units to produce more force?**
    A. α-motor neurons become less active.
    B.   All motor units fire at the same frequency.
    C.   Slow motor units receive more inhibitory feedback.
    D.   Newly recruited motor units fire at a lower frequency.
    E.   Slow motor units fire at a lower frequency.

Answer = D. To generate more force from a muscle, additional motor units must be recruited; greater and greater excitatory input (not **A**) is required to begin recruiting the larger motor units. Hence, the initially recruited units will be firing at a much greater frequency (not **B, C,** or **E**) than the larger units just recruited.

152. **The T-tubule system:**
    A.   stores calcium in smooth muscle
    B.   is a part of the sarcoplasmic reticulum in cardiac muscle but not in smooth muscle
    C.   is a part of the sarcoplasmic reticulum in smooth muscle but not in cardiac muscle
    D.   conducts the action potential in smooth muscle
    E.   conducts the action potential in skeletal muscle

    Answer = E. The T-tubule system is an extension of the plasma membrane (not **B** or **C**) and helps conduct the action potential in skeletal muscle to near the SR. It is, for the most part, absent in smooth muscle (not **A**) and cardiac muscle (not **D**).

153. **Curare, a substance that competitively blocks the acetylcholine receptor, is occasionally used to relax muscles during surgery. Which one of the following postoperative treatments aids in recovery from curare?**
    A.   botulinus toxin, to block ACh release
    B.   neostigmine, an acetylcholinesterase inhibitor
    C.   nifedipine, to block Ca^{2+} channels
    D.   tetrodotoxin, to block Na^+ channels
    E.   none of the above

    Answer = B. Increasing the amount of acetylcholine in the synaptic cleft lets acetylcholine act on the postsynaptic membrane and compete with the curare. Blocking ACh release (**A**) would make matters worst, as would tetrodotoxin (**D**), which would prevent the generation of action potentials. Nifedipine would have little effect on the neuromuscular junction (**C**).

Use Fig. 1-11, which shows motor unit recruitment to answer questions 154 and 155.

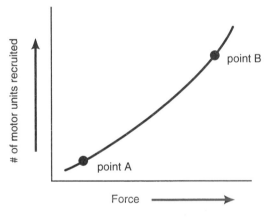

FIG. 1-11

154. **Compared to the motor units recruited at point B, the motor units recruited at point A:**
    A.   have greater glycogenolytic metabolism
    B.   are larger
    C.   use more ATP
    D.   produce more force
    E.   have greater oxidative metabolism

    Answer = E. Motor units recruited first tend to be smaller (not **B**) and normally have a higher level of oxidative metabolism (not **A** or **C**) compared to the larger motor units that are recruited as greater and greater force is needed (not **D**).

155. **When the motor units at point B are recruited, the motor units that were recruited at point A are:**
    A.   fatigued
    B.   generating no force
    C.   firing at a higher frequency
    D.   larger
    E.   in rigor

Answer = C. To recruit more motor units requires higher and higher frequencies; hence, those units that were recruited first are now firing at a higher frequency.

156. **Calcium influx across a muscle cell membrane is important for:**
     A.   the rapid upstroke of the skeletal muscle action potential
     B.   skeletal muscle relaxation
     C.   the plateau phase of the smooth muscle action potential
     D.   smooth muscle relaxation
     E.   the falling phase of the smooth muscle action potential

     Answer = C. The influx of calcium is the essential ionic event that produces the plateau potential in smooth (and cardiac) muscles.

157. **Afferent nerves from the muscle spindles provide information about:**
     A.   tension only
     B.   length, velocity, and tension
     C.   length only
     D.   length and velocity
     E.   tension and velocity

     Answer = D. This is a recall question.

Questions 158-161. Use Fig. 1-12 and the key to identify the muscles described in questions 158-161.

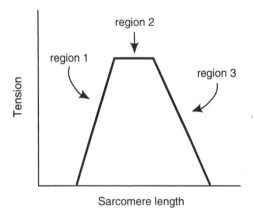

FIG. 1-12

Key for questions 158–161:
"A" = skeletal muscle
"B" = cardiac muscle
"C" = smooth muscle
"D" = none of the muscle types
"E" = all three of the muscle types

158. **Muscle that normally operates in region 1**

     Answer = B. Cardiac muscle clearly operates in region 1.

159. **Muscle that normally operates in region 3**

     Answer = D. None of the muscles normally operates in this range.

160. **Muscle that is not described by the diagram**

Answer = C. Smooth muscle cannot be defined by a simple sarcomere length/tension relationship.

161. **Muscle that normally operates in region 2**

Answer = A. Skeletal muscles tend to operate at the maximum point.

Questions 162–164. Use the following diagram and key to match with questions 162–164. (—) A muscle lifts two different weights and generates the following data:

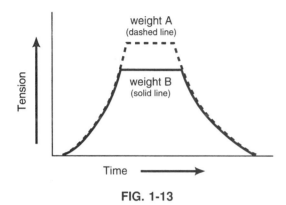

FIG. 1-13

Key for questions 162–164:
"A" = weight A
"B" = weight B
"C" = A and B are equal

162. **The contraction(s) with the shortest isotonic phase**

Answer = A. The muscle has a shorter isotonic phase when lifting weight A because weight A is heavier. Consequently, the muscle has to spend more of the twitch time generating tension.

163. **The contraction(s) with the fastest velocity of shortening**

Answer = B. Recall the force-velocity curve. As the force that a muscle has to develop increases, its velocity of shortening decreases.

164. **The contraction(s) that move(s) the weight the greatest distance**

Answer = B. Weight B is less than weight A. The muscle can move the lighter weight farther because it spends less time developing tension and, hence, has more time to move the weight.

165. **A motor unit is:**
A. a single muscle fiber innervated by several motor neurons
B. all of the muscle fibers innervated by several motor neurons
C. all of the muscle fibers innervated by a single motor neuron
D. a single muscle fiber innervated by a single motor neuron

Answer = C. By definition.

166. The skeletal muscle α-motor neuron is the "final common pathway" for a motor unit for all of the following reasons EXCEPT:

A. it integrates information from muscle spindle afferents
B. it responds to only one neurotransmitter
C. all its muscle fibers contract at the same time
D. it integrates information from Golgi tendon afferents
E. it integrates information from the brain

Answer = **B**. *Remember you are looking for the exception.* The α-motor neuron responds to both excitatory (EPSP) and inhibitory (IPSP) input and, hence, responds to more than one neurotransmitter.

167. The channels opened by acetylcholine at the neuromuscular junction conduct:

A. Na^+ and Ca^{2+} to raise the membrane voltage to a positive potential
B. K^+ and Ca^{2+} to raise the membrane voltage to zero potential
C. Na^+ and Ca^{2+} to raise the membrane voltage to a negative potential
D. K^+ and Na^+ to raise the membrane voltage to a positive potential
E. Na^+ and K^+ to raise the membrane voltage to zero potential

Answer = **E**. The reversal potential of the acetylcholine gate channels (Na^+ and K^+) in the neuromuscular junction is near zero.

168. The neuromuscular junction contains:

A. acetylcholine receptors but no regenerative sodium channels
B. no acetylcholine receptors
C. both acetylcholine receptors and regenerative sodium channels
D. regenerative sodium channels
E. neither acetylcholine receptors nor regenerative sodium channels

Answer = **A**. There are acetylcholine receptors at the motor endplate, but the regenerative sodium channels that generate the action potential are not at that site.

169. The graded potential at the neuromuscular junction:

A. opens Ca^{2+} channels in the T-tubules
B. is conducted some distance from the motor endplate
C. hyperpolarizes the endplate membrane below threshold for an action potential
D. opens acetylcholine channels in the membrane surrounding the motor endplate
E. opens Ca^{2+} channels in the sarcoplasmic reticulum

Answer = **B**. The electronic spread of the depolarization (not **C**) from the neuromuscular junction to the neighboring cell membrane is responsible for causing the neighboring fast sodium channels to open (not **A** or **E**). Acetylcholine-sensitive channels are located in the motor endplate and are relatively insensitive to membrane potentials (not **D**).

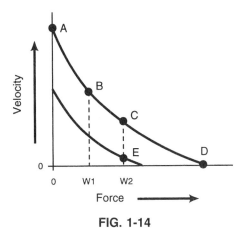

FIG. 1-14

170. Point corresponding to the peak force during an isometric contraction.

Answer = D. By definition, an isometric contraction is one that involves no movement; i.e., velocity is zero.

171. Point corresponding to the muscle generating the greatest type II afferent nerve activity while lifting weight 2 (W2).

Answer = C. The type II afferent from the stretch receptors responds to increases in velocity with an increase in afferent activity. The muscle identified by point C is generating the greatest velocity.

172. Point corresponding to the greatest distance moved when lifting EITHER weight 1 (W1) or weight 2 (W2)

Answer = B. Point B indicates generation of the greatest velocity, the situation in which the weight was moved the farthest.

173. Muscle contraction in the patellar tendon reflex (a deep tendon reflex) results from:
    A. activation of motor units due to stretch of the Golgi tendon organs
    B. activation of motor units due to stretch of the muscle spindles
    C. increased type Ib afferent nerve activity inhibiting the contracting motor units
    D. decreased type Ia afferent nerve activity inhibiting the contracting motor units
    E. increased type II afferent nerve activity inhibiting the contracting units

Answer = B. The sudden and rapid stretching of the patellar tendon stretches the quadriceps, which causes the afferent activity from its muscle spindle to increase. This excites the α-motor neuron, causing a twitch that is an attempt to return the muscle spindle to its original length.

174. A patient places her hands together, palm-to-palm, and pushes. If the muscles of one arm are fast and the muscles of the other are slow, what must happen to maintain her hands in a steady position?
    A. More slow motor units must be recruited at a higher frequency.
    B. More fast motor units must be recruited at a higher frequency.
    C. More fast motor units must be recruited at a lower frequency.
    D. Fewer slow motor units must be recruited at a lower frequency.
    E. Fewer fast motor units must be recruited at a higher frequency.

Answer = A. Since fast motor fibers generate greater force per contraction than slow motor fibers, a greater number of slow units will have to be recruited. In addition, a higher frequency of neuronal activity allows the slow motor units to generate greater force than is obtained with a single twitch contraction.

PART 1: GENERAL PHYSIOLOGY

1.   Which of the following would both decrease heart rate?
      A.   cutting the sympathetic nerves to the heart; infusion of acetylcholine
      B.   stimulation of sympathetic nerves to the heart; infusion of a drug that blocks the effects of acetylcholine
      C.   infusion of epinephrine; infusion of a drug that blocks the effects of acetylcholine
      D.   infusion of a drug that blocks the effects of norepinephrine; cutting the vagus nerve
      E.   stimulation of the vagus nerve; the infusion of epinephrine

      Answer = A.   Cutting the sympathetic nerves to the heart and the infusion of acetylcholine would both decrease heart rate.

2.   If no action potential reached the AV node, a QRS interval that is abnormally long would suggest that the ectopic pacemaker driving the ventricle is located:
      A.   in the common bundle of His
      B.   just before the branch point for the left and right bundle of His
      C.   in a Purkinje cell located at the end of the left bundle branch
      D.   in the AV node
      E.   in any ventricular area, but probably firing at a rate of > 70 beats/min

      Answer = C.   If the ectopic pacemaker is located in the AV node or common bundle of His, the action potential will spread in a reasonably normal fashion and the QRS interval should be of a normal duration (hence, **A, B,** and **D** are incorrect). Choices **C** and **E** would each produce a prolonged QRS interval, but choice **E** would not be expected since the pacemaker rate of a ventricular muscle cell would be much slower, i.e., 15–20 beats/min.

3.   In cardiac muscle, the strength of a contraction would be increased by all the following *EXCEPT:*
      A.   inhibition of Na:Ca exchange
      B.   lengthening the sarcomeres
      C.   phosphorylation of the SR calcium pump
      D.   inhibition of the Na:K pump
      E.   a decrease in heart rate

      Answer = E.   *Remember you are looking for the exception.* A decrease in heart rate is associated with a decrease in contractility due to a decrease in the calcium content of the SR because the calcium efflux process is active for a longer period of time.

Questions 4–7. Refer to Fig. 2-1.

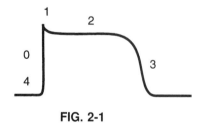

FIG. 2-1

4.   A decrease in potassium conductance is associated with which of the following phases of the ventricular action potential?
      A.   0
      B.   1
      C.   2
      D.   3
      E.   4

Answer = B. An increase in calcium conductance and a decrease in potassium conductance produce the plateau potential and the electrical silence of the normal S-T segment.

5. **Phase 2 corresponds to which component of the EKG?**
   A. P-wave
   B. P-R interval
   C. QRS complex
   D. S-T segment
   E. T-wave

Answer = D. Phases 3 and 4 are associated with either increasing potassium conductance or a high level of potassium conductance.

6. **An increase in sodium conductance produces which phase of the ventricular action potential?**
   A. 0
   B. 1
   C. 2
   D. 3
   E. 4

Answer = A. The rapid opening of sodium channels produces phase 0, whereas phase 1 is associated with inactivation of the fast sodium channels.

7. **What is the major effect that tetrodotoxin would have on the above action potential?**
   A. completely prevent the action potential
   B. decrease the slope of phase 0
   C. greatly suppress the amplitude of phase 2
   D. greatly prolong the duration of the action potential
   E. depolarize the membrane potential during phase 4

Answer = B. Since tetrodotoxin blocks the fast sodium channels, it suppresses the rapid depolarization associated with phase 0; but the calcium channels, which open at a slower rate, are not blocked, and they produce an action potential with a normal phase 2. The duration is not greatly affected because tetrodotoxin does not affect either the calcium or potassium channels.

8. **During stimulation of the sympathetic nerves to the heart:**
   A. heart rate decreases
   B. heart rate increases, but contractility does not change
   C. heart rate and contractility increase
   D. heart rate and contractility decrease
   E. heart rate increases, but contractility decreases

Answer = C. Stimulation of the sympathetic nerves releases norepinephrine, which increases both the heart rate and contractility.

9. **The electrical silence observed during the P–R interval is due to the fact that:**
   A. all the cardiac cells are at the resting membrane potential
   B. the action potential in AV node cells has a small magnitude
   C. the action potential is conducted through a small mass of tissue
   D. there is a lack of fast sodium channels in AV node cells
   E. all the ventricular muscle cells are depolarized

Answer = C. Because of the small mass of tissue comprising the AV node and common bundle of His, extra-cellular recording from surface electrodes can detect the depolarization wave. Choices **A** and **E** are not true because atrial cells are depolarized but ventricular cells are at their resting membrane potential. Choices **B** and **D** are correct statements, but they not the reason for the electrical silence.

10. **Stimulation of the parasympathetic nerves to the heart has the greatest effect on the rate of action potential conduction in:**
   A. atrial muscle cells
   B. the AV node
   C. the bundle of His
   D. ventricular cells
   E. The effect is similar for all cardiac cells.

   Answer = B. The vagal nerve has the greatest effect on the rate of conduction in the AV node; hence, the PR interval changes more than the duration of the P wave. Conduction velocity in cells with fast sodium channels (**A, C,** and **D**) is not dramatically slowed, which makes choice **E** incorrect.

11. **Stimulation of the vagus nerve may result in a decrease in contractility of the ventricle because:**
   A. the muscle cells in the ventricles are heavily innervated by parasympathetic fibers, which directly inhibit calcium influx
   B. the decrease in heart rate leads to enhanced calcium efflux via the Na:Ca exchanger
   C. the decrease in heart rate leads to an increase in calcium influx via calcium channels
   D. acetylcholine causes a receptor-mediated inhibition of the calcium pump that is located on the SR
   E. The statement is false; stimulation of the vagus nerve increases the contractility of the ventricle because it enhances calcium influx.

   Answer = B. The level of contractility is determined primarily by the amount of Ca released from the SR. When heart rate is slow, as will occur with vagal stimulation, most of the time the ventricular muscle cells are at their resting membrane potential. This allows the continued efflux of Ca via the Na:Ca exchanger, results in a decrease in the SR calcium stores, and decreases cardiac contractility (not **E**). The ventricles receive no parasympathetic innervation (not **A**). At a slow heart rate, the plateau phase of the action potential lasts longer, and, hence, more Ca may influx; but this influx of calcium is insufficient to counteract the increase in calcium efflux (not **C**). ACh does not directly affect the calcium pump (not **D**).

   Questions 12–17. Refer to Fig. 2-2.

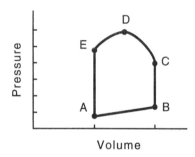

   FIG. 2-2

12. **In a healthy individual at rest, which phase of the above pressure-volume loop occupies the most time?**
   A. A-B
   B. B-C
   C. C-D
   D. D-E
   E. E-A

   Answer = A. Since resting heart rate is slow (60–80 beats/min), most of the cardiac cycle is spent in diastole (A-B).

13. **During which interval can dP/dt be used to evaluate the strength of myocardial contraction?**
   A. A-B
   B. B-C
   C. C-D
   D. D-E
   E. E-A

Answer = B. While the heart is developing pressure but not moving blood (isometric contraction; B-C), dP/dt is a useful index of cardiac contractility. Pressure changes between C-D are dependent not only on cardiac contractility but also on the status of the arterial system.

14. All the valves of the heart are closed during which of the following periods?
    A. A-B
    B. C-D
    C. C-E
    D. D-E
    E. E-A

    Answer = E. All the valves of the heart are closed during both isometric contraction (B-C: not a choice) and during isometric relaxation (E-A).

15. Anemia produces an increased likelihood of a bruit in the base of the aorta. During which part of the pressure–volume loop would you expect to hear such a bruit?
    A. A-B
    B. B-C
    C. C-D
    D. D-E
    E. E-A

    Answer = C. Because a low hematocrit reduces blood viscosity, the likelihood of exceeding the Reynolds number is increased at the high flow rates that are produced during the rapid ejection phase of the cardiac cycle.

16. The mitral valve opens at which point on the pressure–volume loop?
    A. A
    B. B
    C. C
    D. D
    E. E

    Answer = A. When the pressure in the left ventricle drops below that in the left atrium, the mitral valve opens and the ventricle begins to fill.

17. If only contractility increased before the next beat of this heart, you would expect for the next beat that:
    A. point E would shift to the left
    B. point B would shift to the right
    C. point C would shift upward
    D. point C would shift downward
    E. stroke volume would decrease

    Answer = A. The increase in contractility will cause stroke volume to increase (not **E**) by emptying more (shifting point E to the left). Point B would not be affected on the next beat, and any subsequent change in point B would be dependent on what happens to venous return on the subsequent beats. Afterload was not changed; hence, point C should not shift.

18. The following pairs relate a specific tissue to one of its most intense vasodilator stimuli. All the pairs are correct *EXCEPT*:
    A. brain:hypocapnia
    B. intestine:ingested lipids
    C. skeletal muscle:metabolic factors
    D. skin:decreased sympathetic tone
    E. kidney:decrease in arterial pressure

    Answer = A. *Remember you are looking for the exception.* Hypercapnea (not hypocapnea) is a powerful brain vasoconstrictor. All of the other pairs are appropriate. Recall that the kidney exhibits a high degree of autoregulation; therefore, decreases in arterial pressure are associated with an intrinsically induced vasodilation.

19. **A resting normal adult receives an intravenous infusion of isotonic saline at a rate of 1 liter/h over a 3-h period. This would cause:**
    A. reduction of plasma atrial natriuretic peptide (ANP)
    B. renal antidiuresis
    C. a significant rise of arterial pressure
    D. an increase of lymph flow
    E. a rise of plasma renin activity

    Answer = D. The gradual expansion of the plasma and extracellular fluid volumes would increase lymph flow, increase ANP (not **A**), and activate the low and high pressure baroreceptors. The baroreceptors send information to the CNS that results in a decrease in sympathetic nerve activity (vasodilation, a decrease in heart rate, and a decrease in renin secretion (not **E**) that helps to maintain arterial blood pressure (not **C**). Furthermore, renal sodium excretion would be increased (not **B**).

20. **Which of the following is true about the baroreflex mechanism?**
    A. Acute increases in arterial pressure cause a decrease in heart rate.
    B. Acute increases in arterial pressure cause an increase in heart rate.
    C. Acute decreases in arterial pressure cause a decrease in heart rate.
    D. Acute changes in arterial pressure do not alter heart rate.
    E. Acute decreases in arterial pressure cause arterial vasodilation.

    Answer = A. As pressure to the baroreceptors increases, the increased firing from the baroreceptors results in an activation of parasympathetic nerve activity to the heart and a decrease in sympathetic nerve activity to the heart and peripheral vascular beds (vasodilation).

21. **An increase in the number of perfused capillaries:**
    A. decreases the oxygen diffusion distance
    B. increases the surface area for exchange
    C. increases the arterial oxygen content
    D. choices A and B only
    E. choices B and C only

    Answer = D. As more capillaries are perfused, arterial blood is brought closer to the metabolically active tissue, decreasing the distance that oxygen will have to diffuse. As more capillaries are being perfused, there is a greater area of capillary membranes participating in the exchange process. Arterial oxygen content is determined by the lungs, not directly by the number of peripheral capillaries being perfused.

22. **An *increase* in capillary filtration coefficient is likely to occur when:**
    A. plasma oncotic pressure falls
    B. the number of capillary pores increases
    C. interstitial fluid pressure rises
    D. capillary surface area decreases
    E. there is a decrease in arterial blood pressure

    Answer = B. The capillary filtration coefficient is directly proportional to the number and types of pores present in the capillary membrane and to the surface area (not **D**). Neither the plasma oncotic pressure nor the interstitial fluid pressure is a direct determinant of the filtration coefficient. A decrease in arterial blood pressure would be associated with a decrease in both capillary pressure and the number of capillaries being perfused.

23. **Which of the following is most likely to produce delayed diastolic filling of the left ventricle?**
    A. aortic stenosis
    B. tricuspid regurgitation
    C. mitral stenosis
    D. pulmonic stenosis
    E. increasing heart rate from 80 to 100 beats/min

    Answer = C. Mitral stenosis (high resistance to flow across the left ventricular AV valve) would delay diastolic filling because a higher than normal pressure gradient is needed to drive blood from the left atrium into the ventricle. Both aortic and pulmonic stenosis (ventricular outflow defects) would have little effect on the rate of diastolic filling of the left ventricle (not **A** or **D**). Tricuspid regurgitation would affect the filling of the right ventricle, not the left (not **B**). A small increase is heart rate would have little effect on ventricular filling (not **E**), but very large increases in heart rate can decrease the efficiency of ventricular filling.

24. **Which of the following factors contribute(s) to the maintenance of balance between the outputs of the left and right ventricles?**
    A. reflex activity via sympathetic nerves
    B. reflex activity via parasympathetic nerves
    C. circulating epinephrine levels
    D. Frank-Starling law of the heart
    E. all of the above

    Answer = D. Only the Frank-Starling law of the heart (i.e., alterations in preload have a direct effect on stroke volume) contributes to matching the outputs of the two ventricles. Choices **A, B,** and **C** will affect the output of both ventricles in a similar manner.

25. **In a healthy individual, a 10 mm Hg increase in venous pressure across a skeletal muscle vascular bed will result in a decrease in its:**
    A. interstitial pressure
    B. interstitial volume
    C. interstitial protein concentration
    D. movement of fluid into its interstitial space
    E. lymph flow

    Answer = C. The increase in venous pressure will cause an increase in capillary pressure and, thus, increase the rate of filtration via the Starling forces. The increase in filtration will increase interstitial volume, pressure, and lymph flow; and the increase in lymph flow will cause the protein concentration to decrease.

26. **The amplitude of the pulse pressure in the aorta is:**
    A. directly proportional to stroke volume
    B. directly proportional to aortic capacitance
    C. directly proportional to peripheral resistance
    D. calculated by adding one-third of the difference between the systolic and the diastolic pressure to the diastolic pressure
    E. greater in the proximal than in the distal aorta

    Answer = A. If you rearrange the capacitance equation ($C = \Delta V/\Delta P$) to ($\Delta P = \Delta V/C$), then it is apparent that pulse pressure (ΔP) is directly proportional to stroke volume (ΔV) and inversely proportional to the capacitance (not **B**). Peripheral resistance does not directly determine pulse pressure (not **C**); but it is a major determinant of mean arterial pressure (not **D**), which is calculated from the expression presented in **D**. Pulse pressure increases due to summation of reflection waves and changes in capacitance in the more distal (not **E**) vessels.

27. **All of the following are true for the venous system compared to the arterial system *EXCEPT* that in the veins:**
    A. pressure is lower
    B. compliance is greater
    C. flow is greater
    D. blood volume is greater
    E. wall tension is less

    Answer = C. *Remember you are looking for the exception.* Flow is equal throughout each segment of the vascular system. Most of the blood is stored in the venous system at a very low pressure (**A** and **D**). The venous system has a very high compliance (**B**); and, since the venous vessels have lower pressure and are similar in size or slightly larger than their arterial counterparts and pressure is lower, wall tension is much less (**E**).

28. **If cardiac output remained constant, a decrease in left ventricular end-diastolic volume would occur over time if:**
    A. contractility decreased
    B. the afterload on the heart decreased
    C. heart rate decreased
    D. a calcium channel blocking drug were administered
    E. None of the above would cause a decrease in left ventricular end-diastolic volume.

    Answer = B. A decrease in afterload will allow the ventricles to eject more blood at a given end-diastolic volume and, thus, to maintain the same cardiac output; the end-diastolic volume will decrease. Any factor that would decrease contractility (**A, B,** or **D**) would cause left ventricular end-diastolic volume to increase in order to maintain cardiac output. A decrease in heart rate would also require an increase in stroke volume, which would tend to cause left ventricular volume to increase.

29. A patient has a normal arterial blood pressure and cardiac output at rest, but the mitral valve is leaky (insufficient). You would expect all of the following *EXCEPT*:
   A. an increase in left ventricular end-diastolic pressure
   B. an increase in left ventricular end-diastolic volume
   C. a systolic murmur
   D. a decrease in afterload
   E. a decrease in mean pulmonary venous pressure

   Answer = E. *Remember you are looking for the exception.* During systole, blood flows backward through the mitral valve, causing an increase (not a decrease; **E**) in pulmonary venous pressure. The increase in pulmonary venous pressure (**A**) and volume (**B**) will cause greater filling of the ventricle, leading to an increase in end-diastolic pressure and volume. The blood flowing backward through the valve during systole will produce a systolic murmur (**C**). Since arterial blood pressure was normal in this patient (see question), afterload must be considered normal.

30. An increase in preload alone should be associated with an increase in all of the following *EXCEPT*:
   A. stroke volume
   B. end-systolic volume
   C. arterial pulse pressure
   D. end-diastolic volume
   E. end-diastolic pressure

   Answer = B. *Remember you are looking for the exception.* Inspection of any figures showing the effect of an increase in preload (**D** and **E**) reveals that the ventricles are able to increase the amount of shortening (increase in stroke volume; **A**) so that the same end-systolic volume is reached. The increase in stroke volume will produce an increase in the volume of blood entering the aorta (an increase in arterial pulse pressure; **C**).

31. A patient receives a transfusion of 1,000 ml of whole blood. Which of the following would be expected to decrease?
   A. left atrial pressure
   B. cardiac output
   C. mean circulatory filling pressure
   D. arterial pressure
   E. arterial resistance

   Answer = E. Since most of the blood will remain in the circulatory system, blood volume will be increased. The increased filling of the vascular system leads to an increase in mean circulatory filling pressure (not **C**) and an increase in left atrial pressure (not **A**). This shifts the vascular function curve to the right, which tends to increase cardiac output (not **B**), leading to an increase in arterial pressure (not **D**). The increase in blood pressure will cause a decrease in baroreceptor drive and a reflex decrease in arterial resistance (**E**).

32. A patient is inadvertently given an infusion of 1,000 ml of 0.9% saline. All of the following will help restore right atrial pressure to normal *EXCEPT*:
   A. stress relaxation
   B. increase in capillary pressure
   C. increase in lymph flow
   D. increase in urine flow
   E. decrease in sympathetic nerve activity to peripheral venous tissues

   Answer = C. *Remember you are looking for the exception.* All of the above occur in response to a volume overload. However, the increase in lymph flow does not help to bring right atrial pressure back to normal. Stress relaxation (**A**) helps return mean systemic filling pressure to normal. The increase in capillary pressure (**B**) helps shift fluid into the interstitial spaces. The increase in urine flow (**C**) gets rid of the excess volume, reducing blood volume and, hence, restoring right atrial pressure to normal. A decrease in sympathetic drive to the veins (**D**) also increases the capacitance of the venous system, reducing mean systemic filling pressure.

33. During the rapid ejection phase of the cardiac cycle:
   A. the mitral valve is open
   B. aortic pressure is rising
   C. the aortic valve is closed
   D. ventricular volume is at its lowest volume
   E. the first heart sound starts during this phase

Answer = B. As the blood rapidly enters the aorta, aortic pressure rises. The mitral valve closed at the beginning of the isovolumic contraction phase, whereas the aortic valve opens and signals the beginning of the rapid ejection phase. The first heart sound occurs mostly during the isovolumic contraction phase.

34. A patient absorbs 300 ml/min of oxygen. The oxygen content of blood taken from the femoral artery = 18 ml/100 ml; blood taken from the pulmonary artery has an oxygen content of 13 ml/100 ml; and blood taken from the femoral vein has an oxygen content of 140 ml/100 ml. If the patient has a heart rate of 60 beats per min, the patient's stroke volume is:
    A. 10 ml
    B. 12.5 ml
    C. 80 ml
    D. 100 ml
    E. 120 ml

    Answer = D. Cardiac output is equal to the oxygen consumption (300 ml/min)/arterial minus mixed venous oxygen concentration, obtained from a pulmonary arterial sample (18 ml/100 ml − 13 ml/100 ml = 5 ml/100 ml or 0.05 ml/ ml) = **6,000 ml/min.** Stroke volume = cardiac output/heart rate (6,000 ml/min/60 strokes/min = **100 ml/stroke**).

35. The viscosity of blood:
    A. increases when streaming occurs
    B. decreases with increases in hematocrit
    C. is less than that of plasma
    D. increases at very low flow rates
    E. has no influence on Reynolds' number

    Answer = D. At very low flow rates, the red blood cells (RBC) aggregate and collide, causing the viscosity to increase. As velocity increases and streaming occurs, the viscosity decreases (not **A**). The number of RBC is a major factor determining viscosity (not **B**) and explains why blood has a greater viscosity than plasma (not **C**). Blood viscosity is one of the factors that determines Reynolds' number (not **E**).

36. Assuming the arterial–venous pressure gradient remains constant, flow through a vessel will decrease:
    A. if a vessel in parallel constricts
    B. 8-fold if the radius is halved
    C. if the hematocrit is decreased
    D. 16-fold if the radius is doubled
    E. if another vessel is added in series

    Answer = E. Since flow through a vessel bed is determined by the total in-series resistance and the pressure gradient, the constriction of a vessel in parallel (not **A**) will not affect the flow unless the pressure gradient is changed. Since resistance is a function of the radius to the 4th power, a 50% decrease in radius should cause a 16-fold decrease flow (not **B**). The decrease in hematocrit will decrease viscosity and, hence, increase flow (not **C**). Increasing the radius will increase flow (not **D**). Adding another vessel in series will increase the total resistance and, thus, decrease flow (**E**).

37. Assume at this point in the capillary network that filtration equals absorption, plasma oncotic pressure = 30 mm Hg, interstitial oncotic pressure = 8 mm Hg, and interstitial hydrostatic pressure = −2 mm Hg. What is the capillary hydrostatic pressure?
    A. 20 mm Hg
    B. 22 mm Hg
    C. 24 mm Hg
    D. 36 mm Hg
    E. 40 mm Hg

    Answer = A. The implication is that no net filtration is occurring at this site. Hence, the forces favoring filtration = the forces favoring absorption. Capillary hydrostatic pressure + interstitial oncotic pressure (P_{cap} + 8 mm Hg) = plasma oncotic pressure + interstitial hydrostatic pressure (30 mm Hg + [−2 mm Hg] = 28 mm Hg): P_{cap} = 28 mm Hg − 8 mm Hg = **20 mm Hg.**

38. **An increase in protein concentration in the interstitial fluid would tend to cause all of the following *EXCEPT*:**
   A. an increase in lymph flow
   B. an increase in interstitial oncotic pressure
   C. a decrease in capillary filtration
   D. edema
   E. a decrease in net transcapillary oncotic pressure gradient

   Answer = C. *Remember you are looking for the exception.* Increasing the protein concentration (i.e., oncotic pressure; **B**) would increase the forces favoring filtration and, hence, would increase lymph flow (**A**). It would also increase, not decrease (*not* **C**), the amount of filtration. There would be a tendency for the accumulation of fluid, yielding edema (**D**), and the oncotic pressure gradient would be decreased (**E**).

39. **Vasoconstriction of all arterioles, with no change in aortic or venous pressure, would decrease all of the following *EXCEPT*:**
   A. cardiac output
   B. pressure at the venous end of the capillary
   C. filtration across capillaries
   D. pressure at the arterial end of the capillary
   E. arterial–venous oxygen difference

   Answer = E. *Remember you are looking for the exception.* When pressure stays constant and resistance is increased, flow (cardiac output) is decreased (**A**). Since constriction of the arteriole reduces flow across all capillary beds, pressure at the arterial and venous ends of the capillaries is decreased (**B** and **D**); there will also be a corresponding decrease in mean capillary pressure, causing a decrease in the rate of filtration (**C**). Since flow is decreased, tissue will extract more oxygen per ml of flow; hence, the arterial–venous oxygen difference will be increased (*not* **E**).

40. **Vascular permeability is highest in the:**
   A. liver
   B. skin
   C. heart
   D. skeletal muscle
   E. kidney

   Answer = A. The liver has the leakiest capillaries, which explains why ascites fluid has such a high protein content compared to that of edematous fluid from most other parts of the body.

41. **The function of the papillary muscles and chordae tendinae is to:**
   A. hold open the semilunar valves during systole
   B. keep the AV valves from bulging into the aorta and pulmonary arteries during systole
   C. keep the AV valves from bulging into the atria during ventricular contraction
   D. increase backflow into the ventricles during diastole
   E. hold the AV valves open during diastole

   Answer = C. The papillary muscles and chordae tendinae help prevent or minimize the amount of bulging into the atria during systole.

42. **Under normal circumstances, the largest drop in blood pressure in the systemic circulatory system occurs over which of the following vascular segments?**
   A. venae cavae
   B. small and large veins and venules
   C. aorta
   D. small arteries and arterioles
   E. capillaries and venules

   Answer = D. The small arteries and arterioles have the highest resistance and, hence, cause the largest drop in pressure along this segment of the vascular system.

43. **In the SA node, the dominant event that causes the sharp change in membrane potential from −45 to +20 millivolts is the:**
   A. opening of voltage-gated TTX (tetrodotoxin)-sensitive sodium channels
   B. opening of potassium channels
   C. opening of chloride channels
   D. opening of ligand-gated sodium channels
   E. opening of voltage-gated calcium channels

   Answer = E. In the ventricular and atrial muscle cells, action potentials are generated by the opening of voltage-gated TTX-sensitive sodium channels. In the SA node, however, the dominant event is the opening of calcium channels.

44. **Even though blood pressure may fall as a result of hemorrhage, cerebral blood flow is maintained constant because of:**
   A. autoregulation
   B. reactive hyperemia
   C. active hyperemia
   D. Starling equilibrium
   E. increased metabolism

   Answer = A. The brain, more than almost any organ, has the inherent ability to autoregulate its blood flow. This is not caused by either reactive or active hyperemia or to an increase in metabolism, although all of these factors can affect cerebral blood flow.

45. **All of the following processes or mechanisms help the body regulate mean arterial blood pressure *EXCEPT*:**
   A. sympathetic outflow to the splanchnic bed
   B. parasympathetic outflow to the heart
   C. activation of the renin–angiotensin system
   D. locally induced alteration in organ blood flow
   E. carotid baroreceptor

   Answer = D. *Remember you are looking for the exception.* Locally induced alteration in organ blood flow is very important for the maintenance of the integrity of any organ. It, however, presents a challenge to the cardiovascular system because it tends to have a negative effect on the maintenance of arterial blood pressure.

46. **In an otherwise healthy individual at rest, an increase in afterload is likely to be associated with all of the following *EXCEPT*:**
   A. a decrease in stroke volume
   B. a decrease in ventricular end-diastolic volume
   C. an increase in diastolic blood pressure
   D. an increase in end-systolic volume
   E. an increase in cardiac mass

   Answer = B. *Remember you are looking for the exception.* Afterload has a negative effect on stroke volume (**A**) because more time is spent generating pressure needed to overcome the increase in afterload (increase in diastolic pressure; **C**) than is spent on shortening. Hence, the heart does not empty as well (**D**) which results in a tendency for end-diastolic volume to increase (not decrease; **B**). A serious consequence of an increase in afterload and the resulting increase in wall tension is hypertrophy of the heart (**E**).

47. **When comparing the right ventricle to the left ventricle, all of the following are true for the left ventricle *EXCEPT*:**

   A. muscle mass is greater in the left ventricle
   B. depolarization starts first in the left ventricle
   C. pressure generated in the left ventricle is greater
   D. the left ventricle does more work
   E. the left ventricle starts to eject blood first

   Answer = E. *Remember you are looking for the exception.* Even though the left ventricle starts to depolarize first, shortening (ejection of blood) start first in the right ventricle because the afterload for the right ventricle (pulmonary arterial pressure) is so much less than that for the left ventricle. All of the other factors are true.

48. **Endothelium-derived relaxing factor (EDRF) influences blood flow by:**
 A. increasing blood pressure
 B. directly increasing cardiac output
 C. dilating resistance vessels upstream of capillaries
 D. dilating capillaries
 E. decreasing tissue oxygen utilization

Answer = C. EDRF is released from capillary vascular endothelium and causes arteriolar vasodilation. If anything, vasodilators tend to decrease blood pressure (not **A**). EDRF has little effect on the heart (not **B**) since it does not circulate at a high level in the blood (i.e., it is a locally released factor). Capillaries themselves do not dilate (not **D**), and EDRF has little effect on tissue oxygen utilization (not **E**).

49. **The most important physiological regulator of resistance in cutaneous (skin) blood vessels is:**
 A. lactic acid
 B. adenosine
 C. potassium
 D. norepinephrine
 E. carbon dioxide

Answer = D. Blood flow through the skin is primarily determined by the thermoregulatory requirements of the body and very little by locally released metabolic products. Hence, norepinephrine released from the sympathetic nerves to the skin is the primary physiological regulator.

50. **During vigorous exercise, all of the following organs are likely to have greatly increased blood flow *EXCEPT* the:**
 A. heart
 B. skeletal muscles
 C. lungs
 D. kidneys
 E. skin

Answer = D. *Remember you are looking for the exception.* During rigorous exercise, the skeletal muscles produce locally released factors that cause vasodilation (**B**) and, hence, increase venous return, leading to an increase in cardiac output and a subsequent increase in coronary blood flow (**A**). The increase in cardiac output also means that pulmonary blood flow is increased (**C**). The metabolic heat produced by the muscles causes an increase in skin blood flow (**E**) to help lose heat to maintain body temperature. The kidney and other organs that are not participating in the exercise experience an increase in sympathetic nerve activity, which tends to reduce blood to these tissues (*not* **D**).

Questions 51–52. Refer to Fig. 2-3.

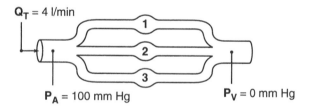

Q_T = 4 l/min

P_A = 100 mm Hg P_V = 0 mm Hg

FIG. 2-3

51. **If pressure at P_A and P_V remains constant, the resistance in circuit 1 is decreased, and the resistances in circuit 2 and 3 do not change, then:**
 A. flow through circuit 1 decreases
 B. flow through circuit 2 increases
 C. total flow (Q_T) increases
 D. none of the above occurred
 E. cannot determine from the data given

Answer = C. Flow is determined simply by the pressure gradient across the circuit divided by the total resistance of the circuit. Since resistance decreased in circuit 1 and remained constant in circuits 2 and 3, total resistance decreased and total flow (Q_T) increased. The flow in circuit 1 had to increase because resistance decreased, whereas flow in circuit 2 did not change. Clinically, this is what occurs during mild exercise.

52. If total flow (Q_T) remains constant, resistance in circuit 1 increases, and the resistances in circuit 2 and 3 do not change, then:
A. flow through circuit 1 decreases
B. flow through circuit 2 decreases
C. flow through circuit 3 decreases
D. B and C only
E. P_A decreases

Answer = A. When flow remains constant, any change in resistance must be accompanied by a proportional change in pressure. Hence, when resistance increases in circuit 1, it causes the total resistance to increase; and, consequently, pressure has to increase. The increase in pressure (not **E**) then causes flow in circuits 2 and 3 to increase (not **B** or **C**), and the increase in resistance through circuit 1 causes flow through circuit 1 to decrease.

53. When a well conditioned athlete at rest is placed in a warm environment, the following will occur:
A. increased total peripheral resistance
B. decreased heart rate
C. increased cardiac output
D. increased blood pressure
E. none of the above

Answer = C. When a person is placed in a warm environment, body temperature is maintained by a thermoregulatory reflex involving an increase in blood flow through the skin. This vasodilation (not **A**) causes a slight initial decrease in blood pressure (not **D**) that is sensed by the baroreceptors, leading to an increase in heart rate (not **B**) and cardiac output and, thus, minimizing any change in blood pressure.

54. The major factor that explains the decrease of total peripheral resistance during exercise is:
A. decreased sympathetic nervous activity
B. increased systemic filling pressure
C. local regulation of the skeletal muscle vascular bed
D. increased arterial pressure
E. increased muscle capillary hydrostatic pressure

Answer = C. The locally released products of muscle metabolism and the decrease in tissue oxygen levels are the major determinants of skeletal muscle blood flow during exercise. There is an increase in sympathetic nervous system outflow (not **A**) that actually tends to decrease blood flow to the other uninvolved peripheral organs and leads to an increase in systemic filling pressure, arterial blood pressure, and (possibly) muscle capillary hydrostatic pressure; but none of these factors explains or causes the decrease in peripheral resistance.

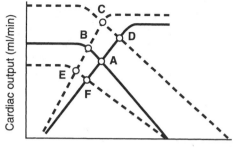

FIG. 2-4

The following represent various cardiovascular changes shown in Fig. 2-4. Please match the moves shown below with the statements given subsequently. Assume that unmentioned variables are constant.

    A.   A to C
    B.   A to B
    C.   C to D
    D.   A to F
    E.   E to A

55.   **Increased blood volume together with increased contractility:**

Answer = A.   What you need to do is determine the effect that an increase in blood volume and an increase in contractility will have on both the vascular function and the cardiac output curves. An increase in blood volume will shift the vascular function curve to the right with little change in slope, whereas an increase in contractility will shift the cardiac function curve to the left and increase the slope. Going from point A to point C (**A**) is the only correct possibility in the above pairs of points. Note, however, that going from F to C would also be reasonable.

56.   **Increased parasympathetic nerve activity to heart together with decreased arterial resistance:**

Answer = E.   What you need to do is determine the effect of an increase in parasympathetic drive to the heart (a decrease in contractility; decrease in slope of the cardiac output curve) and a decrease in arterial resistance (an increase in the slope of the vascular function curve with little or no shift). Going from point E to point A (**E**) is the only correct possibility in the above pairs of points.

57.   **Increased peripheral resistance:**

Answer = D.   What you need to do is determine what effect an increase in peripheral resistance will have on the curves for both the vascular function (a counter-clockwise rotation of the curve) and the cardiac output (no direct effect on the curve). Going from point A to point F (**D**) is the only correct possibility in the above pairs of points. Note, however, that going from B to E would also be reasonable.

58.   **A patient receives a strong blow to the head and is brought to the hospital, complaining of headache and various neurological symptoms. Upon examination, you find a blood pressure of 220/160 (this patient's normal value is 120/80). Appropriate treatment for this patient is:**
    A.   intravenous infusion of a drug that decreases arterial pressure
    B.   intravenous infusion of a drug that increases renal function
    C.   an X-ray to determine whether the patient has a subdural hematoma
    D.   using leeches to decrease blood volume
    E.   intravenous infusion of a drug that dilates the arterioles

Answer = C. What you need to recognize is that the head injury plus the marked increase in blood pressure may indicate a cerebral ischemic response resulting from the accumulation of blood or fluid within the CSF. Such accumulation compresses the vasculature, leading to an increase in arterial blood pressure, which can maintain blood flow to the brain. Hence, you need to first determine if subdural hematoma is a possibility (**C**). If a hematoma is present, any drug or procedure that would lower blood pressure (not **A, D,** or **E**) might cause the brain tissue to become underperfused, leading to a rapid deterioration of the patient's cerebral function. Although the blood pressure increase might compromise the kidneys, their ability to autoregulate, the lack of any statement about renal dysfunction, and the lack of a critical necessity to address a renal problem make **B** an unlikely first choice.

59. **A 25% loss of blood volume is likely to:**
    A. increase unstressed volume
    B. decrease the plasma levels of vasopressin
    C. increase tissue interstitial pressure
    D. increase the plasma levels of angiotensin II
    E. increase the plasma levels of ANF

    Answer = D. Hemorrhage will cause a decrease in the unstressed volume (not **A**). The subsequent decrease in arterial and venous pressure will—via the low pressure receptors, the high pressure baroreceptors, and the atrial volume receptors—cause vasopressin levels to increase (not **B**), activate the renin–angiotensin system, and decrease the secretion of ANF (not **E**). The decrease in blood pressure will result in an increase in sympathetic nerve activity to the peripheral tissues (arteriolar constriction), leading to a decrease in mean capillary pressure and a movement of fluid from the interstitial to the vascular space, which will cause interstitial pressure to decrease (not **C**).

60. **Assuming that cardiovascular reflexes are allowed to operate, a decrease in cardiac output due to an infarct is likely to cause an increase in all of the following** *EXCEPT:*
    A. parasympathetic nerve activity
    B. venous pressure
    C. mean systemic filling pressure
    D. release of renin
    E. heart rate

    Answer = A. *Remember you are looking for the exception.* A pure decrease in the cardiac function curve will result in a decrease in cardiac output and an increase in right atrial pressure and venous pressure (**B**), leading to a decrease in blood pressure. This will reflexively increase sympathetic, not parasympathetic, outflow (*not* **A**), which will stimulate renin secretion (**D**), cause an increase in heart rate (**E**), and increase mean systemic filling pressure.

61. **The QT interval shortens with increases in heart rate because:**
    A. norepinephrine directly shortens the duration of ventricular muscle action potentials
    B. the duration of ventricular muscle cell action potentials intrinsically decreases as heart rate increases
    C. parasympathetic stimulation shortens the duration of ventricular muscle action potentials
    D. sodium channels inactivate faster as heart rate increases
    E. potassium channels fail to open during the plateau phase (phase 2) of the ventricular action potential

    Answer = B. An intrinsic characteristic of the heart is that the QT interval (action potential duration) shortens as the heart rate increases. This occurs in isolated strips of cardiac tissue in response to electrical pacing without the involvement of norepinephrine (NE). This is probably a characteristic of the refractive period and may be due to increased activity or level of activation of potassium channels (not **E**). Neither NE (not **A**) nor ACh (not **C**) directly affects the duration of the action potentials of cardiac muscle cells. Sodium channel inactivation (**D**) in heart cells is already very fast, and sodium channels have very little to do with the duration of the cardiac action potential.

62. **Increasing the rate at which cardiac muscle cells are electrically stimulated causes the strength of contraction to** __(X)__ **because the amount of calcium that** __(Y)__ **during phase 4** __(Z)__

	X	Y	Z
A.	increase	influxes	increases
B.	increase	influxes	decreases
C.	increase	effluxes	decreases
D.	decrease	effluxes	increases
E.	increase	influxes	remains constant

PART 2: CARDIOVASCULAR PHYSIOLOGY

141

Answer = C.   Recall that one of the factors that increases contractility is an increase in heart rate (X: increase). As the heart rate increases, the heart spends less time at the resting membrane potential (phase 4); hence, less time is available for the efflux of calcium (Y: effluxes) via the Na:Ca exchanger, which decreases (Z: decreases) the rate of calcium efflux, which leads to an increase in calcium stores within the SR of the heart.

Question 63. Refer to Fig. 2-5.

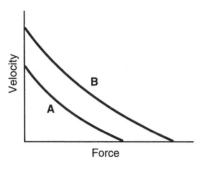

FIG. 2-5

63.   **Which of the following would cause the heart to go from curve A to curve B in Fig. 2-5?**
   A.   activation of the parasympathetic nervous system
   B.   infusion of a drug that blocks calcium channels
   C.   release of epinephrine from the adrenal medulla
   D.   decrease in the intracellular sodium concentration
   E.   infusion of an acetylcholine esterase inhibitor

Answer = C.   Going from curve A to curve B describes the effects of increasing contractility. Epinephrine is the only factor in the above list that increases cardiac contractility. All of the other factors actually decrease cardiac contractility.

64.   **An increase in preload is likely to be associated with:**
   A.   a decrease in stroke volume
   B.   an increase in end systolic volume
   C.   a decrease in diastolic arterial blood pressure
   D.   a decrease in ventricular end diastolic volume
   E.   an increase in the ejection fraction

Answer = E.   When preload (an increase in ventricular end diastolic volume; not **D**) increases (Frank-Starling mechanism), the heart is able to eject the increase in volume (increased stroke volume; not **A**). End systolic volume remain the same (not **B**); hence, the fraction of the end-diastolic volume ejected (ejection fraction) is increased. The increase in stroke volume would probably not be associated with a decrease in diastolic pressure.

Questions 65–67. Refer to Fig. 2-6.

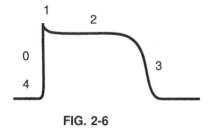

FIG. 2-6

65. **The T wave of the EKG is caused by which phase of the ventricular action potential?**
    A.   1
    B.   2
    C.   3
    D.   4
    E.   none of the above

Answer = C. The T wave is the repolarization wave and, hence, is caused by phase 3 of the ventricular action potential.

66. **The P wave of the EKG is caused by which phase of the ventricular action potential?**
    A.   1
    B.   2
    C.   3
    D.   4
    E.   none of the above

Answer = E. The P wave reflects the depolarization wave in the atria and is not associated with the ventricular action potential.

67. **A change in extracellular potassium concentration would have the greatest effect on which phase of the ventricular action potential?**
    A.   1
    B.   2
    C.   3
    D.   4
    E.   none of the above

Answer = D. The resting membrane potential of ventricular cells is determined primarily by the relatively high permeability of the cell membrane to potassium. Hence, during phase 4, the membrane potential is most sensitive to changes in [K].

68. **A patient's EKG has an upward deflection of the P wave in the lead II and lead III recordings, but no P wave is present in the lead I recording. The most likely cause is:**
    A.   atrial repolarization occurs completely vertically
    B.   atrial depolarization occurs completely horizontally
    C.   ventricular depolarization occurs completely horizontally
    D.   atrial repolarization occurs completely horizontally
    E.   atrial depolarization occurs completely vertically

Answer = E. The absence of a P wave in lead I alone indicates that the axis of the atrial (not ventricular; **C**) depolarization (not repolarization; **A** and **D**) wave must be perpendicular (vertical) to lead I (right arm–left arm). If it were horizontal (**B**), lead I would be very large.

69. **An increase in the rate of intraventricular pressure development during isovolumic contractions could be caused by:**
    A.   inhibition of the Na:Ca exchanger
    B.   a decrease in afterload
    C.   stimulation of the parasympathetic vagus nerve
    D.   decreasing the heart rate
    E.   increasing the duration of ventricular action potentials

Answer = A. Inhibition of the Na:Ca exchanger increases the calcium content of the ventricular cells and leads to an increase in contractility, which causes the dP/dt to increase. Factors **C–E** cause contractility to decrease, whereas factor **B** should have little effect on dP/dt.

Questions 70–71. Refer to Fig. 2-7.

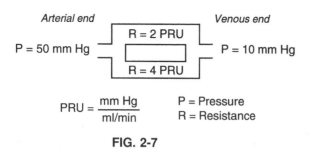

FIG. 2-7

70.   Total flow through this network would equal:
   A.   6.67 ml/min
   B.   53.3 ml/min
   C.   37.5 ml/min
   D.   30 ml/min
   E.   15 ml/min

Answer = D.   Flow = delta P/resistance. Total resistance in a parallel circuit = $1/R_T$ = $1/R_1$ + $1/R_2$. $1/R_T$ = 2/4 + 1/4. RT = 4/3 = 1.33. Flow = (50 mm Hg − 10 mm Hg) = 40 mm Hg/1.33 PRU = 30 ml/min.

71.   If the pressure at the venous end increased from 10 to 20 mm Hg without any changes in resistance, the flow through the vessel with a resistance of 2 PRU would equal:
   A.   7.5 ml/min
   B.   22.5 ml/min
   C.   5 ml/min
   D.   11.25 ml/min
   E.   15 ml/min

Answer = E.   Flow = delta P/resistance. Therefore, flow = (50 mm Hg − 20 mm Hg) = 30 mm Hg/2 PRU = 15 ml/min.

72.   The coronary circulation has a relatively high resistance to blood flow because:
   A.   coronary blood vessels are smaller in diameter than blood vessels to other organs
   B.   cardiac venous pressure is less than that in other organs
   C.   perfusion of the left ventricle occurs mainly during diastole
   D.   epinephrine, which dilates the blood vessels in other organs, causes constriction in the heart
   E.   coronary blood vessels are especially sensitive to the constrictor effect of angiotensin II

Answer = C.   Unlike all the other capillary beds in the body, cardiac muscle has a constant rhythmic compression caused by its contraction, which generates such a high pressure that the vessels may actually be compressed. This results in a high resistance to flow during a substantial part of the cardiac cycle. The vessels are not of a different size (not A). Venous pressure is not a determinant of resistance (not B), and choices D and E do not cause high resistance.

73.   Blood flow to resting skeletal muscles is:
   A.   independent of the central nervous system
   B.   likely to decrease with increased carotid sinus nerve activity
   C.   likely to increase in response to locally administered norepinephrine
   D.   likely to increase in response to locally administered vasopressin
   E.   none of the above

Answer = E.   None of the above is correct for resting skeletal muscle. It is influenced by the CNS (not A). An increase in carotid sinus nerve activity would occur when blood pressure was increased, which should cause a reflex decrease in sympathetic nerve activity to the peripheral tissue (increase in blood flow; not B) to return blood pressure to normal. Both norepinephrine and vasopressin (not D or E) will cause vasoconstriction and, hence, should decrease blood flow.

144   SECTION II: QUESTIONS AND ANSWERS

74. Decreased blood volume is likely to be associated with all the following *EXCEPT:*
    A. decreased arterial blood pressure
    B. increased systemic filling pressure
    C. decreased firing of the carotid sinus nerve
    D. reabsorption of interstitial fluid into the vascular compartment
    E. increased heart rate

Answer = B. *Remember you are looking for the exception.* A decrease in blood volume will decrease (not increase) mean systemic filling pressure, causing a downward shift in the vascular function curve to the left; this will cause cardiac output and arterial blood pressure to decrease (**A**). The decrease in arterial blood pressure will evoke less nerve activity from the baroreceptors (**C**) and, hence, will cause a reflex increase in heart rate (**E**). Both the arteriolar vasoconstriction and the decrease in mean systemic filling pressure will cause mean capillary pressure to decrease, resulting in a net reabsorption of fluid from the interstitial to the plasma compartment (**D**).

75. If heart rate, end-diastolic pressure, and total peripheral resistance remain constant but mean arterial pressure increases, which of the following must also occur?
    A. decreased venous return
    B. decreased mean venous pressure
    C. decreased end-systolic volume
    D. increased right atrial pressure
    E. decreased stroke work

Answer = C. Cardiac output (increase in stroke volume) must increase for mean arterial blood pressure to increase without the other variables' changing. In addition, the cardiac function curve shifts upward to the left with no change in the slope of the vascular function curve. Venous return has to increase (**A**). Mean venous pressure has to be similar or to increase for the increase in venous return to occur (**B**). Right atrial pressure decreases (**D**) as the consequence of shift in the cardiac function curve. Since stroke volume and arterial blood pressure increase, stroke work increases.

Questions 76–77. Refer to Fig. 2-8 of renal function curves.

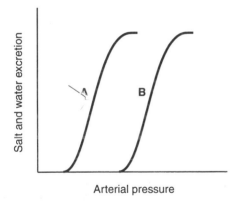

FIG. 2-8

76. A hypothetical substance shifts the renal function curve from A to B. Assuming that caloric, salt, and water intakes remain constant, this causes:
    A. a long-term reduction in arterial blood pressure
    B. an initial decrease of renal salt and water excretion
    C. an decrease in body weight
    D. a decrease in arterial resistance
    E. none of the above

Answer = B. A rightward shift in the renal function curve indicates that a greater pressure is required to excrete the same salt intake. The initial effect is that the arterial blood pressure is no longer adequate to cause the kidneys to excrete the daily salt and water intake. Hence, salt and water are retained (increase in body weight; not **C**), gradually leading to an increase in cardiac output that increases arterial blood pressure (not **A**). Arterial resistance increases (not **D**) as the initial increase in cardiac output is brought back to normal by activation of autoregulatory events in the periphery.

77. **All the following may be true for this hypothetical substance** *EXCEPT:*
   A.   it may be a diuretic acting on the distal nephron
   B.   it may stimulate hormone secretion by glomerulosa cells
   C.   it may increase the secretion of renin
   D.   it may vasoconstrict the afferent arteriole
   E.   it may increase secretion from the adrenal medulla

Answer = A. *Remember you are looking for the exception.* A diuretic would be expected to shift the renal function curve to the right, not to the left (*not* **A**). Increases in the production of aldosterone (**B**), renin (**C**), or systemic catecholamines (**E**) would cause rightward shifts in the renal function curve. Vasoconstriction of the afferent arterioles (**D**) would decrease GFR and, hence, shift the renal function curve to the right.

78. **A generalized systemic inflammatory condition (known as anaphylaxis) will cause:**
   A.   increased renal fluid output
   B.   hypertension
   C.   decreased blood volume
   D.   decreased interstitial fluid pressure
   E.   increased level of atrial natriuretic factor

Answer = C. Anaphylaxis is associated with a massive inflammatory response that will cause peripheral vaso-dilation leading to hypotension (not **B**) and an increase in capillary permeability, which leads to an increase in interstitial oncotic pressure. The hypotension causes a decrease in renal fluid output (not **A**). An increase in capillary pressure caused by the vasodilation and the increase in interstitial oncotic pressure caused by the increased capillary permeability both cause a shift of fluid into the interstitial spaces from the plasma compartment (i.e., a decrease in blood volume), which leads to an increase in interstitial fluid pressure (not **D**). The decrease in blood volume will decrease the secretion of atrial natriuretic factor (not **E**).

79. **An individual with anaphylaxis (see question 78) would benefit from all of the following** *EXCEPT:*
   A.   an intravenous infusion of fluid having a high protein content
   B.   a drug that increases arterial resistance
   C.   a drug that decreases capillary permeability
   D.   a drug that decreases heart rate
   E.   a drug that increases cardiac contractility

Answer = D. *Remember you are looking for the exception.* The patient will benefit from any procedure or drug that prevents the anaphylaxis-induced vasodilation, fluid shifts, and/or decrease in arterial blood pressure. A drug that decreases heart rate will decrease cardiac output and, hence, lower (not increase) arterial blood pressure. The administration of a fluid with a high protein concentration (**A**) would help shift fluid back into the vascular system by increasing the plasma oncotic pressure and, hence, increasing blood volume, assuming that the protein can remain in the vascular system. A drug that increases arterial resistance (**B**) will increase blood pressure and decrease capillary pressure, which will shift fluid back into the vascular system. Helping to restore capillary permeability (**C**) will decrease the rate at which plasma protein is lost from the vascular system and, hence, will help restore blood volume. Improving the ability of the heart to increase cardiac output (**E**) will help maintain arterial blood pressure.

80. **A drug that reduces arrhythmia could act by:**
   A.   decreasing (making more negative) the threshold for calcium channels
   B.   shortening the duration of the relative refractory period
   C.   partially inhibiting the K_1 potassium channel
   D.   activating β-adrenergic receptors in the heart
   E.   activating muscarinic receptors in the heart

Answer = E. To reduce arrhythmia, you need to reduce the chances for the generation of a spontaneous ectopic potential. Activating muscarinic receptors will hyperpolarize the cardiac muscle and reduce the chances for producing an ectopic beat. However, any agent that tends to depolarize the resting membrane potential (**C** or **D**) would make it easier to reach threshold (**A**) and, thus, would be more likely to cause an arrhythmia. Shortening the relative refractory period (**B**) would make it easier for a secondary event to initiate an action potential and, hence, would make an arrhythmia more likely to occur.

81. **An inverted T wave (downward deflection) in the EKG would most likely be caused by:**
    A.   ventricular repolarization occurring from endocardium to epicardium
    B.   ventricular repolarization occurring from epicardium to endocardium
    C.   ventricular depolarization occurring from epicardium to endocardium
    D.   ventricular depolarization occurring from endocardium to epicardium
    E.   an abnormal delay in AV nodal conduction

    Answer = A. Since the normal direction for the repolarization wave (not **C** or **D**) is from epicardium to endocardium (not **B**), reversing this sequence (from endocardium to epicardium) will produce an inverted T wave. A delay in AV node conduction will not affect the normal sequence of electrical events in the ventricles (not **E**).

82. **The average critical closing pressure of an arterial bed is about _____ mm Hg and would be significantly (higher or lower) if the sympathetic nerves were stimulated.**

	Average Closing Pressure	Effect of Sympathetic Nerve Stimulation
A.	0 mm Hg	Higher
B.	7 mm Hg	Higher
C.	7 mm Hg	Lower
D.	20 mm Hg	Higher
E.	20 mm Hg	Lower

    Answer = D. When perfusion pressure falls below 20 mm Hg in normal vascular beds, flow to that organ stops. This is thought to be caused by tension within the vascular system and by the tendency for viscosity to increase as velocity decreases. Increasing the level of sympathetic nerve activity raises the pressure at which the critical closing pressure occurs. Hence, pressures below 60 mm Hg in a patient can lead to anoxic damage to vital organs such as the kidneys.

83. **Which of the following is most likely to produce a diastolic murmur?**
    A.   aortic stenosis
    B.   pulmonic stenosis
    C.   ventricular septal defect
    D.   mitral stenosis
    E.   tricuspid regurgitation

    Answer = D. A diastolic murmur will occur when (1) blood flows across some valve during diastole that normally does not allow blood to flow during diastole or (2) blood flows through a stenotic valve that normally is open during diastole; hence, mitral stenosis will produce a diastolic murmur. All of the other situations will produce murmurs that occur during systole.

Questions 84–85. Refer to Fig. 2-9 showing a slow action potential for a normal individual a heart rate of 60 beats/min.

FIG. 2-9

84. **Blocking the parasympathetic activity to the heart would:**
    A.   increase the height of the depolarization in phase b
    B.   make the threshold of the action potential more positive
    C.   increase the rate of depolarization during phase a
    D.   prolong the duration of the action potential
    E.   increase the interval between action potentials

    Answer = C. Removing parasympathetic activity would result in a sympathetic-like effect on the heart, i.e., an increase in heart rate (not **E**) and a lowering of the threshold potential (not **B**), making it easier to reach threshold. The rate of depolarization during phase a would be increased but not the height (not **A**), and the duration of the action potential would not be prolonged (a slight shortening might occur; not **D**).

85. **Voltage-gated sodium channels that can be blocked with tetrodotoxin are responsible for:**
   A.   phase a
   B.   phase b
   C.   phase c
   D.   Voltage-gated sodium channels are not involved in action potentials in sinoatrial cells.

   Answer = D.   The fast voltage-gated sodium channels are not present in the SA node "slow" action potential.

86. **Compared to sinoatrial cells, ventricular contractile cells will have:**
   A.   an action potential with a shorter duration
   B.   a more negative resting membrane potential
   C.   a slower depolarization during the action potential
   D.   a slower conduction velocity
   E.   a smaller amplitude action potential

   Answer = B.   Ventricular cells have a much more negative resting membrane potential than sinoatrial cells. The ventricular action potential has a longer duration (not **A**), a more rapid depolarization (not **C**), and a much faster conduction velocity (not **D**), and is much larger in amplitude (not **E**).

87. **The tension in the wall of an aneurysm *increases* with:**
   A.   increasing luminal diameter
   B.   decreasing transmural pressure
   C.   increasing wall thickness
   D.   decreasing intravascular pressure
   E.   increasing interstitial pressure

   Answer = A.   According to Laplace's Law, wall tension is directly proportional to the diameter of the vessel and the transmural pressure; hence, choices **B, D,** and **E** will decrease the transmural pressure and lead to a decrease in wall tension. The wall tension is also inversely proportional to the thickness of the wall (not **E**).

Questions 88–89. Please refer to Fig. 2-10. The solid lines refer to the normal situation, while the dashed lines refer to an undiagnosed pathologic situation.

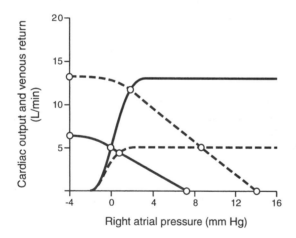

FIG. 2-10

88. **This individual's normal values for cardiac output, right atrial pressure, and mean systemic filling pressure are, respectively:**
   A.   4.5 l/min, 1 mm Hg, and 7 mm Hg
   B.   5 l/min, 0 mm Hg, and 7 mm Hg
   C.   5 l/min, 9 mm Hg, and 14 mm Hg
   D.   12 l/min, 8 mm Hg, and 14 mm Hg
   E.   12 l/min, 0 mm Hg, and 7 mm Hg

Answer = B. Reading from the intersection of the two solid lines, the cardiac output (5 liters/min) and right atrial pressure (0 mm Hg) can be obtained, while the x-axis intercept of the vascular function curve gives you the mean systemic filling pressure (7 mm Hg).

89. **The most likely explanation for the change in cardiac output for an individual with cardiac function and venous return curves indicated by the dashed lines is:**
    A.   increased arterial resistance and decreased contractility
    B.   increased venomotor tone and decreased contractility
    C.   increased venomotor tone and decreased myocardial fiber length
    D.   increased arterial resistance and increased extracardiac pressure
    E.   increased arterial resistance and increased myocardial fiber length

    Answer = B. A parallel shift to the right in the vascular function curve could have been produced by an increase in venomotor tone, whereas an increase in arterial resistance would have caused a counter-clockwise rotation of the vascular function curve (not **A, D,** or **E**). The new cardiac function curve shows that contractility decreased. At the new steady state, the higher right atrial pressure indicates that myocardial fiber length is increased (not **C**).

Questions 90–95. Refer to Fig. 2-11.

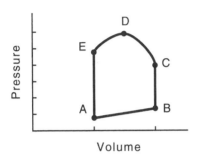

FIG. 2-11

90. **If only afterload increased before the next beat of this heart, you would expect for the next beat that:**
    A.   point E would shift to the left
    B.   point B would shift to the right
    C.   point A would shift to the left
    D.   point C would shift downward
    E.   stroke volume would decrease

    Answer = E. When afterload increases, more time is spent generating pressure during B-C, and the aortic valves will open at a higher pressure; i.e., C will shift upward (not **D**). Since less time will be available for emptying, points E and A will shift to the right (not **A** and **C**), which means that stroke volume will decrease (**E**). Since preload did not change, point B would not change (not **B**); any subsequent change in B would be dependent on what happens to venous return on the subsequent beats.

91. **If only preload increased before the next beat of this heart, you would expect for the next beat that:**
    A.   point E would shift to the left
    B.   point B would shift to the right
    C.   point A would shift to the left
    D.   point C would shift downward
    E.   stroke volume would decrease

    Answer = B. Since end-diastolic volume determines the preload, point B will shift to the right. Points E and A will remain very similar (**A** and **C** are wrong), as stated by the Frank-Starling law of the heart. Point C (afterload; **D**) was not changed. Stroke volume will increase (not **E**).

92. A patient develops an insufficient (leaky) aortic valve. Where along the pressure–volume loop would you expect to hear a murmur?
   A. B-C
   B. C-D
   C. C-E
   D. E-A
   E. E-B

Answer = E. The insufficient aortic valve will let blood flow back from the aorta into the ventricle whenever aortic pressure exceeds ventricular pressure, i.e., between E-A and A-B (not a choice).

93. A patient develops an insufficient (leaky) mitral valve. You would expect to hear a murmur during all phases of the pressure–volume loop *EXCEPT*:
   A. A-B
   B. B-C
   C. B-E
   D. E-A
   E. E-B

Answer = A. *Remember you are looking for the exception.* The insufficient mitral valve will let blood flow back from the left ventricle into the left atrium whenever the pressure in the ventricle exceeds the pressure in the left atrium, i.e., between B-A. Between A-B, atrial pressure exceeds ventricular pressure and the mitral valve is normally open.

94. A patient develops a stenosis of the mitral valve. You would expect to hear a murmur during which phases of the pressure–volume loop?
   A. A-B
   B. B-C
   C. C-D
   D. D-E
   E. E-A

Answer = A. A stenotic mitral valve causes turbulent flow to occur when blood is flowing from the atrium into the ventricle, i.e., during diastole (A-B).

95. A patient develops a stenosis of the aortic valve. You would expect to hear a murmur during which phase of the pressure–volume loop?
   A. A-B
   B. B-C
   C. C-E
   D. E-A

Answer = C. The stenotic aortic valve causes turbulent flow to occur; blood flows rapidly from the ventricle into the aorta, i.e., during systole (C-E). Often the murmur is referred to as having a "diamond-shaped" quality.

96. When systemic arterial blood pressure increases, the myogenic response:
   A. is inhibited by elevations in circulating angiotensin II produced by the blood vessel renin–angiotensin system
   B. augments the rise in arterial pressure by redistributing blood from veins to arteries, thus increasing venous return and causing a rise in cardiac output
   C. reduces the luminal diameter of arterioles, which causes a rise in total peripheral resistance and, thus, a normalization of blood flow
   D. acts to maintain blood flow to the brain and heart and, thus, balances the demands of an increased sympathetic nerve activity
   E. all of the above

Answer = C. The myogenic response is a local (intrinsic) process that helps maintain tissue blood flow near normal levels. All of the other statements are false.

97. A patient with no baroreceptor function would most likely suffer from:
    A. hypertension
    B. hypotension
    C. increased blood pressure lability
    D. no obvious problem in regulating arterial blood pressure

    Answer = C. The baroreceptors play a dominant role in maintenance of arterial blood pressure within narrow limits; hence, in their absence, blood pressure is very labile (not **D**). The long-term regulation of arterial blood pressure is dominated by the renal output–arterial blood pressure relationship and by the long-term status of the arterial system. Therefore, the lack of the baroreceptors would not be expected to produce long-term hypertension or hypotension (not **A** or **B**).

98. Which of the following is most likely to produce sinus bradycardia (rate below 60/min)?
    A. removal of three units of blood
    B. moderate exercise
    C. standing erect from a supine position
    D. carotid sinus massage
    E. painful fracture of left arm

    Answer = D. Direct massage of the carotid baroreceptors can activate the baroreceptors, sending neuronal data indicating an increase in blood pressure; this will induce a reflex increase in heart rate (increased parasympathetic activity) and a decrease in peripheral resistance (decreased sympathetic activity). All of the other situations are associated with activation of the sympathetic nervous system and, hence, with an increase in heart rate.

99. The blood–brain barrier:
    A. is part of the cerebral autoregulatory system that protects the brain from large increases in arterial pressure
    B. occurs because cerebral arterioles are surrounded by a thick basement membrane and a large mass of vascular smooth muscle
    C. is produced by the impermeable type IV collagen secreted by cerebral endothelial cells
    D. results in a diminished movement of vasoactive peptides into the brain tissue
    E. none of the above

    Answer = D. The cerebral capillaries (not **C**) that form the blood–brain barrier have a tight endothelial lining that keeps out or impedes the movement of small peptides and other molecules into the brain tissue. The cerebral arteries are not the basis for the blood–brain barrier (not **B**). Autoregulation has nothing to do with the blood–brain barrier (not **A**), but rather with the intrinsic ability of the CNS to maintain cerebral blood flow in the face of alterations in blood pressure.

100. Which of the following is most likely to occur in anaphylactic shock?
    A. a rise in total peripheral resistance and a rise in the resistance to venous return
    B. hypotension and tachycardia
    C. reduced plasma levels of angiotensin and aldosterone
    D. a decrease in hematocrit
    E. none of the above

    Answer = B. In anaphylactic shock, the release of vasodilatory substances causes a profound peripheral vaso-dilation (not **A**), leading to a decrease in blood pressure (hypotension), which results in a reflex increase in heart rate and the secretion of renin/angiotensin II and aldosterone (not **C**). The arteriolar vasodilation and an increase in the permeability of capillaries to proteins causes capillary pressure to increase and protein to leak into the interstitial spaces. Both the vasodilation and the permeability contribute to a shift of fluid from the vascular into the interstitial spaces. Both the vasodilation and the permeability contribute to a shift of fluid from the vascular into the interstitial space, which causes the hematocrit to increase (not **D**).

101. Left ventricular heart failure is associated with an increased:
    A. left ventricular contractility
    B. left ventricular end-diastolic pressure
    C. left ventricular stroke volume
    D. output from the right heart
    E. venous return

Answer = B. The failing left ventricle will have an increase in end-diastolic pressure (and volume) since its contractility is decreased (not **A**); and, to maintain the normal cardiac output, the Frank-Starling mechanism is used. Stroke volume will be decreased since most likely the failing heart will result in reflex activation of the sympathetic nervous system, leading to an increase in heart rate, which means a decrease in stroke volume (not **C**). Right heart output and venous return will not be increased but will equal what the left heart is able to pump (not **D** or **E**).

102. During a run of several miles at a strenuous pace, all of the following hemodynamic variables would be elevated *EXCEPT*:
   A.   mean systemic filling pressure
   B.   arterial blood pressure
   C.   stroke volume
   D.   cerebral blood flow
   E.   coronary blood flow

Answer = D. *Remember you are looking for the exception.* Strenuous exercise will cause an increase in mean arterial blood pressure (**B**); but, because of the ability of the brain to autoregulate blood flow, cerebral blood flow will not be increased (*not* **D**). There will be a large increase in sympathetic nerve activity that will cause nonessential vascular beds and the venous system to constrict, leading to an increase in both mean systemic filling pressure (**A**) and arterial pressure (**B**). The increase in cardiac contractility will result in both a heart rate- and stroke volume-induced increase (**C**) in cardiac output, which will cause the coronary vessels to vasodilate (**E**).

103. Under normal physiological conditions, the most important underlying determinant of cardiac output is:
   A.   mean systemic pressure
   B.   blood volume
   C.   heart rate
   D.   stroke volume
   E. V_{O_2}

Answer = E. The sum of the metabolic needs of the tissues of the body as determined by the level of oxygen consumption will be the determinant of the cardiac output at any given time. All of the other factors can affect the status of the vascular system, but none of them is as important as the oxygen consumption (not **A, B, C,** or **D**).

Questions 104–107. An adult man weighing 70 kg and having a normal resting cardiac output of 5 l/min has been observed to have a long-standing (years) elevation of his aortic systolic pressure (160 mm Hg) and a diastolic pressure of 55 mm Hg. Match the following words and phrases to questions 104–107.
   A.   renal hypertension
   B.   normal flow
   C.   laminar flow
   D.   turbulent flow
   E.   atherosclerosis
   F.   high sympathetic nerve activity
   G.   arterial-venous fistula
   H.   aortic valve regurgitation
   I.   aortic stenosis
   J.   increased
   K.   decreased
   L.   normal

104. What is the most likely diagnosis?

Answer = H. Aortic valve regurgitation is the best choice, since it would result in a high initial stroke volume (large pulse pressure); but since much of that stroke volume returns to the left ventricle via the defective aortic valve, net cardiac output can be normal. In contrast, a patient with an arterial–venous fistula would also have a large pulse pressure, but cardiac output at rest would be very high (not **G**). A patient with aortic stenosis would not have an elevated systolic pressure or such a low diastolic blood pressure (not **H**).

105. **Upon X-ray of the heart, the size of the left ventricle would be:**

Answer = J. This heart is being overfilled by inappropriate return of blood from the aorta, which will cause the heart to be enlarged. The added work associated with the marked increase is stroke volume, which will cause the left ventricle to hypertrophy.

106. **Stroke volume of this patient would be:**

Answer = J. The initially ejected stroke volume will be very large, but most of it will return to the left ventricle via the defective valve.

107. **You would expect the mean arterial pressure to be:**

Answer = L. Mean arterial pressure is equal to one-third the pulse pressure (~35 mm Hg) plus the diastolic pressure (55 mm Hg), i.e., 90 mm Hg, which is a normal arterial pressure. Obviously, pulse pressure and systolic pressure are increased while diastolic pressure is reduced.

108. **Stroke work of the human left ventricle is likely increased by:**
     A.   severe hemorrhage
     B.   ventricular tachycardia (heart rate > 250/min)
     C.   pulmonary valve stenosis
     D.   mitral stenosis
     E.   chronic hypertension

Answer = E. Left ventricular stroke work is dependent on both stroke volume and the pressure generated to pump it. Chronic hypertension (increased blood pressure) causes the left ventricular afterload to be increased and, hence, greatly increases the work the heart has to perform to pump out the stroke volume. Hemorrhage is associated with a reduced venous return, a low blood pressure, and a sympathetically driven high heart rate, all of which lead to a decrease in both stroke volume and arterial blood pressure (afterload) and, hence, a decrease in stroke work (not **A**). Both pulmonary valve stenosis and mitral stenosis decrease the filling of the left ventricle and tend to reduce cardiac output and blood pressure, with reflex increases in heart rate; this again leads to a decrease in stroke work (not **C** or **D**). Ventricular tachycardia with very high heart rates is associated with reduced filling of the heart and a small stroke volume; and if afterload is not altered, then stroke work is greatly reduced.

109. **Which of the following is most likely seen in ventricular septal defect without cyanosis?**
     A.   a decrease in pulmonary artery pressure
     B.   a decrease in oxygen saturation of left ventricular blood
     C.   a mid-diastolic heart murmur
     D.   an increase in oxygen saturation of right ventricular blood
     E.   a decrease in right ventricular stroke work

Answer = D. With a septal defect, blood will exit the left ventricle through both the aortic valve and the septal defect. Hence, during systole (not **C**), totally oxygenated left ventricular blood (not **B**) enters the right ventricle, which leads to a large increase in oxygen saturation of right ventricular blood. As left ventricular blood enters the right ventricle via the septal defect, the volume and pressure in the right ventricle are increased, leading to an increase in right ventricular stroke volume that causes an increase in pulmonary arterial pressure (not **A**). The elevated end-diastolic volume and the increase in afterload (increased pulmonary artery pressure) lead to an increase in stroke work (not **E**).

110. **All of the following will be found in aortic stenosis *EXCEPT*:**
     A.   increased left ventricular stroke work
     B.   increased rate of rise in systolic aortic blood pressure
     C.   increased systolic pressure gradient across the aortic valve
     D.   EKG evidence of left axis deviation
     E.   a systolic ejection heart murmur

Answer = B. *Remember you are looking for the exception.* Aortic stenosis produces an increase in the work (**A**) the heart has to perform, which leads to left ventricular hypertrophy (**D**). The stenotic valve is a high-resistance site and requires a large pressure gradient to produce the flow (**C**); hence, there is a systolic ejection murmur (**E**). Because of the stenotic valve, the rate at which blood is ejected into the root of the aorta is reduced; therefore, there will be a decrease (*not* **B**) in the rate that systolic aortic blood pressure rises.

111. **Which of the following is likely to exhibit the shortest phase 4 of the cardiac action potential?**
    A. Purkinje fiber
    B. SA node cell
    C. atrial muscle
    D. ventricular muscle
    E. AV node cell

    Answer = A. The Purkinje fibers have the longest duration of the action potential and, hence, have the shortest phase 4.

112. **According to the Laplace relation for the heart, if pressure doubles and the radius of the left ventricle remains constant, what must happen to wall thickness for wall tension to remain constant?**
    A. increase 1.5-fold
    B. increase 2-fold
    C. increase 4-fold
    D. decrease 2-fold
    E. decrease 4-fold

    Answer = B. Wall tension = pressure times radius divided by wall thickness. Hence, if pressure doubles and the radius does not change, wall thickness must double in order for tension to remain constant.

113. **Movement of fluid from the capillaries to the interstitial space:**
    A. occurs because the capillary wall is only slightly permeable to fluid
    B. occurs when the balance of forces favors filtration over reabsorption
    C. requires that the capillary wall be impermeable
    D. occurs only in cases that produce edema, such as heart failure or hypertension

    Answer = B. The movement of fluid from the capillaries to the interstitium is a dynamic process that is constantly changing, depending on the moment-to-moment status of the balance of the Starling forces (hydrostatic and oncotic) causing either net filtration or net reabsorption (not **D**) at any particular site within the body. Although the permeability (not **C**) of the capillary is an important determinant of the rate of fluid movement, it does not determine the direction (not **A**).

114. **Blood flow to skeletal muscle:**
    A. accounts for approximately 70% of the cardiac output at rest
    B. is greater at rest than renal blood flow on a per-gram basis
    C. stays constant during exercise because oxygen extraction increases
    D. is elevated in chronically hypertensive patients
    E. depends primarily on local metabolic activity

    Answer = E. Skeletal muscle blood flow is determined, in large part, by the level of local metabolism that releases various products that cause local vasodilation. Hence, skeletal muscle blood flow can increase dramatically during exercise (not **C**). Skeletal muscle blood flow at rest is quite low (not **A**) and on a per-gram basis is very low in comparison to the very high kidney blood flow (not **B**). Chronic hypertension does not affect local blood flow as much as it affects the pressure needed to supply muscle with the normal blood flow (not **D**).

115. **Which of the following is most likely associated with an increase in the area under the left ventricular pressure–volume loop, left axis deviation in the EKG pattern, and a systolic ejection murmur?**
    A. mitral stenosis
    B. tricuspid stenosis
    C. aortic regurgitation
    D. pulmonic regurgitation
    E. aortic stenosis

    Answer = E. These data suggest that afterload is increased (increased area under the left ventricular pressure–volume curve), leading to ventricular hypertrophy (not **A, B,** or **D**), which causes the left axis deviation in the EKG and the systolic ejection murmur; these factors make aortic stenosis (**E**) the best choice. Mitral and tricuspid stenosis would both produce diastolic murmurs and make the left ventricle smaller than normal, if anything (not **A** or **B**). Both aortic and pulmonary regurgitation would cause diastolic murmurs (not **C** or **D**).

116. **Complete left bundle branch block is most likely associated with which of the following EKG changes?**
    A. prolonged duration of QRS complex
    B. increased amplitude of T wave
    C. lengthened ST interval
    D. prolonged P-R interval
    E. elevated ST segment

Answer = A. When a bundle is blocked, conduction of the action potential to the area supplied by that branch is slowed, causing a prolongation of the QRS complex; and, consequently, it will shorten the length of the ST segment (not **C**). Because the conduction of the action potential is spread out over time, the repolarization wave (T wave) is less synchronized and, therefore, has a lower amplitude (not **B**). The PR interval should not be altered by a direct effect of a bundle branch block (not **D**). Although the ST segment duration may be shortened, there will still be a period during which all of the ventricular muscle cells are depolarized (not **E**).

117. **Which of the following principles puts a dilated heart at a clear disadvantage?**
    A. Starling's law of the heart
    B. Poiseuille's law
    C. Fick's law
    D. Laplace's law
    E. Reynolds' number

Answer = D. The tension that the heart has to develop when its diameter is increased (and, consequently, its thickness is decreased) is greatly increased, as shown by Laplace's law (T = Pr/w, where T = wall tension, P = pressure, r = radius, and w = wall thickness). Starling's law relates the end-diastolic volume to stroke volume (not **A**); Poiseuille's law defines the determinants of flow in the vascular system (not **B**); Fick's law defines the determinants of diffusion (not **C**); and Reynolds' number helps us determine whether turbulent flow will occur.

118. **Rapid expansion of extracellular volume is compensated for by all of the following *EXCEPT*:**
    A. increased secretion of atrial natriuretic peptide
    B. reduced secretion of renin
    C. reduced secretion of vasopressin
    D. increased renal sympathetic nerve activity
    E. reduced aldosterone secretion

Answer = D. *Remember you are looking for the exception.* Rapid expansion of the extracellular compartment increases the firing rate of both low- and high-pressure baroreceptors, causing a reflex decrease in sympathetic nerve activity; this in turn contributes to the decrease in both renin (and, hence, aldosterone) and vasopressin secretion. The stretching of the atria will also directly stimulate the secretion of atrial natriuretic peptide.

119. **Drugs that block L-type calcium channels would be expected to:**
    A. increase heart rate by enhancing the firing rate of the sinoatrial node
    B. trigger vasoconstriction
    C. lower blood pressure
    D. increase the force of contraction of the heart
    E. lengthen the plateau phase of the cardiac action potential

Answer = C. Blocking the L-type calcium channels causes smooth muscle relaxation (not **B**), a slowing of the heart rate (not **A**), and a decrease in cardiac contractility (not **D**); it would also tend to shorten the plateau phase of the cardiac action potential (not **E**).

120. **The portion of the cardiac conductile system with the slowest rate of conduction is the**
    A. atrial muscle
    B. atrioventricular node
    C. bundle of His
    D. Purkinje system
    E. ventricular muscle

Answer = B. The AV node cells have the slowest conduction velocity of all of the cells in the conduction system. All of the other types of cells contain fast sodium channels and have higher conduction velocities.

121. **What effect does tetrodotoxin (TTX) have on the firing rate of isolated sinoatrial nodal cells?**
 A. increases the rate
 B. decreases the rate
 C. no change in rate

 Answer = C. Since the sinoatrial cells have no fast sodium channels, TTX has little effect on any component of the slow action potential.

Questions 122–126. These questions concern the cardiac action potential and related electrophysiological occurrences. Match the ionic events listed below (phrases A–L) to the items in questions 122–125. A phrase may be used once, twice, or not at all. Some questions may be answered by two phrases.
 A. decrease in the outward potassium current
 B. increase in the outward potassium current
 C. decrease in the inward potassium current
 D. increase in the inward potassium current
 E. decrease in the inward fast sodium current
 F. increase in the inward fast sodium current
 G. decrease in the outward fast sodium current
 H. increase in the outward fast sodium current
 I. decrease in the inward calcium current
 J. increase in the inward calcium current
 K. decrease in the outward calcium current
 L. increase in the outward calcium current

122. **The early-to-mid portion of the pacemaker potential of the sinoatrial node:**

 Answer = A (J). The slowly depolarizing pacemaker potential is produced by both a decrease in an outward potassium current (i_k) and an increase in an inward sodium/calcium current (i_f; not a listed choice) that produce the slowly depolarizing pacemaker potential. Late in phase 4, there is an increase in Ca^{2+} current.

123. **The QRS complex of the electrocardiogram:**

 Answer = F. The opening of fast sodium channels produces the rapid spread of depolarization that causes the QRS complex of the EKG.

124. **The T wave of the electrocardiogram:**

 Answer = B. The opening of potassium channels causes an increase in an outward potassium current that returns the ventricular muscle cells to their resting membrane potential; this process is the cause of the T wave.

125. **The ST segment of the EKG:**

 Answer = A and J. The ST segment of the EKG is associated with the plateau potential of the ventricular action potential; hence, it is the increased inward flow of calcium and the decreased outward flow of potassium that produce the plateau potential.

126. **The "rapid" upstroke of the sinoatrial nodal action potential:**

 Answer = J. Rather than the opening of fast sodium channels, it is the opening of calcium channels that produces the "rapid" upstroke of the sinoatrial node.

127. **Which of the following produces a decrease in the slope of phase 4 depolarization of SA node pacemaker cells?**
    A. direct application of epinephrine
    B. direct application of norepinephrine
    C. cardiac sympathetic nerve stimulation
    D. direct application of acetylcholine
    E. direct application of atropine

Answer = D. Acetylcholine (ACh) causes an increase in potassium conductance that results in a hyperpolarization of sinoatrial cell membrane potential and a decrease in the slope of the phase 4 potential. Atropine (by blocking the effect of ACh), epinephrine, norepinephrine, and stimulation of the cardiac sympathetic nerve all lead to a net increase in the slope of the diastolic depolarization.

Use Fig. 2-12 to answer questions 128–129.

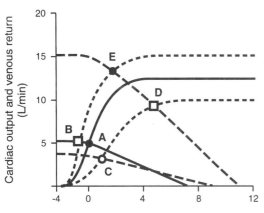

FIG. 2-12

128. **Which point would represent the expected value for cardiac output during the first 10 minutes of an angiotensin II infusion? (Assume no direct cardiac effects of angiotensin II, but that all compensatory cardiovascular systems are working.)**
    A. point A
    B. point B
    C. point C
    D. point D
    E. point E

Answer = C. Angiotensin II increases blood pressure by causing both arterial and venous vasoconstriction, which leads to a rightward and downward shift of the vascular function curve. The increase in blood pressure induces a withdrawal of sympathetic nerve activity and an increase in parasympathetic nerve activity to the heart, which depresses the cardiac function curve. Hence, point C is the logical cardiac output for a short-term infusion of angiotensin II.

129. **Point B in Fig. 2-12 could best be described as the cardiac output during:**
    A. acute volume expansion
    B. withdrawal of cardiac vagal tone
    C. moderate sustained isometric exercise
    D. left ventricular heart failure
    E. an i.v. infusion of norepinephrine

Answer = B. To go to point B requires that the event caused just the cardiac function curve to shift to the left, which is precisely what withdrawal of vagal (parasympathetic) nerve activity would do. Volume expansion would shift the vascular function curve and reflexively shift the cardiac function curve (not **A**). Sustained exercise and an infusion of norepinephrine would result in activation of sympathetic nerve activity to the heart and to the vasculature; hence, both curves would be shifted (not **C** or **E**). Heart failure would shift the cardiac function curve downward and to the right (not **D**).

130. **At a heart rate of 70 beats/min, coronary artery blood flow is greatest:**
   A. immediately after the second heart sound
   B. when dP/dt has reached its maximum
   C. immediately after the mitral valve has closed
   D. immediately after the aortic valve has opened
   E. during the rapid ejection phase of the cardiac cycle

   Answer = A. When the ventricle starts to relax and ventricular pressure falls below arterial pressure, coronary blood flow reaches its peak value. During systole (**B–E**), flow to the left ventricle is depressed by the contracting muscle.

131. **An increase in arterial pulse pressure is mostly like to be found in:**
   A. aortic insufficiency
   B. aortic stenosis
   C. mitral insufficiency
   D. mitral stenosis
   E. pulmonary insufficiency

   Answer = A. Since much of the blood pumped into the aorta returns to the left ventricle via the insufficient aortic valve, the pulse pressure is very high. Aortic stenosis impedes the ability of the left ventricle to eject blood (not **B**). Both mitral insufficiency and stenosis impede the overall filling of the left ventricle and tend to decrease pulse pressure (not **C** or **D**). Since pulmonary insufficiency tends to decrease the output of the right ventricle, it also tends to decrease filling of the left ventricle; hence, pulse pressure tends to be low (not **E**).

132. **A person with no innervation of the heart and a person with a normally innervated heart run at an identical pace. Which of the following would be greater in the person with no innervation of the heart?**
   A. blood flow to the active muscle masses
   B. venous return
   C. stroke volume
   D. cardiac output
   E. heart rate

   Answer = C. Since the denervated heart will have a smaller increase in heart rate (not **E**) than the heart of the individual with an intact nervous system, the increase in venous return caused by the vasodilation of the exercising muscle beds will produce a larger increase in end-diastolic volume and, hence, a larger increase in stroke volume in the denervated heart. The increases in cardiac output and venous return will be similar in both individuals (not **B** or **D**) because the metabolic needs of the exercising muscles are similar; i.e., the level of exercise is similar (not **A**).

133. **Closure of the aortic valve is associated with all of the following EXCEPT:**
   A. dicrotic notch on the aortic pressure wave
   B. the second heart sound
   C. relaxation of the ventricle
   D. rapid filling of the left ventricle
   E. T-wave of the EKG

   Answer = D. *Remember you are looking for the exception.* The ventricle begins to relax (**C**), as evidenced by the appearance of the T-wave of the EKG (**E**), which closes the aortic valve, causing the dicrotic notch (**A**) and the second heart sound (**B**). The opening of the mitral valve (*not* **D**) is associated with the rapid filling of the left ventricle.

134. **A decrease in cardiac output due to a large hemorrhage that results in a sustained decrease in arterial blood pressure is likely to be associated with a decrease in all of the following EXCEPT:**
   A. parasympathetic nerve activity
   B. venous pressure
   C. mean systemic filling pressure
   D. release of renin
   E. plasma pH

Answer = D. *Remember you are looking for the exception.* The sustained and large decrease in arterial blood pressure leads to an increase in renin release (*not* **D**). A large hemorrhage associated with a sustained decrease in arterial blood pressure suggests that reflexive compensation for the blood loss is not adequate and, hence, that venous pressure (**B**) and mean systemic filling (**C**) pressure have not returned to normal. The baroreflex leads to a decrease in parasympathetic nerve activity (**A**). The inability to adequately perfuse peripheral tissues leads to the production of lactic acidosis (**E**).

135. **A generalized systemic inflammatory condition (known as anaphylaxis) will cause all of the following *EXCEPT*:**
   A. increased sympathetic nerve activity
   B. arterial vasodilatation
   C. decreased blood volume
   D. protein accumulation in the interstitial fluid
   E. increased level of atrial natriuretic factor

   Answer = E. *Remember you are looking for the exception.* In anaphylactic shock, peripheral vasodilation (**B**) and leakage of protein into the interstitial fluid compartment (**D**) lead to loss of fluid from the vascular compartment (**C**) and activation of the baroreflex (**A**) and, hence, to the collapse of the vascular system. The very low venous pressure and, hence, atrial pressure lead to a decrease, not an increase, in atrial natriuretic factor secretion (*not* **E**).

136. **All patients in shock are suffering from an inadequate cardiac output. The intravenous infusion of fluid to help restore blood pressure is logical for all types of shock *EXCEPT*:**
   A. anaphylactic shock
   B. cardiogenic shock
   C. loss of autonomic control due to a CNS lesion
   D. hemorrhagic shock
   E. shock induced by severe burns

   Answer = B. *Remember you are looking for the exception.* In cardiogenic shock, it is the inability of the acutely failing heart to supply an adequate cardiac output that produces the shock, whereas the other types of shock are associated with a collapse of the vascular system. Infusion of saline will often help restore the inadequate vascular volume in all of these patients except those suffering from cardiogenic shock. Patients with cardiogenic shock can be harmed by the infusion of saline because an additional increase in preload might acutely further compromise the already failing heart.

137. **All of the following are likely to occur in hemorrhagic shock *EXCEPT*:**
   A. a rise in total peripheral resistance
   B. hypotension and tachycardia
   C. increased plasma levels of angiotensin
   D. a decrease in hematocrit
   E. increased mean systemic filling pressure

   Answer = E. *Remember you are looking for the exception.* Activation of the sympathetic nervous system (**A**), mobilization of interstitial fluid (producing a decrease in hematocrit; **D**), and secretion of vasoactive peptides (**C**) caused by a severe decrease in blood volume and blood pressure (**B**) will tend to minimize the decrease (*not* **E**) in mean systemic filling pressure. During hemorrhagic shock, these reflexes are not able to increase the mean systemic filling pressure above that found before the hemorrhage until the fluid volume has been restored.

138. **Left ventricular heart failure due to a stenotic aortic valve is associated with:**
   A. eccentric hypertrophy
   B. pulmonary edema
   C. decreased pulmonary wedge pressure
   D. expanded jugular neck veins when the patient is in the upright position
   E. increased diastolic compliance

   Answer = B. When the left ventricle fails, blood accumulates within the left atrium and pulmonary circulation. This causes an increase in pulmonary capillary pressure and, therefore, pulmonary wedge pressure (not **C**); hence, pulmonary edema will occur. Unless the right heart is also involved, the neck veins should not be distended since no accumulation of fluid in the systemic circulation has occurred (not **D**). The constant pumping against an increased afterload leads to a concentric hypertrophy (not **A**), which is associated with an elevated stroke volume at a normal or reduced afterload. The thickened ventricular walls that reduce the internal diameter of the heart also cause serious diastolic filling problems associated with the decrease in diastolic compliance (not **E**).

139. **In a patient suffering from heart failure induced by a stenotic pulmonary valve, all of the following procedures or treatments might be beneficial *EXCEPT*:**
   A.   administering digitalis
   B.   administering a diuretic
   C.   administering a catecholamine
   D.   administering an angiotensin-converting enzyme inhibitor
   E.   placing the patient on a low-salt diet

Answer = C. *Remember you are looking for the exception.* A stenotic pulmonary valve will lead to congestive heart failure because the right heart can only pump a normal cardiac output at a markedly elevated right atrial pressure. The increase in atrial pressure is associated with a parallel increase in venous and capillary pressure that causes the formation of dependent edema and venous congestion, especially in the splanchnic circulation. Administering catecholamines would tend to increase mean systemic filling pressure and lead to a further increase in venous congestion (*not* **C**). Digitalis will help the failing heart by increasing its contractility (**A**). Administering a diuretic or placing the patient on a low-salt diet will decrease the blood volume and, hence, help reduce the edema and venous congestion (**B** and **E**). Administration of an angiotensin-converting enzyme inhibitor will lower blood pressure and increase cardiac output (**D**), which will reduce the venous congestion and decrease the work load of the failing heart.

140. **In an arterial blood sample, which of the following would be expected to decrease during hemorrhagic shock?**
   A.   epinephrine
   B.   angiotensin II
   C.   anion gap
   D. P_{CO_2}
   E.   cortisol

Answer = D. The hypotension and reduced mean systemic filling pressure induced by the hemorrhage activate both high- and low-pressure baroreceptors that cause reflex increases, not decreases, in the adrenal secretion of epinephrine (not **A**) and cortisol (not **E**) and in the renal secretion of renin (angiotensin II; not **B**). In addition, reduced blood pressure to the carotid baroreceptors stimulates respiration, which decreases the P_{CO_2}. The reduced perfusion of peripheral tissues leads to the production of lactic acidosis, which causes the anion gap to increase, not decrease (not **C**), and contributes to the hyperventilation that results in a decrease in P_{CO_2}.

141. **At rest, patients with a mild form of right ventricular congestive heart failure will have:**
   A.   hypotension
   B.   elevated central venous pressure
   C.   reduced cardiac output
   D.   increased cardiac reserve
   E.   elevated left atrial pressure

Answer = B. Patients at rest with a mild form of congestive right ventricular heart failure will most likely have a normal arterial blood pressure (not **A**) and cardiac output (not **C**); but their ability to increase cardiac output, i.e., cardiac reserve, is reduced (not **D**). Central venous pressure (and right atrial pressure) will be elevated because (by definition) the right ventricle is failing to generate a normal cardiac output at a normal filling pressure. Since cardiac output at rest is normal, there is no reason for left atrial pressure to be elevated (not **E**).

RESPIRATORY PHYSIOLOGY

1. **Pulmonary edema forms preferentially at the lung base because:**
   A. P_{O_2} is less at the base
   B. P_{CO_2} is higher at the base
   C. intravascular pressure is greater at the base
   D. lymphatic drainage is less at the base
   E. vascular resistance is higher at the base

   Answer = C. Because we are upright, the hydrostatic fluid column within the thoracic cavity causes the venous and thus the capillary hydrostatic pressure at the base of our lungs to be higher than that at the apex; thus, the safety factor preventing edema formation is much smaller at the base. Because of the decrease in V_A/Q as you go from the apex to the base of the lung, both **A** and **B** are correct statements but have little to do with the tendency to produce edema. If anything, the lower PA_{O_2} might tend to cause arterial vasoconstriction, which would tend to counteract the increase in hydrostatic forces. Actually, lymph flow is higher at the base because more filtration is occurring (not **D**). The vascular resistance at the base is lower because the higher intravascular pressure mechanically dilates the pulmonary vascular bed (not **E**).

2. **If PA_{O_2} = 200 mm Hg and PA_{CO_2} = 20 mm Hg, what is PI_{O_2}?**
   A. 180 mm Hg
   B. 225 mm Hg
   C. 153 mm Hg
   D. 250 mm Hg
   E. 32 mm Hg

   Answer = B. The inspired partial pressure of O_2 must be greater than the alveolar O_2. The PA_{O_2} = PI_{O_2} − PA_{CO_2}/R. Using an R value of 0.80 (a reasonable estimate), we divide the PA_{CO_2} of 20 mm Hg by 0.8. This = 25 mm Hg. Add the PA_{O_2} of 200 mm Hg, and the PI_{O_2} = **225 mm Hg**.

3. **An increase in Pa_{CO_2} is caused by:**
   A. decreased diffusing capacity for CO
   B. increased V_{CO_2}/V_A
   C. increased shunt fraction
   D. V_A/Q mismatch
   E. decreased physiological dead space

   Answer = B. An increase in arterial P_{CO_2} is caused by either an increase in production or a decrease in ventilation; hence, when V_{CO_2}/V_A increases (**B**), there is either an increase in production (V_{CO_2}) or a decrease in ventilation (1/V_A). Because CO_2 is ~20 times as permeable as O_2, arterial P_{CO_2} is not affected by changes in diffusing capacity for CO (not **A**), which gives an index of the permeability of the lungs to O_2. Shunts and V_A/Q mismatch affect arterial P_{O_2} but have little effect on arterial P_{CO_2}. (not **C** or **D**) A decrease in dead space would tend to increase alveolar ventilation and thus decrease arterial P_{CO_2} (not **E**).

4. **The normal pattern of phrenic nerve activity is generated by impulses from the:**
   A. pons
   B. cerebrum
   C. medulla
   D. cerebellum
   E. hypothalamus

   Answer = C. This is a "recall" question.

5. **Contraction of the diaphragm would cause:**
    A.   a decrease in the volume of air in the lungs
    B.   an increase in airways pressure
    C.   a decrease in intrapleural pressure
    D.   movement of the ribs toward the spinal cord
    E.   a decrease in intra-abdominal pressure

    Answer = C.   Contraction of the diaphragm decreases intrapleural pressure and creates a pressure gradient for air to flow into the lungs, causing them to expand (not **A**). Pressure throughout the lung and bronchial tree is decreased (not **B**). As the lungs expand, the ribs are pushed up and away from the spinal cord (not **D**). Finally, the diaphragm contraction pushes down on the abdominal cavity, causing intra-abdominal pressure to increase (not **E**).

6. **The V_A of an 80-inch tall, 200-pound man with a tidal volume of 700 ml and a breathing rate of 20 breaths/min is about:**
    A.   140,000 ml/min
    B.   12,400 ml/min
    C.   4,000 ml/min
    D.   10,000 ml/min
    E.   14,000 ml/min

    Answer = D.   Since the man weighs 200 pounds, his dead space is ~200 ml and his tidal volume is 700 ml. His V_A is 500 ml (700 ml − 200 ml) times 20 breaths/min = **10,000 ml/min**.

7. **On the accompanying compliance curve of a lung, the middle of expiration is:**

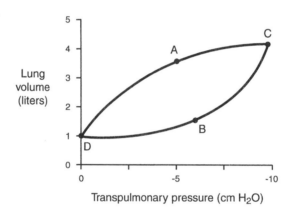

    FIG. 3-1

    A.   A
    B.   B
    C.   C
    D.   D

    Answer = A.   Points D and C are the resting value and the end inspiration and, hence, the beginning of expiration (**C**). Inspection of the hysteresis curve for the lung in any textbook indicates that point A occurs during the middle of expiration.

8. **All of the following are true of V_A and Q in the lungs of a healthy, standing individual *EXCEPT*:**
    A.   Q is greater at the base than at the apex
    B. V_A is greater at the apex than at the base
    C. V_A/Q is greater at the apex than at the base
    D.   differences in V_A/Q from apex to base are less during exercise
    E.   the V_A/Q distribution causes higher PA_{O_2} at the apex than at the base

    Answer = B.   *Remember you are looking for the exception.* Recall that both V_A and Q increase (**A**) as you go from the apex to the base, but Q increases more than V_A; this accounts for V_A/Q being greater at the apex than at the base (not **C**). Regional differences in V_A/Q are affected by posture and by the magnitude of the cardiac output and become much smaller during exercise (not **D**). The higher V_A/Q occurring at the apex will cause the PA_{O_2} to be higher (not **E**).

9. **If the P_{O_2} in a blood sample is not changed, which of the following will cause a decrease in the content of oxygen in the blood?**
   A. an increase in 2,3 diphosphoglycerate (DPG)
   B. a decrease in temperature
   C. an increase in pH
   D. a decrease in P_{CO_2}
   E. an increase in hemoglobin

   Answer = A. 2,3 DPG shifts the oxygen dissociation curve to the right. All of the other changes cause the curve to be shifted to the left, which means an increase in the oxygen content.

10. **Most of the lung volume is in the:**
    A. alveoli
    B. bronchioles
    C. segmental bronchi
    D. lobar bronchi
    E. trachea

    Answer = A. Like the capillaries of the vascular system, the alveoli contain most of the air in the lung.

11. **If the water vapor pressure in saturated air is 47 mm Hg when barometric pressure is 760 mm Hg and the temperature is 37 C, what is the water vapor pressure at 380 mm Hg in saturated air at the same temperature?**
    A. 47 mm Hg
    B. 23.5 mm Hg
    C. 35.3 mm Hg
    D. 11.8 mm Hg
    E. Insufficient information is available to answer.

    Answer = A. Water vapor pressure is independent of the barometric pressure; once air is warmed to 37 C and saturated with water vapor, it is 47 mm Hg.

12. **One hundred percent O_2 administration will reverse hypoxemia in all of the following conditions *EXCEPT*:**
    A. arterial–venous shunt
    B. V_A/Q mismatch
    C. hypoventilation
    D. decreased D_{CO}
    E. loss of cabin pressure in an airplane

    Answer = A. *Remember you are looking for the exception.* Because gas exchange can never occur in the blood that is shunted over to the venous side, no amount of oxygen will correct hypoxia resulting from an A–V shunt. The hypoxia in all of the other conditions will be improved by administration of 100% O_2.

13. **To accomplish a metabolic compensation for a respiratory acidosis, there would be:**
    A. an increase in plasma bicarbonate
    B. a decrease in plasma bicarbonate
    C. an increase in Pa_{CO_2}
    D. a decrease in Pa_{CO_2}
    E. a decrease in hemoglobin concentration

    Answer = A. Respiratory acidosis is caused by an increase in Pa_{CO_2}. To bring the ratio between CO_2 and HCO_3 back toward normal, the kidney generates new bicarbonate, thus increasing the plasma bicarbonate and bringing the pH back toward 7.4.

14. **If one were to inflate the lungs of a lightly anesthetized adult human to 2 liters over FRC:**
    A. a forced expiration would occur within 10 sec
    B. no breathing movements would occur after 10 sec
    C. rapid inspiratory and expiratory movements would occur within 10 sec
    D. inspiration would continue for about 1 more liter
    E. airways resistance would be increased from the value at FRC

Answer = B. A 2-liter forced inspiration would initiate the Hering-Breuer inflation reflex even in an adult; hence, inspiratory activity would stop (not **C** or **D**). There is no forced expiratory component to this reflex (not **B**). Actually, airways resistance is decreased as the lungs inflate (not **E**).

15. **All else being equal, which of the following gases will equilibrate most quickly across an alveolar membrane?**
    A. O_2
    B. He
    C. CO
    D. CO_2
    E. All gases diffuse at the same rate.

    Answer = D. CO_2 is the most permeable. He is very impermeable and is used to measure total lung volume. CO is used as a tracer for the permeability of the pulmonary membranes to O_2, which is about 20 times less permeable than CO_2 (not **A**, **B**, or **C**).

16. **Airways resistance:**
    A. is greater during inspiration than during expiration
    B. is lower when near FRC than when near TLC
    C. is increased by sympathetic stimulation
    D. is decreased in asthma
    E. is increased by histamine

    Answer = E. Histamine does cause bronchoconstriction. The vascular bed of the lung is sensitive to transmembrane forces; any time the lung is expanded, so is the diameter of the vessels and vice versa (not **A** or **B**). Sympathetic stimulation dilates the pulmonary vasculature (not **C**). Asthma is associated with bronchoconstriction (not **D**).

17. **The equilibrium point of the lungs and chest wall is at:**
    A. residual volume
    B. tidal volume
    C. total lung capacity
    D. functional residual capacity
    E. vital capacity

    Answer = D. By definition, the equilibrium point is called functional residual capacity (FRC).

18. **Which of the following is transformed to the active state during passage through the pulmonary circulation?**
    A. angiotensin I
    B. norepinephrine
    C. vasopressin
    D. endothelin I
    E. prostaglandin E_2

    Answer = A. The lung is rich in converting enzymes; hence, angiotensin I is converted to angiotensin II. The lung has little effect on norepinephrine and vasopressin (not **B** or **C**). Endothelin I and prostaglandin E_2 can be produced and released by the lung, but they are released in an active form (not **D** or **E**).

19. **Occlusion of the left pulmonary artery would cause:**
    A. an increase in shunt fraction
    B. an increase in PI_{O_2}
    C. an increase in anatomical dead space
    D. a decrease in anatomical dead space
    E. an increase in physiological dead space

    Answer = E. Since the left lung is now receiving air but not blood, the air in the left bronchial tree is not exposed to gas exchange (increase in physiological dead space). Shunt fraction is not affected by occlusion of the arterial supply (not **A**). Inspired oxygen is not affected by what happens in the lung (not **B**). Anatomical dead space will not change (not **C** or **D**).

20. **All of the following will cause an increase in pulmonary vascular resistance *EXCEPT*:**
    A.   a decrease in Pa_{O_2}
    B.   a decrease in Pa_{CO_2}
    C.   a decrease in FI_{O_2}
    D.   a decrease in cardiac output
    E.   a decrease in arterial pH

    Answer = B. *Remember you are looking for the exception.* An increase in Pa_{CO_2} causes pulmonary vasoconstriction (not **B**), while factors or situations that cause a decrease in P_{O_2} or pH will cause pulmonary vasoconstriction (**A**, **C**, and **E**). Pulmonary vascular resistance is inversely proportional to the cardiac output (**D**) since the increase in flow passively dilates the pulmonary vessels.

21. **Which of the following is always true of normal blood?**
    A.   An increase in P_{CO_2} causes an increase in Cl^- inside red blood cells.
    B.   An increase in P_{CO_2} causes a decrease in HCO_3^- inside red blood cells.
    C.   A decrease in P_{CO_2} causes a decrease in O_2 bound to hemoglobin.
    D.   The P_{CO_2} inside the red blood cell is higher than in the plasma.
    E.   The P_{O_2} inside the red blood cell is higher than in the plasma.

    Answer = A. An increase in Pa_{CO_2} causes an increase in the formation of carbonic acid inside the red blood cells because carbonic anhydrase is present in abundance. The carbonic acid dissociates to hydrogen ions and bicarbonate (increases bicarbonate concentration; not **B**). The latter exits the red blood cells in exchange for extracellular chloride; hence, $[Cl^-]$ inside the red blood cell increases (the chloride shift). A decrease in P_{CO_2} causes a increase in O_2 bound to hemoglobin (the Bohr effect; not **C**). The P_{CO_2} and P_{O_2} can both be higher or lower than what is found in plasma depending on the location in the vascular system. If the O_2 or CO_2 is diffusing into the red blood cells, then the plasma concentration of these gases will be higher than that in the RBC and vice versa (not **D** or **E**).

22. **When people are very cold, their lips and nail beds may turn blue. This occurs because:**
    A.   the rate of oxygen removal from the blood is increased
    B.   skin metabolism is decreased
    C.   the oxygen dissociation curve is shifted to the left by a decrease in temperature
    D.   the blood pH is increased by a decrease in temperature
    E.   deoxygenated hemoglobin has a different three-dimensional structure than oxygenated hemoglobin

    Answer = E. Because of circulatory stagnation and the continued, albeit very slow, rate of metabolism, deoxygenated hemoglobin accumulates. Because it has a different three-dimensional structure than oxygenated hemoglobin, it changes the capillary beds from red to blue in appearance. Choice **A** is the opposite of what occurs at a low temperature. Choice **B** is true but not related to the tissue beds' taking on a blue color. Choices **C** and **D** are true; but, because they tend to increase the oxygenated hemoglobin concentration, both actually counteract the tendency of capillary beds to "turn blue."

23. **During acclimation to altitude:**
    A.   the sensitivity of carotid bodies to hypoxia increases
    B.   the sensitivity of central chemoreceptors to hypoxia increases
    C.   the sensitivity of carotid sinuses to hypoxia increases
    D.   the HCO_3^- concentration in the blood increases
    E.   the HCO_3^- concentration in the brain decreases

    Answer = E. Acclimation to high altitude involves a gradual decrease in HCO_3^- in both plasma (not **D**) and CSF (brain), with consequential normalization of the CSF and plasma pH. The decrease in HCO_3^- allows for a greater decrease in P_{CO_2} by removing the inhibitory effect of the CSF-induced alkalosis. The sensitivity of the carotid bodies to a decrease in P_{O_2} is very stable (not **A**). Neither the central chemoreceptors (not **B**) nor the carotid sinuses (not **C**) act as oxygen sensors.

24. Which of the following arterial gases and pH most likely were obtained from a person who arrived at an altitude of 10,000 ft. 30 min before the sample was taken?

	P_{O_2}	P_{CO_2}	pH
A.	55	36	7.42
B.	70	20	7.42
C.	33	50	7.28
D.	70	20	7.53
E.	55	25	7.53

Answer = A. The initial response to high altitude involves a P_{O_2}-induced hyperventilation that is dampened by the pursuant increase in both peripheral and central pH. Hence, **A** is the best choice. Choice **B** is what might be expected following acclimation to high altitude. Choice **C** is not logical because a decrease in P_{CO_2} should occur. Choices **D** and **E** are not logical because the alkalosis would prevent that large an increase in ventilation.

25. Chronic severe hypoxia would be expected to cause or lead to all of the following *EXCEPT*:
    A. pulmonary hypertension
    B. right ventricular hypertrophy
    C. increase in mean circulatory filling pressure
    D. decrease in right ventricular end diastolic pressure
    E. increase in hematocrit

Answer = D. *Remember you are looking for the exception.* Severe hypoxia causes pulmonary vasoconstriction (i.e., pulmonary hypertension) that increases the afterload on the right ventricle, causing right ventricular hypertrophy. Furthermore, the increase in afterload causes the preload to increase (i.e., right ventricular end diastolic pressure). The increase in ventricular preload causes an increase in venous filling and, hence, increases mean circulatory filling pressure. There also will be a tendency for fluid to shift out of the vascular system, causing some hemoconcentration as well as stimulation of red blood cell production. Recall that any time cardiac output is impinged upon, there will be a tendency for fluid (salt and water) retention, which will also contribute to the increase in mean circulatory filling pressure (**C**), in right ventricular end diastolic pressure, and in hematocrit (**E**).

26. Which of the following would cause the greatest immediate increase in V_A?
    A. an increase in arterial pressure to 150 mm Hg evoked by i.v. injection of saline
    B. ventilation with 10% O_2
    C. ventilation with 10% CO_2
    D. injection of mild acid to decrease arterial pH to 7.30
    E. ventilation with 80% N_2, 20% O_2

Answer = C. The most physiologically important stimulus to ventilation is P_{CO_2}; hence, increasing the inspired CO_2 from 0% to 10% (~ mm Hg) would produce a near-maximal stimulation of ventilation. Choice **A** would decrease ventilation. Choice **B** would not reduce PO enough to cause a significant stimulation of ventilation. Choice **D** is not nearly as potent a signal as Choice **B**, whereas Choice **E** is basically room air.

27. All of the following are true of pulmonary surfactant *EXCEPT* that it:
    A. floats on water
    B. is lipoproteinaceous
    C. is formed in alveolar type II cells
    D. decreases lung compliance
    E. is insufficient in premature babies

Answer = D. *Remember you are looking for the exception.* Pulmonary surfactant increases, not decreases, compliance. All of the other statements are true.

28. In an individual with an obstructive ventilatory defect, all of the following would be increased *EXCEPT*:
    A. TLC
    B. FRC
    C. FEV_1
    D. RV
    E. airways resistance

Answer = C. *Remember you are looking for the exception.* FEV_1 is decreased because the dynamic compression of the airways (airways resistance is increased; **E**) makes it hard to move air out of the lung. The loss of elastic recoil of the lung that is associated with obstructive defects causes TLC and FRC to increase. With the increase in FRC, RV must also increase.

29. If the barometric pressure is 300 mm Hg, the PI_{O_2} of a healthy subject will be:
    A. 63 mm Hg
    B. 53 mm Hg
    C. 3 mm Hg
    D. 13 mm Hg
    E. 45 mm Hg

Answer = B. Correct for the partial pressure of H_2O ($300 - 47$ mm Hg $= 253$ mm Hg total gas pressure). Second, O_2 equals 21% of the gas, so 253 mm Hg $\times 0.21 = $ **53 mm Hg**.

30. According to Fick's Law, if the partial pressure difference across a membrane does not change but both the surface area and thickness are doubled, the rate of transfer of the gas across the membrane will:
    A. be halved
    B. be doubled
    C. increase 4-fold
    D. decrease 4-fold
    E. not change

Answer = E. Recall that Fick's Law of diffusion states that the rate of diffusion is directly proportional to the partial pressure gradient (stays constant), directly proportional to the surface area (doubled), and inversely proportional to the thickness of the membrane (doubled). The changes in the latter two factors cancel each other out, and no net change should occur.

31. Which of the following changes in P_{O_2} would have the greatest effect on the amount of O_2 (ml O_2/100 ml) in the blood?
    A. from 0 mm Hg to 20 mm Hg
    B. from 20 mm Hg to 40 mm Hg
    C. from 50 mm Hg to 70 mm Hg
    D. from 80 mm Hg to 100 mm Hg
    E. from 100 mm Hg to 150 mm Hg

Answer = B. First, recall the sigmoid shape of the normal hemoglobin–oxygen dissociation curve, with the steepest part of the curve between 20 and 40 mm Hg P_{O_2}. Above a P_{O_2} of 50 mm Hg, the curve is quite flat; whereas below a P_{O_2} of 20 mm Hg, the curve is definitely less steep. Hence, a change in P_{O_2} from 20 to 40 mm Hg will cause the greatest change in O_2 content.

32. If a person with $PA_{O_2} = 125$ mm Hg and $PA_{CO_2} = 20$ mm Hg doubles V_A without changing metabolic rate, PA_{O_2} will become:
    A. 75 mm Hg
    B. 110 mm Hg
    C. 115 mm Hg
    D. 132 mm Hg
    E. 138 mm Hg

Answer = E. First, PA_{O_2} will increase because the person is going to hyperventilate. Since PA_{CO_2} is determined by the rate of CO_2 production divided by V_A, PA_{CO_2} will decrease to 10 mm Hg. Based on the alveolar gas equation (assuming that R = 0.8), 10 mm Hg (PA_{CO_2})/0.8 = ~12.5 mm Hg increase in PA_{O_2}. Subtract this from the inspired O_2 of 150 mm Hg (125 mm Hg + [20/0.8 = 25 mm Hg] = 150 mm Hg inspired O_2), and the new PA_{O_2} is ~**138 mm Hg**.

33. An individual has a residual volume of 2 liters, a vital capacity of 6 liters, and a functional residual capacity of 3 liters. What is the total lung capacity?
   A. 3 liters
   B. 4 liters
   C. 8 liters
   D. 9 liters
   E. 11 liters

   Answer = C. Total lung volume is vital capacity plus residual volume (6 + 2 liters = 8 liters). FRC is the volume of the lung when the glottis is open and the chest wall is relaxed.

34. All of the following are true of pulmonary vascular resistance *EXCEPT* that it:
   A. increases with increasing cardiac output
   B. increases with decreasing Pa_{O_2}
   C. increases with increasing Pa_{CO_2}
   D. is greater at the top than at the bottom of the lungs
   E. is more affected by alveolar gases than by blood gases

   Answer = A. *Remember you are looking for the exception.* Pulmonary vascular resistance decreases as cardiac output increases because the increase in vascular pressure causes the diameter of the vessels to increase (*not* A). All of the other choices are true.

35. FEF 25–75% (MMFR) is a reflection of:
   A. lung compliance only
   B. airways resistance only
   C. both lung compliance and airways resistance
   D. expiratory muscle force
   E. CO_2 retention

   Answer = C. Expiratory muscle force has little impact on FEF 25–75% since outflow rate is effort-limited. FEF 25–75% is determined by both lung compliance and the airways resistance.

36. A patient has the following blood gases and pH: Pa_{CO_2} = 64 mm Hg, Pa_{CO_2} = 62 mm Hg, pH = 7.36. Which of the following best fits these data?
   A. respiratory compensation for hypoxemia
   B. respiratory compensation for metabolic alkalosis
   C. metabolic compensation for respiratory acidosis
   D. uncompensated metabolic acidosis
   E. uncompensated respiratory acidosis

   Answer = C. An acidosis (pH = 7.36) with an increase in Pa_{CO_2} (Pa_{CO_2} = 62 mm Hg) indicates a primary respiratory problem. Since the pH of the patient is about normal, the kidneys have had time to generate new bicarbonate to compensation for the respiratory acidosis.

37. All of the following can be measured with just an air-filled spirometer *EXCEPT*:
   A. FRC
   B. FEV_1
   C. FVC
   D. tidal volume
   E. FEF 25–75% (MMFR)

   Answer = A. *Remember you are looking for the exception.* To measure FRC (functional residual capacity) you need to know the total lung volume, which requires the use of some technique such as N_2 washout or dilution of He to measure the volume of air remaining in the lung at the end of a forced expiration. All of the other factors are measured by a spirometer.

38. A patient has the following blood gases and pH:
Pa_{O_2} = 48 mm Hg
Pa_{CO_2} = 43 mm Hg
pH = 7.38
The patient was placed on a ventilator and given 100% O_2. The blood gases became:
Pa_{O_2} = 68 mm Hg
Pa_{CO_2} = 36 mm Hg
pH = 7.41
You should conclude that the patient's primary (i.e., most severe) problem is:
A. hypoventilation
B. shunt
C. V_A/Q mismatch
D. an obstructive ventilatory defect
E. anemia

Answer = B. The patient showed only minor improvement in Pa_{O_2}, despite the fact that the Pa_{CO_2} was reduced after the patient was placed on the ventilator. This latter finding shows that alveolar ventilation was increased by the ventilation. Hence, a large fraction (a shunt) of blood was not being exposed to the 100% O_2. The normal Pa_{CO_2} proves that the patient was not hypoventilating (not A); the increase in inspired O_2 should have increased the Pa_{O_2} if V_A/Q mismatch (or an obstructive ventilatory defect were the problem (not C or D). Anemia may reduce the content of O_2, but it should not reduce the Pa_{CO_2} (not E).

39. A diver is breathing 10% O_2 at a pressure of 1,500 mm Hg. The diver's body temperature is 37 C, and Pa_{CO_2} = 32 mm Hg. What is the Pa_{O_2}?
A. 63 mm Hg
B. 105 mm Hg
C. 110 mm Hg
D. 113 mm Hg
E. 145 mm Hg

Answer = B. First correct the pressure of the gas for the vapor pressure of water (1,500 mm Hg − 47 mm Hg = 1453 mm Hg); then calculate the partial pressure of oxygen (0.10 × 1,453 mm Hg = 145 mm Hg). Now use the alveolar gas equation:
Pa_{O_2} = inspired O_2 − Pa_{CO_2}/R = 145 − 32 mm Hg/0.8 = 105 mm Hg

40. Bacteria penetrating the respiratory zone of otherwise healthy lungs are removed by:
A. cilia
B. white blood cells
C. lymphocytes
D. macrophages
E. platelets

Answer = D. Bacteria that penetrate the respiratory zone (having escaping the mucus and cilia action along the bronchial tree) are engulfed by macrophages.

41. A 130-pound Olympic racer at the end of the Super G has a tidal volume of 2,500 ml and a breathing rate of 25 breaths/min. What is the racer's alveolar ventilation (to the nearest l/min)?
A. 6 liters/min
B. 9 liters/min
C. 59 liters/min
D. 62 liters/min
E. 63 liters/min

Answer = C. Alveolar ventilation is tidal volume minus dead space volume times breathing rate: 2,500 ml/breath − 130 ml/breath = 2,370 ml/breath × 25 breaths/min = 59.3 liters/min. Dead space is approximately equal to 1 ml per pound of body weight.

42. **Respiratory compensation for metabolic acidosis occurs as a result of effects of pH on:**
   A.   peripheral chemoreceptors only
   B.   central chemoreceptors only
   C.   both central and peripheral chemoreceptors
   D.   pontine chemoreceptors
   E.   carotid baroreceptors

   Answer = C. Both the central and peripheral chemoreceptors are sensitive to pH. Choices **D** and **E** are not chemoreceptors.

43. **The apneustic center is:**
   A.   located in the medulla and provides inspiratory drive
   B.   located in the medulla and provides expiratory drive
   C.   located in the pons and provides inspiratory drive
   D.   located in the pons and provides expiratory drive
   E.   located in the hypothalamus and provides expiratory drive

   Answer = C. This is a "recall" question.

44. **Which of the following would you expect to find in an individual who has lived at 10,000 feet above sea level for three weeks?**
   A.   increased CSF pH
   B.   decreased CSF pH
   C.   decreased plasma pH
   D.   decreased CSF bicarbonate concentration
   E.   increased CSF bicarbonate concentration

   Answer = D. A patient acclimatized to high altitude would be expected to have a near-normal arterial (not **C**) and CSF pH (not **A** or **B**); but, because of the decrease in Pa_{CO_2} (induced by the hyperventilation caused by the hypoxia), the bicarbonate concentration is reduced (not **E**).

45. **The greatest flow during forced expiration occurs near total lung capacity:**
   A.   due to dynamic compression of airways
   B.   due to maximal diaphragmatic force
   C.   because minimal intraalveolar pressure is achieved
   D.   because greatest intrapleural pressure achieved
   E.   because maximal surface tension is achieved

   Answer = E. The maximal surface tension developed by the alveoli being at their largest size produces the greatest force for expiration without contributing to the dynamic compression of the airways (not **A**), which reduces flow. Diaphragmatic forces (not **B**) lead to higher intrapleural pressure, which causes dynamic compression of the airways. Maximal intra-alveolar pressures (not **C**) are achieved. Choice **D** leads to dynamic compression of the airways.

46. **A patient transported to your emergency room is unconscious and cyanotic; the initial blood gases and pH are $Pa_{O_2} = 36$ mm Hg, $Pa_{CO_2} = 90$ mm Hg, pH = 7.01. You place the patient on a ventilator with room air, a tidal volume of 800 ml/breath, and a rate of 10 breaths/min. The second blood gas reading, 10 min later, is: $Pa_{O_2} = 101$ mm Hg, $Pa_{CO_2} = 36$ mm Hg, pH = 7.30. This history is consistent with:**
   A.   carbon monoxide poisoning
   B.   adult respiratory distress syndrome
   C.   diabetes mellitus
   D.   barbiturate poisoning
   E.   emphysema

   Answer = D. This patient has acute respiratory acidosis caused, for some reason, by hypoventilation. By depressing the respiratory centers, barbiturates cause a person to become unconscious and suppress ventilation enough to cause cyanosis. Simply ventilating such a patient will rapidly improve the blood gas profile and relieve most of the acidosis. The remaining acidosis might be due to a lactic acidosis caused by the prolonged hypoxia and is slower to be corrected. Carbon monoxide poisoning would not be associated with reduced Pa_{O_2} (not **A**). Adult respiratory distress syndrome is a severe respiratory problem that cannot be corrected simply by placing a patient on a ventilator (not **B**). A patient with diabetes mellitus should have a metabolic acidosis, not a respiratory acidosis (not **C**). Simply ventilating a patient who has emphysema would not be able to correct the severe hypoxia, nor would you expect that the patient's CO_2 would be quite so high or the pH quite so low (not **E**).

47. A decrease in blood pressure stimulates breathing by effects on:
   A. the carotid bodies
   B. the central chemosensitive cells
   C. the gamma efferents
   D. the cerebrum
   E. the carotid sinuses

   Answer = E.   The carotid sinuses reflexly affect ventilation; a decrease in blood pressure to the sinuses stimulates breathing.

48. A liquid-ventilated lung compared to a gas-ventilated lung:
   A. has reduced airways resistance
   B. has pronounced hysteresis
   C. is more compliant
   D. requires greater pressure to inflate
   E. has increased residual volume

   Answer = C.   Inspection of the static pressure–volume curve for lungs inflated with air or saline clearly shows that the liquid-ventilated lung is more compliant. Saline has a higher viscosity than air; hence, airways resistance will be higher (not A). Without the surface tension of the gas–liquid junction, hysteresis is much less in the saline-filled lung (not B). By definition of compliance, the liquid-filled lung requires less pressure to inflate (not D). The elastic forces of the lung are not affected by filling the lung with saline. Since residual volume of the lung is determined by the elastic properties of the lung and thorax, liquid-ventilated lungs should have a similar residual volume (not E).

49. If the V_A of an individual with a Pa_{O_2} of 100 mm Hg and a Pa_{CO_2} of 40 mm Hg were doubled, Pa_{O_2} would become:

   A. 50 mm Hg
   B. 80 mm Hg
   C. 125 mm Hg
   D. 150 mm Hg
   E. 200 mm Hg

   Answer = C.   Assuming that there is no change in CO_2 production and the R value is 0.8, a doubling of V_A would cause Pa_{CO_2} to decrease from 40 to 20 mm Hg. (20 mm Hg/0.8 = 25 mm Hg.) Since PI_{O_2} was 150 mm Hg (100 mm Hg + 40 mm Hg/0.8 = 150 mm Hg), the new Pa_{O_2} = 150 − 25 = **125 mm Hg**.

50. All of the following would decrease airways resistance EXCEPT:
   A. positive pressure inflation of the lungs
   B. negative pressure inflation of the lungs
   C. sympathetic stimulation
   D. vagal stimulation
   E. spontaneous inspiration

   Answer = D.   *Remember you are looking for the exception.* Vagal stimulation will cause bronchoconstriction and, hence, an increase in airways resistance (not D). All of the other events will dilate the airways and, thus, cause bronchodilation.

51. A decrease in diffusing capacity will cause:
   A. hypoxemia only
   B. hypercapnia only
   C. hypoxemia and hypercapnia
   D. a decrease in 2,3 DPG
   E. anemia

   Answer = A.   Because O_2 is 20 times less permeable than CO_2, a decrease in diffusing capacity will cause hypoxemia, but not hypercapnia (not B or C). Hypoxemia will increase 2,3 DPG (not D) and the synthesis of RBC (opposite of anemia).

52. **A 170-pound man with a body temperature of 37 C has a tidal volume of 800 ml and a breathing rate of 10 breaths/min. What is his minute volume?**
   A. 0.6 liters
   B. 7.5 liters
   C. 8.0 liters
   D. 6.3 liters
   E. 7.8 liters

   Answer = B. The minute volume is simply the tidal volume times the frequency (800 ml/breath × 10 breaths/min = 8.0 liters/min); hence, the minute volume is **8.0 liters**.

53. **The primary respiratory control center is located in the:**
   A. cerebrum
   B. medulla
   C. pons
   D. carotid body
   E. hypothalamus

   Answer = B. The medulla.

54. **Pa_{O_2} is greater at the apex than at the base of the lung because:**
   A. blood flow is greater at the apex
   B. ventilation is greater at the apex
   C. D_{CO} is less at the apex
   D. V_A/Q is greater at the apex
   E. shunt fraction is greater at the base

   Answer = D. V_A/Q is greater at the apex because the decrease in ventilation is less than the decrease in blood flow as you approach the apex of the lung (see figure in any text showing the relationship between height and blood flow, ventilation, and V_A/Q). D_{CO} is not different between the various zones. Shunting is not a normal physiological event.

55. **A patient with a body temperature of 37 C is ventilated with 30% O_2 when the barometric pressure is 754 mm Hg. What is the patient's PI_{O_2}?**
   A. 98 mm Hg
   B. 148 mm Hg
   C. 162 mm Hg
   D. 212 mm Hg
   E. 226 mm Hg

   Answer = D. To estimate the PI_{O_2}, we need to first subtract the water vapor pressure (47 mm Hg) from the atmospheric pressure (754 − 47 = 707 mm Hg). Since the patient is being ventilated with 30% O_2 (707 × 0.30) = the PI_{O_2} is **212 mm Hg.**

56. **If the length of a tube is reduced to half and the diameter is also reduced by half, the resistance to flow through the tube will:**
   A. not change
   B. decrease 4-fold
   C. increase 2-fold
   D. increase 8-fold
   E. increase 16-fold

   Answer = D. The factors that determine the flow of air through the tracheal system are the same that determine the flow of blood (see Poiseuille's law). Hence, when the length of a tube is cut in half, resistance is cut in half. When the diameter is cut in half, the resistance increases 16-fold. Hence, the combined effect would be an 8-fold increase in the resistance to flow.

57. **All of the following are true for CO_2 *EXCEPT*:**
   A.   approximately 60% is in the form of HCO_3^-
   B.   an increase in Pa_{CO_2} increases Cl^- in red blood cells
   C.   less than 3% is in the dissolved form
   D.   about 30% is bound to hemoglobin
   E.   the CO_2 carrying capacity of blood is decreased by increasing P_{O_2}

   Answer = C. *Remember you are looking for the exception.* Approximately 6% of the CO_2 is simply dissolved in plasma (not **C**). All of the other choices are true.

58. **A 130-lb patient has a Pa_{CO_2} of 80 mm Hg, a tidal volume of 1.5 liter, and a ventilation rate of 40 breaths per min; metabolic rate is approximately 80% elevated for a resting person of this size. Which of the following must be true for this patient?**
   A.   decreased diffusing capacity
   B.   increased anatomical dead space
   C.   anemia
   D.   increased shunt fraction
   E.   increased physiological dead space

   Answer = E. This patient should have a rate of alveolar ventilation of ~1.37 liter/breath $\times$ 40 breaths/min = 54.8 liters/min, almost 10 times the expected normal value; furthermore, the metabolic rate is not increased enough to produce the reported level of hypercapnia. The hypercapnia indicates that alveolar ventilation is markedly reduced; hence, the best choice is an increase in the physiological dead space (possibly an occluded right pulmonary artery). Because CO_2 is 20 times more permeable than oxygen, a decrease in diffusing capacity (**A**) will affect O_2 long before it affects Pa_{CO_2}. Anatomical dead space is determined by the size of the individual and should be about 130 ml for this patient. Even a 3-fold increase in the anatomical dead space would not produce a major decrease in alveolar ventilation (not **B**). Anemia does not affect the ability of the lung to equilibrate CO_2 (not **C**). A large shunt fraction will affect O_2 but will have little effect on CO_2 because any increase in CO_2 will stimulate the respiratory drive; hence, Pa_{CO_2} is normal in patients with shunts (not **D**).

59. **At FRC, the intrapleural pressure of a healthy person lying in bed is about (compared to atmospheric pressure):**
   A. -20 cm H_2O
   B. -5 cm H_2O
   C.   0 cm H_2O
   D.   5 cm H_2O
   E.   20 cm H_2O

   Answer = B. This is a "recall" question that can be answered by reviewing the relationship between lung volume changes and intrapleural pressure.

60. **Which of the following would have the greatest effect on Pa_{CO_2}?**
   A.   a 50% reduction in V_A
   B.   a 50% reduction in hemoglobin concentration
   C.   a decrease in FI_{O_2} to 18%
   D.   an increase in inspired CO_2 to 5%
   E.   a 100% increase in 2,3 DPG

   Answer = A. Assuming no change in the value for R (0.8), a 50% reduction in V_A would cause the Pa_{CO_2} to double (40 to 80 mm Hg), which would cause the Pa_{O_2} to decrease from ~100 mm Hg to ~50 mm Hg. Although **B** would reduce the content of O_2, Pa_{CO_2} would not be affected. A decrease in FI_{O_2} to 18% from a normal value of 20% would have only a slight effect (not **C**). The increase in FI_{CO_2} would lead to an initial increase in Pa_{CO_2}, which would stimulate V_A, resulting in a smaller increase in Pa_{CO_2} than the ($760 - 47 = 713 \times 0.05$) ~36 mm Hg initial increase; but enhanced ventilation would minimize the increase in Pa_{CO_2} (not **D**). Hence, the final Pa_{CO_2} would be significantly less than that found in **A**. Although a change in 2,3 DPG would affect the P_{50} for the oxyhemoglobin dissociation curve, it would not affect the Pa_{O_2} at a high P_{O_2}.

61. **A patient with a moderately severe reduction in diffusing capacity will mostly like have which of the following?**
   A.   a near normal resting P_{O_2}, which will decrease markedly during severe exercise.
   B.   a very low resting P_{O_2} that prevents the patient from performing even light exercise
   C.   hypoxemia, which will not become more severe during exercise
   D.   hypercapnea that will become very severe during exercise
   E.   equally severe hypoxemia and hypercapnea, both of which will become more severe during exercise

   Answer = A.   Because the time needed for O_2 exchange to equilibrate is much less than is available, a moderately impaired diffusing capacity will still allow O_2 to equilibrate with the alveolar gas under resting conditions (not **B** or **C**) but not when exercising (not **C**). Because CO_2 is 20 times more permeable than O_2, a moderate reduction in the diffusing capacity for oxygen has no effect on CO_2 (not **D** or **E**).

62. **Tuberculosis grows best in areas of high P_{O_2}. Where in the lung does tuberculosis usually concentrate?**
   A.   base
   B.   apex
   C.   near the heart
   D.   near lymphatic vessels
   E.   near pulmonary veins

   Answer = B.   The highest P_{O_2} occurs at the apex, where the ventilation V/Q ratio is highest.

63. **An individual is diagnosed as having pulmonary hypertension/cor pulmonale. The most likely cause of this condition is:**
   A.   hypoxia
   B.   hypercapnea
   C.   ketoacidosis
   D.   Kussmaul respiration
   E.   tricuspid valve stenosis

   Answer = A.   Hypoxia is the most potent constrictor of the pulmonary arterioles and hence is the most likely cause of pulmonary hypertension. Hypercapnea has little direct effect on the pulmonary vasculature (not **B**). Acidosis does cause some vasoconstriction (which is enhanced if hypoxia is present), but nothing like that produced by hypoxia itself (not **C**). Kussmaul respiration is a slow, deep breathing pattern associated with metabolic acidosis (not **D**). Tricuspid valve stenosis would produce an increase in right ventricular pressure but no increase is pulmonary artery pressure (not **E**).

Questions 64–67. Match the following laboratory values with the conditions listed for the next four questions (use each answer no more than once).

	Pa_{O_2} (mm Hg)	Pa_{CO_2} (mm Hg)	Arterial pH	Ca_{O_2} (ml/100 ml)	Hemoglobin (g/100 ml)
A.	120	20	7.19	20	15
B.	95	38	7.36	5	16
C.	52	30	7.34	17	16
D.	50	80	7.21	16	15
E.	108	34	7.51	10	8

64. **Hypoventilation**

   Answer = D.   Hypoventilation will cause an increase in Pa_{CO_2} and a decrease in Pa_{O_2}, leading to a respiratory acidosis. The hemoglobin and the content of O_2 are appropriate for the Pa_{CO_2}.

65. **Diabetes mellitus (metabolic acidosis)**

   Answer = A.   The low arterial pH of metabolic acidosis will cause a compensatory increase in ventilation, leading to a decrease in Pa_{CO_2} and an obligatory increase in Pa_{O_2}. The hemoglobin and the content of O_2 should be appropriate for the Pa_{O_2}.

66. **Carbon monoxide poisoning**

174   SECTION II: QUESTIONS AND ANSWERS

Answer = B. By binding to hemoglobin, the CO will greatly decrease the O_2 carrying capacity of the hemoglobin; hence, the hemoglobin should be normal but the content of O_2 should be inappropriately low for the Pa_{O_2}. The decreased delivery of oxygen to the tissue will cause a lactic acidosis to develop; hence, both arterial pH and Pa_{CO_2} will tend to be lower than normal.

67.   **Adult respiratory distress syndrome (ARDS)**

Answer = C. In ARDS, the patient has a markedly reduced diffusing capacity, causing the development of a hypoxia that the hyperventilation (lower than normal Pa_{CO_2}) does not correct. This hypoxia does lead to a slight metabolic acidosis (lactic acidosis) that contributes to the hyperventilation. Remember that a major decrease in diffusing capacity has little effect on the very permeable CO_2.

68.   **Which condition do the following values for an arterial blood sample represent?**
       $P_{O_2} = 52$ mm Hg
       $P_{CO_2} = 60$ mm Hg
       pH = 7.05
       $[HCO_3^-] = 16$ mM
       A.   respiratory acidosis only
       B.   metabolic acidosis only
       C.   respiratory acidosis and metabolic acidosis
       D.   respiratory acidosis and metabolic alkalosis
       E.   respiratory alkalosis and metabolic acidosis

Answer = C. This patient has a mixed acidosis. The bicarbonate is either inappropriately low or the P_{CO_2} is inappropriately high. Either the kidneys should be attempting to compensate for the respiratory acidosis (increasing HCO_3), or the patient is hypoventilating and cannot respond appropriately (hyperventilating to decrease the P_{CO_2}) to the metabolic acidosis.

69.   **An average intrapleural pressure of -1 cm H_2O at FRC suggests:**
       A.   decreased lung compliance
       B.   increased lung compliance
       C.   increased airways resistance
       D.   decreased airways resistance
       E.   decreased residual volume

Answer = B. Compliance is determined by the formula: lung volume/ distention pressure. If the distending pressure is -1 cm H_2O at FRC (normal value = -5 cm H_2O), then compliance is very high, and the patient has a flabby lung syndrome. At FRC, airways resistance has no role in determining intrapleural pressure, but it becomes an important determinant of the intrapleural pressure when a person is actually breathing.

70.   **Arteriovenous oxygen extraction is increased by a decrease in:**
       A.   pH
       B. CO_2
       C.   2,3 diphosphoglycerate
       D.   temperature

Answer = A. A decrease in pH will increase arteriovenous oxygen extraction. (As tissues become more metabolically active, the local pH decreases, which helps unload oxygen). Decreases in all of the other factors increase hemoglobin affinity for O_2.

71.   **Within zone II in the lung, flow occurs:**
       A.   during diastole only
       B.   during systole and diastole
       C.   during systole only
       D.   periodically during diastole

Answer = C. Flow in zone II only occurs when arterial pressure is greater than alveolar pressure and (simultaneously) alveolar pressure is greater than venous pressure. Hence, flow only occurs in zone II during systole.

Questions 72–74. Use the following data to answer questions 72–74. A patient was attached to a spirometer that had an initial volume of 10 liters of air. One liter of pure He was added to the spirometer when the patient was at functional residual capacity (FRC), and the patient rebreathed into the spirometer for 12 min while CO_2 was absorbed and replaced by oxygen to maintain constant spirometer volume at end expiration. At the end of the 12-min breathing period, the He concentration was 7%. The patient then exhaled into the spirometer as completely as possible from FRC; the exhalation increased the spirometer volume by 1.1 liters. The patient then took a maximal inspiration and then exhaled as completely as possible. The total volume exhaled during this latter maneuver was 5.0 liters.

72. The patient's functional residual capacity was closest to which of the following?
    A.   5.00 liters
    B.   6.00 liters
    C.   2.36 liters
    D.   3.29 liters
    E.   3.63 liters

    Answer = D.   The initial concentration of He was equal to (1 liter He)/(11 liters total spirometer volume). After equilibrating with the system, the He concentration was 7%; hence, the total volume of the system was (1 liter He)/(0.07 liters He)/liter = 14.29 liters. By subtracting the initial volume in the spirometer system of 11 liters, the volume in the patient's lung after a maximal forced expiration the FRC (14.29 liters − 11 liters) is **3.29 liters**.

73. The patient's residual volume was closest to which of the following?
    A.   1.10 liters
    B.   1.80 liters
    C.   2.19 liters
    D.   3.29 liters
    E.   5.26 liters

    Answer = C.   Subtract the value for the maximal forced expiration (1.1 liters) from the FRC value (3.29 liters) to find the residual volume: **2.19 liters**.

74. The patient's total lung capacity was approximately:
    A.   8 liters
    B.   7 liters
    C.   6 liters
    D.   5 liters
    E.   4 liters

    Answer = B.   The patient's vital capacity was 5 liters; this value plus the patient's residual volume of 2.2 liters gives a total lung capacity of ~**7 liters**.

75. A patient's test reveals a blood hemoglobin of 15 g/100 ml, a Pa_{O_2} of 55 mm Hg, a Pa_{CO_2} of 31 mm Hg, an arterial pH of 7.43, and an arterial O_2 saturation of 78%. As each gram of hemoglobin binds 1.34 ml of O_2, and as the solubility coefficient for O_2 is 0.003 ml/100 ml/mm Hg, this patient's arterial O_2 content is:
    A.   20.1 ml/100 ml
    B.   0.17 ml/100 ml
    C.   20.3 ml/100 ml
    D.   15.9 ml/100 ml

Answer = D. The arterial content of O_2 can be calculated from the data:
1) hemoglobin] $\times$ Hb binding $\times$ arterial O_2 sat. = O_2 content of Hb
   15 g/100 ml $\times$ 1.34 g/ml $\times$ 0.78 = 15.7 ml/100 ml
2) Pa_{O_2} $\times$ sol. coefficient of O_2 = ml of soluble oxygen
   55 mm Hg $\times$ 0.003 ml/100 ml/mm Hg = 0.17 ml/100 ml/mm Hg
3) Thus, this patient's arterial O_2 content = 15.9 ml/100 ml.

76. **Referring to the patient in question 75, one would conclude that the patient:**
    A.   is anemic
    B.   is hypoventilating
    C.   has an alveolar–arterial P_{O_2} difference that is greater than normal
    D.   has an arterial O_2 content that is greater than normal

    Answer = C. The finding that the patient has a lower than normal Pa_{CO_2} indicates that he is not hypoventilating (not **B**); the normal hemoglobin level indicates that he is not anemic (not **A**); and his oxygen content is lower than that of someone with a normal Pa_{CO_2} (not **D**) This patient could have a diffusion defect, with oxygen being the factor that is driving respiration, which also explains the lower than normal Pa_{CO_2}.

77. **Which of the following has the least effect on Pa_{O_2}?**
    A. V_A
    B. FI_{O_2}
    C. V_{O_2}
    D.   hemoglobin concentration

    Answer = D. V_A, FI_{O_2}, and V_{O_2} all have direct effects on the PA_{O_2} and can cause major increases or decreases in Pa_{O_2}. Hemoglobin will have little effect on the Pa_{O_2}, but it will affect the arterial content of oxygen.

78. **When someone is breathing 100% oxygen instead of room air:**
    A.   the tendency of alveoli to collapse is significantly reduced
    B.   the oxygen content in normal blood is more than doubled
    C.   the total gas pressure of the systemic venous blood is significantly increased
    D.   mixed venous P_{O_2} will be less than 100 mm Hg
    E.   the quantity of CO_2 added to the blood in the systemic capillaries is significantly increased

    Answer = D. Since there is only a small increase in the oxygen content (not **B**) of the blood when breathing 100% oxygen, the normal rate of oxygen uptake by the tissue will still cause the mixed venous P_{O_2} to become less than 100 mm Hg. All of the other choices are wrong.

79. **A compensatory mechanism for reducing V_A/Q mismatch in a region of the lung with higher than average V_A/Q ratio is:**
    A.   bronchoconstriction caused by high PA_{CO_2}
    B.   bronchoconstriction caused by low PA_{CO_2}
    C.   bronchodilation caused by high PA_{CO_2}
    D.   vasoconstriction caused by low PA_{O_2}
    E.   vasoconstriction caused by high PA_{O_2}

    Answer = B. With a higher than average V/Q ratio, the alveolar gases will be high in O_2 and low in CO_2. The lower than normal CO_2 causes bronchoconstriction, which tends to reduce the inflow of air and, thus, normalize the V/Q ratio.

80. **In obstructive lung disease, a patient is most likely to have:**
    A.   low lung compliance
    B.   high functional residual capacity
    C.   high forced expiratory flow rate
    D.   high transpulmonary pressure at a given lung volume
    E.   high ventilation perfusion ratio

Answer = B. There are diverse causes of obstructive lung disease, ranging from loss of elastic recoil (emphysema) to bronchial constriction (asthma and bronchial hypersecretion); but what they all have in common is that the airways become obstructed, which reduces the forced expiratory flow rate (not **C**); compliance is increased (not **A**). Hence, to reduce the work of moving air out of the lungs, a patient will expand the lungs to take advantage of the greater expiratory flow rate and greater transpulmonary pressure gradient associated with expanded lungs. The higher compliance of the lung tissue also causes the transpulmonary pressure to be smaller at any volume (not **D**). The difficulty of bringing air in and out of the lungs will tend to reduce the ventilation perfusion ratio (not **E**).

81. **During a forced exhalation:**
    A. the pleural pressure can be greater than atmospheric pressure
    B. the alveolar pressure is always less than pleural pressure
    C. the transpulmonary pressure increases as the lung volume decreases
    D. the pressure in the bronchi is greater than alveolar pressure
    E. the flow rate increases as the lung volume decreases

    Answer = A. The contraction of the intercostal and abdominal muscles associated with expiration causes the pleural pressure to greatly exceed atmospheric pressure. Alveolar pressure is always greater than pleural pressure (not **B**) and bronchial pressure (not **D**). The transpulmonary pressure decreases as lung volume decreases (not **C**). Inspection of any text flow–volume curve reveals that the flow rate decreases as the lung volume decreases (not **E**).

82. **During heavy muscular exercise, there is an increased production of lactic acid by the muscles. The lactic acid:**
    A. is excreted as lactic acid by the kidneys into the urine
    B. results in a reduction in plasma HCO^-_3
    C. results in hypoventilation
    D. leads to increased hemoglobin affinity for oxygen
    E. causes the anion gap to decrease

    Answer = B. Lactic acid immediately dissociates into a hydrogen ion, which is buffered by the bicarbonate, and a lactate anion, which causes the anion gap to increase (not **E**). Since lactic acid decreases the pH at the site of its production, it decreases the affinity of oxygen for hemoglobin (not **D**). Any systemic decrease in pH caused by the lactic acid will serve to stimulate respiration (not **C**). It is unlikely that the blood levels of lactate will exceed the T_m of the renal transport system for lactate (not **A**).

83. **The following data were obtained regarding a patient: arterial pH = 7.52; Pa_{CO_2} = 50 mm Hg; Pa_{O_2} = 75 mm Hg. This patient:**
    A. is hyperventilating
    B. has respiratory alkalosis
    C. must have an increased plasma HCO_3^- concentration
    D. has a relatively increased V_A
    E. has respiratory acidosis

    Answer = C. The increase in Pa_{CO_2} is a compensatory hypoventilation (not **A** or **D**) due to the metabolic (not **B**) alkalosis (not **E**) caused by an increase in the plasma bicarbonate concentration.

84. **A normal subject is allowed to breathe a primary mixture of inert gas and 15% oxygen for 10 min before switching to a secondary mixture of inert gas with 15% oxygen and 3% carbon dioxide. The effect on the subject's ventilation is most likely to be:**
    A. an increase after breathing the secondary mixture for several minutes
    B. a decrease after breathing the secondary mixture for several minutes
    C. an increase after breathing the secondary mixture for several hours
    D. a decrease after breathing the secondary mixture for several hours

    Answer = A. Raising the inspired CO_2 from 0% to 3% would produce a rapid onset of hypercapnea, which would rapidly increase breathing.

85. The following arterial blood gas data were obtained regarding a healthy human and a human COPD patient.

	Breathing Room Air	Breathing a 40% O_2 Mixture
Healthy	Pa_{O_2} = 100 mm Hg	Pa_{O_2} = 200 mm Hg
	Pa_{CO_2} = 40 mm Hg	Pa_{CO_2} = 40 mm Hg
COPD	Pa_{O_2} = 40 mm Hg	Pa_{O_2} = 70 mm Hg
	Pa_{CO_2} = 65 mm Hg	Pa_{CO_2} = 75 mm Hg

Based on the above data, all of the following statements are true *EXCEPT*:
   A.   the COPD patient is hypoventilating while breathing room air
   B.   breathing the 40% O_2 mixture results in hypoventilation in both the healthy human and the COPD patient
   C. O_2 chemoreceptors are a greater determinant of V_A in the COPD patient than in the healthy human while the persons are breathing room air
   D.   while breathing room air and while breathing 40% O_2 mixture, the COPD patient is breathing less than the healthy human

Answer = B. *Remember you are looking for the exception.* The healthy individual has no evidence of hypoventilation since his or her carbon dioxide level in the arterial blood is well maintained (not **B**). The COPD patient is always hypoventilating (**A**), and breathing oxygen shows that it is the O_2 chemoreceptors that are driving ventilation (**C**). The COPD patient is being subjected to an intense respiratory drive; and, although he or she is not ventilating well, this patient will be breathing very vigorously compared to the healthy individual (**D**).

86.   A patient is found to have a lowered arterial oxygen partial pressure (hypoxemia). Each of the following could be considered as a possible cause of this condition *EXCEPT*:
   A.   ventilation–perfusion mismatch
   B.   low blood hemoglobin concentration
   C.   hypoventilation
   D.   physiological shunting
   E.   high altitude exposure

Answer = B. *Remember you are looking for the exception.* A low blood hemoglobin concentration would present a problem with the appropriate delivery of oxygen to metabolically active tissues; but, in itself, it is not a cause of hypoxemia—in fact, it would be easier to saturate the blood since less oxygen would be required. All of the other factors clearly could be a cause of hypoxemia.

87.   Increasing tidal volume, while keeping all other factors constant, will result in:
   A.   decreased minute ventilation
   B.   increased dead space ventilation
   C.   increased alveolar ventilation
   D.   increased P_{CO_2} in arterial blood
   E.   increased inspiratory reserve volume

Answer = C. Since dead space is a constant (not **B**), any increase in tidal volume will lead to an increase in alveolar ventilation, which will decrease P_{CO_2} in arterial blood (not **D**). Since minute volume is the number of breaths times the tidal volume, it must increase (not **A**). To increase tidal volume, you are using up some of your inspiratory reserve (not **E**).

88.   Tissue P_{O_2} is determined by a balance between:
   A.   cardiac output and venous return
   B.   tissue oxygen use and carbon dioxide production
   C.   tissue metabolism and tissue blood flow
   D.   lung ventilation and perfusion

Answer = C. It is the balance between tissue metabolism and the delivery of oxygen to the tissue (blood flow) that determines P_{O_2}.

89. If tissue oxygen consumption increases to four times normal and tissue blood flow increases to two times normal, then:
   A. tissue interstitial fluid P_{O_2} will decrease
   B. tissue interstitial fluid P_{O_2} will not change
   C. tissue interstitial fluid P_{O_2} will increase
   D. the amount of oxygen removed from the blood each minute will not change

   Answer = **A**. The blood flow increase is not matching the increased tissue oxygen consumption; hence, there will be a significant decrease in tissue interstitial fluid P_{O_2}. There will be a large increase in the amount of oxygen removed each minute.

90. Each of the following conditions causes increased ventilatory drive due to low arterial P_{O_2} (hypoxemia) *EXCEPT*:
   A. severe chronic obstructive pulmonary disease
   B. immediate breathing of a low oxygen level (acute hypoxia)
   C. prolonged breathing of a low oxygen level (chronic hypoxia)
   D. carbon monoxide poisoning
   E. adaptation to high altitude

   Answer = **D**. *Remember you are looking for the exception.* Carbon monoxide poisoning has no effect on the arterial partial pressure of oxygen; it only reduces the arterial content of oxygen (not **D**).

91. Normally, the arterial blood gases do not change significantly during strenuous exercise. Which of the following is thought to stimulate the respiratory center the proper amount to supply the extra oxygen requirements for strenuous exercise and to blow off the extra carbon dioxide?
   A. hydrogen ions from lactic acid produced by exercising muscles
   B. the central and peripheral chemoreceptors
   C. neurogenic factors involving the higher brain centers and proprioceptive reflexes
   D. hypoxia developing within the exercising muscles

   Answer = **C**. It is thought that the higher brain centers and proprioceptive reflexes account for the fact that the blood gases do not change significantly. However, if these reflexes do not maintain the arterial blood gases, then the other factors will come into play.

92. A condition in which hypoxia is always accompanied by hypercapnia is:
   A. diffusion impairment
   B. V_A/Q_C mismatch
   C. physiologic shunt
   D. hypoventilation
   E. anemia

   Answer = **D**. Since diffusion limitations (not **A**, **B**, or **C**) do not normally affect the ability of the lungs to equilibrate carbon dioxide, only hypoventilation will produce a hypercapnia along with hypoxemia. Anemia does not cause a ventilatory defect that would produce hypercapnia (not **E**).

Questions 93–95. Figure 3-2 shows pressure changes for a single tidal breath. From the figure, determine the pressures in questions 93–95.

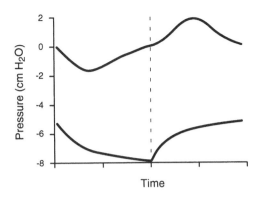

FIG. 3-2

93. Transpulmonary pressure at the end of inspiration
    A. -8 cm H_2O
    B. -5 cm H_2O
    C.   0 cm H_2O
    D.   3 cm H_2O
    E.   8 cm H_2O

Answer = B. Since alveolar pressure is zero at the end of inspiration, the transpulmonary pressure = the pleural pressure at the end of inspiration.

94. Pleural pressure immediately before inspiration
    A. -8 cm H_2O
    B. -5 cm H_2O
    C.   0 cm H_2O
    D.   3 cm H_2O
    E.   8 cm H_2O

Answer = A. Inspection of Fig. 3-2 shows that immediately before inspiration, pleural pressure is -5 cm H_2O.

95. Alveolar pressure at the end of expiration
    A. -8 cm H_2O
    B. -5 cm H_2O
    C.   0 cm H_2O
    D.   3 cm H_2O
    E.   8 cm H_2O

Answer = C. At the end of expiration when the chest wall is relaxed, alveolar pressure is equal to atmospheric pressure or 0 cm H_2O.

96. During inspiration, all of the following increase *EXCEPT:*
    A.   intrapleural pressure
    B.   stroke volume
    C.   venous return
    D.   intra-abdominal pressure
    E.   pulmonary vascular resistance

Answer = A. *Remember you are looking for the exception.* During inspiration, the contraction of the diaphragm decreases (*not* **A**) intrapleural pressure while increasing intra-abdominal pressure (**D**). Because of the negative intrathoracic pressure, there is an increase in venous return (**C**), which leads to a transient increase in stroke volume (**B**) that can produce a transient increase in blood pressure, leading to a reflex slowing of the heart (**B**).

97. **During normal expiration, which of the following increases?**
  A. metabolic rate of the diaphragm
  B. bronchial diameter
  C. pulmonary vascular diameter
  D. alveolar pressure
  E. height of the xiphoid process above the ground

Answer = D. For air to flow from the alveoli to the outside, there must be a pressure gradient; hence, alveolar pressure must become greater than atmospheric pressure. During expiration, the diaphragm is relaxed (not **A**) and intrapleural pressure becomes positive; hence, the diameter of both the blood vessels and the bronchi are decreased (not **B** or **C**). As the chest wall relaxes, the xiphoid process descends (not **E**).

98. **In a normal subject after 10 min of exposure to hypoxia (PA_{O_2} = 50 mm Hg), you would expect that compared to the initial response (first 15 sec) there would be:**
  A. an increase in arterial P_{CO_2}
  B. a decrease in arterial pH
  C. a decrease in activity of the medullary chemoreceptors
  D. a decrease in the pH of the CSF
  E. a decrease in the activity of the peripheral chemoreceptors

Answer = C. A PA_{O_2} of 50 mm Hg would activate the peripheral chemoreceptors (not **E**), causing an increase in ventilation that would lead to a decrease in P_{CO_2} (not **A**). The consequent increase in arterial and CSF pH (the CSF alkalosis; not **B** or **D**) and the decrease in P_{CO_2} will decrease the activity of the medullary chemoreceptors, which are not sensitive to a low partial pressure of oxygen.

99. **A lightly anesthetized patient still capable of spontaneous breathing is artificially ventilated for 10 min at his normal tidal volume but at twice his normal frequency with a gas mixture of 50% O_2 and 50% N_2. On cessation of this artificial ventilation, the patient fails to breathe for 1 min. The most important cause of this temporary apnea is a decreased activity of the:**
  A. peripheral chemoreceptors because of the high P_{O_2}
  B. peripheral chemoreceptors because of the low P_{CO_2}
  C. medullary chemoreceptors because of the high P_{O_2}
  D. medullary chemoreceptors because of the low P_{CO_2}
  E. peripheral chemoreceptors because of the decrease in arterial pH

Answer = D. The patient was being hyperventilated; therefore, the P_{CO_2} was reduced whereas the P_{O_2} was slightly elevated. However, P_{CO_2}, primarily via its effects on the medullary chemoreceptors (not **B**), is the most powerful stimulus for breathing. The slightly elevated P_{O_2} will have no effect on the peripheral chemoreceptors (not **A**), and the medullary chemoreceptors are not sensitive to oxygen (not **C**). The hyperventilation will increase (not **E**) arterial pH.

100. **Prolonged hypoxia may result in:**
  A. pulmonary vasodilation
  B. reduced proportion of pulmonary blood flow to the lung apex
  C. coronary vasoconstriction
  D. decreased right ventricular end diastolic pressure
  E. increased mean circulatory filling pressure

Answer = E. Hypoxia causes a sustained generalized pulmonary vasoconstriction (not **A**) that chronically increases pulmonary arterial blood pressure. The increase in pulmonary arterial pressure tends to increase the relative perfusion of the apex of the lung (not **B**) by minimizing the effects of gravity on pulmonary perfusion. The increased pulmonary vasoconstriction initially decreases cardiac output, leading to reflex increases in salt and water retention. The increased retention of salt and water results in an increase in extracellular volume and a subsequent increase in mean circulatory filling pressure, which contributes to an increase in right ventricular end diastolic pressure (not **D**). The increased right ventricular end diastolic pressure contributes to the increase in preload that helps the right ventricle compensate for the increase in afterload. The prolonged hypoxia will cause coronary vasodilation (not **C**).

Questions 1–4. Data were obtained on one of your class-mates who volunteered to participate in a renal clearance study in order to pay for medical school expenses.

Two hours following the initiation of an inulin infusion:
Plasma inulin = 20 mg/dl
Plasma glucose = 150 mg/dl
Urine flow = 2 ml/min
Urine inulin = 500 mg/dl
Urine glucose = 30 mg/dl

1. What is the GFR?
   A. 130 ml/min
   B. 100 ml/min
   C. 50 ml/min
   D. 25 ml/min
   E. 12 ml/min

   Answer = C. The clearance of inulin is a measure of the glomerular filtration rate. Thus, (urine flow $\times$ urine concentration of inulin)/plasma inulin concentration = (2 ml/min $\times$ 500 mg/dl)/20 mg/dl = 50 ml/min.

2. If you then simply doubled the rate at which the inulin solution was being infused into this otherwise normal medical student, all of the following would be expected to change *EXCEPT*:
   A. plasma inulin concentration
   B. urine inulin concentration
   C. excretion of inulin in the urine
   D. GFR

   Answer = D. *Remember you are looking for the exception.* The rate at which you infuse the inulin solution determines the mass of inulin the student will excrete each minute in the urine when a steady state is reached; it has nothing to do with the GFR. The GFR determines what the plasma inulin concentration will be when the steady state is reached. Hence, plasma inulin concentration (**A**) and the excretion of inulin in the urine (**C**) will double. If urine flow remains constant (no reason to assume it would change), then the concentration of inulin in the urine (**B**) will also double.

3. What was the clearance of glucose?
   A. 60 ml/min
   B. 6 ml/min
   C. 0.6 mg/min
   D. 0.4 ml/min
   E. 0.15 ml/min

   Answer = D. Based on the general clearance equation, (urine$_{glucose}$ $\times$ urine flow)/plasma$_{glucose}$, we have (30 mg/dl $\times$ 2 ml/min)/150 mg/dl; 60 ml/min/150 = 0.4 ml/min.

4. Which is true for the reabsorption of glucose by this student?
   A. approximately 75 mg/min is being reabsorbed
   B. approximately 20 mg/min is being reabsorbed
   C. approximately 150 mg/min is being reabsorbed
   D. glucose reabsorption must be at its maximum level
   E. cannot determine the rate of glucose reabsorption from the data presented

Answer = A. The amount filtered at the glomerulus is equal to 150 mg/dl $\times$ 50 ml/min (GFR) = 75 mg/min. The student is excreting 30 mg/dl $\times$ 2 ml/min = 0.6 mg/min. The amount reabsorbed is equal to the amount filtered minus the amount excreted, or 74.4 mg/min; thus, approximately 75 mg/min was reabsorbed, and sufficient data are presented to determine the rate of glucose reabsorption. Although some glucose is present in the urine, you cannot assume that the T_{max} for glucose has been exceeded.

5. **You discover a new drug that causes GFR to increase but renal blood flow to decrease. This drug does not affect arterial blood pressure. The drug causes:**
   A. constriction of the afferent arteriole
   B. dilation of the afferent arteriole
   C. constriction of the efferent arteriole
   D. dilation of the efferent arteriole
   E. equal constriction of both the afferent and efferent arterioles

   Answer = C. Overall, there was an increase in resistance (not **B** or **D**) because renal blood flow decreased but arterial pressure did not change. Furthermore, either the net glomerular filtration pressure increased (efferent arteriolar constriction), or the K_f for filtration increased. Constriction of the afferent arteriole would decrease net filtration pressure (not **A**). Choice **E** would keep net filtration pressure constant (i.e., no change in GFR) and would decrease renal blood flow.

6. **The macula densa is an important component for all of the following EXCEPT:**
   A. autoregulation of GFR
   B. secretion of renin
   C. regulation of afferent arteriole tone
   D. sensing fluid delivery to the distal tubule
   E. sensing plasma osmolarity

   Answer = E. *Remember you are looking for the exception.* The macula densa does not sense plasma osmolarity, which is sensed primarily within the CNS. The macula densa is thought to sense alterations in the rate of delivery of fluid and/or solute to the distal tubule (**D**). This is an important component for autoregulation of GFR (**A**) by altering afferent arteriolar tone (**C**) and for the release of renin from the juxtaglomerular cells in the afferent arteriole (**B**).

7. **A patient has the following clinical data:**
   urine volume/24 h = 600 ml
   urine osmolality = 1,100 mOsm
   plasma osmolality = 260 mOsm
   blood pressure = 120/80 mm Hg
   plasma potassium = 4.1 mM
   Which of the following could produce these data?
   A. a large increase in antidiuretic hormone secretion
   B. a large increase in aldosterone secretion
   C. a large increase in angiotensin II
   D. the total absence of aldosterone
   E. the total absence of antidiuretic hormone

   Answer = A. The urine osmolarity and urine flow data indicate a high ADH level, which is inappropriate for someone with a low plasma osmolarity. Low plasma osmolarity inhibits ADH secretion. Hence, there is an inappropriate secretion of ADH, which causes water retention by the kidneys, leading to the decrease in plasma osmolarity. A large increase in either aldosterone (**B**) or angiotensin II (**C**) would cause sodium retention but not an abnormal amount of water retention because the body still regulates plasma osmolarity. Furthermore, plasma potassium decreases following a large increase in these two hormones. The total absence of aldosterone (**D**) causes urinary salt loss, and a slight decrease in plasma osmolality might occur; but plasma potassium will increase, while blood pressure will tend to decrease. In the absence of ADH (**E**), plasma osmolarity is high and urine osmolality is very low, with a large volume of urine being produced.

8. A patient has a tumor of the adrenal gland, causing a sustained hypersecretion of aldosterone (primary aldosteronism). Which of the following parameters is elevated above that found in a normal individual ingesting an identical diet?
    A. plasma renin concentration
    B. plasma angiotensin II concentration
    C. plasma K
    D. plasma ANF concentration
    E. plasma chloride concentration

Answer = D. Primary aldosteronism causes an initial salt retention that expands the extracellular fluid compartment and leads to various reflex changes that limit the amount of sodium retained. These changes include such events as a decrease in renin and angiotensin levels (not **A** or **B**) and increases in the secretion of ANF and in arterial blood pressure. In addition, potassium excretion significantly increases, leading to hypokalemia (not **C**). The hypokalemia and the direct effect of aldosterone both enhance H^+ ion secretion by the kidneys, which leads to the development of a metabolic alkalosis (an increase in plasma HCO_3^-), producing a decrease in plasma Cl^- (not **E**).

9. When you are excreting a maximally concentrated urine, the greatest amount of water is being reabsorbed by the:
    A. proximal tubule
    B. descending limb of Henle's loop
    C. ascending thin limb of Henle's loop
    D. thick ascending limb of Henle's loop
    E. collecting ducts

Answer = A. Regardless of the final osmolarity of the urine or the presence of a high level of ADH, the proximal tubule reabsorbs the greatest amount of the filtered water. Recall that the proximal tubule reabsorbs between 60% and 80% of the GFR. This is a classic question that leads many students to wrongly select choice **E**, the collecting ducts. In the presence of ADH, the collecting ducts reabsorb a very high percentage of the water delivered to them, but the absolute volume being reabsorbed is quite small—probably less than 5% of the GFR.

10. When you are excreting a maximally concentrated urine, the fluid in the thin ascending limb of Henle's loop has:
    A. a lower urea concentration than that found in the fluid within an adjacent descending limb
    B. a lower sodium concentration than that in the adjacent interstitial fluid
    C. a lower osmolality than that found in the fluid within an adjacent collecting duct
    D. an osmolality identical to that of the adjacent interstitial fluid
    E. a lower osmolality than that found in the afferent arteriolar blood

Answer = C. Reexamine any textbook figure showing the countercurrent process in the kidneys when ADH is present. Compared to fluid in the adjacent collecting duct (which is in osmotic equilibrium with its interstitial environment in the presence of ADH), the ascending limb fluid has a lower osmolality than the adjacent interstitial fluid (not **D**) due to the reabsorption of sodium without the concurrent reabsorption of water. Note that the urea concentration within the loop of Henle increases somewhat as urine descends into the papilla, primarily due to the reabsorption of water (a small influx may also occur); but as the fluid passes the bend and starts back up the ascending limb of Henle's loop, no water is reabsorbed and little urea enters. Therefore, the urea concentration is similar to or slightly higher than that found in the adjacent descending limb (not **A**). The sodium concentration in the ascending limb is higher than that in the adjacent interstitial fluid because urea makes up a large part of the interstitial osmolality, creating a gradient for the reabsorption of sodium by the thin ascending limb (not **B**). Along the thin limb of Henle's loop, the fluid will not become hypotonic to the arterial blood until you reach the cortical–medullary portion (not **E**) of the thick ascending limb.

11. With ADH present, which of the following is correct for the tubular fluid/plasma ratio for osmolality at the *end* of the structure mentioned?
A.	distal tubule	— the ratio is greater than 1
B.	proximal tubule	— the ratio is less than 1
C.	cortical collecting duct	— the ratio is 1
D.	thick ascending loop of Henle	— the ratio is 1
E.	medullary collecting duct	— the ratio is less than 1

Answer = C. In the presence of ADH, fluid at the end of both the distal tubule and cortical collecting duct will become iso-osmotic with the interstitial fluid within the cortex; thus, the tubular fluid/plasma ratio for osmolality will become 1 but will not exceed 1 (not **A**). The proximal tubule reabsorbs water in an iso-osmotic manner; hence, the ratio will be 1, not less than 1 (not **B**). At the end of the thick ascending limb, the fluid is hypo-osmotic to plasma because it actively reabsorbs sodium without the concurrent reabsorption of water (not **D**). In the presence of ADH, the fluid within the medullary collecting duct becomes hypertonic to the arterial plasma as it equilibrates with the hypertonic environment of the medulla (not **E**).

12. For a patient who has an acute increase in P_{CO_2} (acute respiratory acidosis), you would expect all of the following *EXCEPT*:
    A.   a small decrease in plasma HCO_3^-
    B.   a significant initial decrease in plasma pH
    C.   increased HCO_3^- reabsorption by the kidney
    D.   a gradual increase in plasma pH over the next several days
    E.   an increase in titratable acid excretion for several days

    Answer = A.   *Remember you are looking for the exception.* Because there are multiple buffers in the body, a primary increase in P_{CO2} causes a small increase (2–4 mM; not **A**) in plasma HCO_3^- as the H^+ from the dissociation of H_2CO_3 is buffered by the other buffers (e.g., proteins and hemoglobin). Although the buffers dampen the pH decrease, there will still be a significant decrease in plasma pH (**B**). The increase in P_{CO_2} and the increase in the amount of filtered HCO_3^- cause the kidney to reabsorb more bicarbonate (**C**). The plasma pH will increase over the next several days (**D**) as the kidneys are stimulated by the acidosis and the increase in P_{CO_2} to generate new HCO_3^- from the increased titratable acid excretion and the increased NH_4^+ (**E**).

13. Upon changing from a normal diet to a diet with a very high potassium content, you would expect:
    A.   a large decrease in the amount of potassium being reabsorbed by the proximal tubule
    B.   a decrease in plasma aldosterone, causing increased K secretion by collecting duct cells
    C.   a rapid development of a metabolic alkalosis
    D.   a slight increase in plasma K, causing increased K secretion by cells along the collecting duct
    E.   a parallel increase in urinary sodium excretion

    Answer = D.   Potassium excretion is determined primarily by the amount of potassium secreted by the distal nephron segments and not by an inhibition of reabsorption as occurs for sodium. Hence, there will not be a large decrease in potassium reabsorption by the proximal tubule (not **A**). The expected slight increase in plasma K would stimulate (not **B**) aldosterone secretion. Simply changing potassium intake will have little effect on acid/base balance. The body can regulate sodium balance and potassium balance in an independent manner. Hence, an increase in dietary potassium intake does cause a significant increase in sodium excretion (not **E**); in fact, you might expect a transient retention of sodium caused by the potassium-mediated increase in aldosterone secretion.

14. A decrease in renal arterial blood pressure of 10 mm Hg in a normal kidney will lead to all of the following responses *EXCEPT*:
    A.   a decrease in urinary sodium excretion
    B.   a decrease in efferent arteriolar resistance
    C.   an increase in renin secretion
    D.   a decrease in afferent arteriolar resistance
    E.   a response that maintains GFR and renal blood flow near normal values

    Answer = B.   *Remember you are looking for the exception.* Recall that the kidney can autoregulate both its blood flow and GFR (**E**), but sodium excretion is not autoregulated. As blood pressure decreases, sodium excretion decreases (**A**); there is a proportional decrease in resistance (primarily afferent arteriolar resistance; **D**) as pressure decreases because glomerular capillary pressure remains unchanged. A decrease in renal arterial pressure is a stimulus for an increased renin secretion (**C**).

15. Which of the following acts to decrease GFR and renal blood flow below normal levels?
    A.   autoregulation
    B.   a small increase in efferent arteriolar resistance
    C.   prostaglandin E_2
    D.   a decrease in afferent arteriolar resistance
    E.   a high plasma catecholamine level

Answer = E. Catecholamines cause constriction of both the afferent and efferent arterioles and thus tend to decrease blood flow and GFR. Autoregulation tends to prevent decreases in renal blood flow and GFR (not **A**). A small increase in efferent arteriole resistance would decrease renal blood flow but not GFR, which might increase slightly (not **B**). Prostaglandin E_2 can be produced within the kidneys, but it is a vasodilator substance that tends to increase renal blood flow (**C**). A decrease in afferent resistance increases both GFR and renal blood flow (not **D**).

16. **Following hemorrhage, renal blood flow is normally reduced because of:**
    A. a decrease in activity of the parasympathetic nerves to the kidney
    B. an increase in sympathetic nerve activity to the kidneys
    C. a decrease in hematocrit
    D. an increase in aldosterone secretion
    E. a decrease in renin secretion

Answer = B. There is a generalized increase in sympathetic nerve activity brought on by the decrease in blood pressure induced by the hemorrhage. The increase in sympathetic nerve activity causes renal vasoconstriction, which decreases renal blood flow. There is no evidence that there is any parasympathetic innervation of the kidney (not **A**). Although the hematocrit will decrease as interstitial fluid is reabsorbed back into the plasma compartment, a decrease in hematocrit will tend to decrease viscosity (not **C**) and, thus, increase renal blood flow. The decrease in blood pressure, the increase in sympathetic nerve activity to the kidney, and the decrease in GFR being sensed by the macula densa will all tend to increase renin secretion (not **E**), which leads to an increase in aldosterone secretion; however, aldosterone has no direct vasoactive properties (not **D**) that would decrease renal blood flow.

17. **Phosphate reabsorption by the kidney:**
    A. occurs primarily along the distal tubule and collecting duct
    B. has a genetically fixed transport maximum like that of glucose
    C. is controlled by the secretion of angiotensin II
    D. is influenced by the level of parathyroid hormone
    E. occurs primarily along the thick ascending limb of Henle

Answer = D. Parathyroid hormone directly inhibits phosphate reabsorption and, thus, acts to decrease the T_{max} for phosphate. Most of the phosphate is reabsorbed along the proximal tubule (not **A** or **E**). Phosphate reabsorption behaves like it has a variable (PTH-dependent) transport maximum, not a genetically fixed transport maximum like that of glucose (not **B**). Angiotensin does not control phosphate reabsorption (not **C**).

18. **The initial increase (first 15 min) in plasma HCO_3^- following hypoventilation is associated with:**
    A. a rapid (first 15 min) increase in the production of ammonium by the kidney
    B. an increase in arterial pH
    C. a shift of K^+ into cells
    D. a decrease in the concentration of protein bases ($Prot^-$)
    E. a rapid (first 15 min) increase in the amount of titratable acid excreted by the kidney

Answer = D. Hypoventilation causes a primary increase in P_{CO_2} (acute respiratory acidosis: a decrease in arterial pH; not **B**). As the protein bases become more protonated, there is a decrease in the amount of protein base in the body. As cell protein buffers the increase in hydrogen ions, potassium is shifted out of the cell compartment (not **C**). The renal compensatory response (increased titratable acid excretion and NH_4^+ excretion) will occur over the next few days (not **A** or **E**), not in the initial 15 min.

19. **Which process enables us to produce a urine with a final pH of 4.5?**
    A. Na^+/H^+ exchange pump
    B. diffusion of H^+ from the tubular cell into the tubular fluid
    C. ATP-powered proton pump
    D. cotransport of Na^+ and H^+ into the tubular fluid
    E. cotransport of K^+ and H^+ into the tubular fluid

Answer = C. The ATP-powered proton pump located in the intercalated cells generates the large, ~1,000:1 H^+ ion gradient and, thus, lowers urine pH to 4.5. The Na^+/H^+ exchange pump (not **A**) transports a large number of H^+ ions, but its location within the cells of the leaky proximal tubule prevents it from generating a tubular fluid pH lower than ~6.8. Diffusion of H^+ tends to increase urinary pH because tubular fluid is usually more acidic than plasma fluid (not **B**). Neither process involves a cotransport of H^+ with either sodium or potassium (not **D** or **E**).

20. **The carbonic acid/ bicarbonate system is considered the most important body buffer because:**
   A. both the acid and base components can be independently regulated
   B. it is the only buffer in the body that has a pK close to the normal pH of plasma
   C. it is present in large quantities
   D. carbonic acid is a gas, while HCO_3^- is an electrolyte
   E. none of the above

   Answer = A. The ability of the lungs and kidneys to independently regulate the P_{CO_2} (lungs) and the plasma HCO_3 (kidney) make the carbonic acid/bicarbonate buffer system the most important buffer system. The pK (6.1 1 pH unit from the desired pK of 7.4) for this buffer is not indicative of a good biological buffer (not **B**). Both proteins and HCO_3^- are present in large quantities (not **C**). Choice **D** is true but is not the reason the carbonic acid/ bicarbonate system is considered the most important body buffer.

21. **Any substance that is filtered by the glomerulus and reabsorbed and not secreted by the renal tubules will have a renal clearance that is:**
   A. equal to the clearance of urea
   B. equal to the clearance of inulin
   C. less than the clearance of inulin
   D. greater than the clearance of inulin
   E. equal to the glomerular filtration rate

   Answer = C. Since inulin is filtered and not reabsorbed or secreted, the clearance of any substance that is filtered and reabsorbed but not secreted will always be less than the clearance of inulin (not **B** or **D**). Since the clearance of inulin is equal to the GFR, the clearance of the substance will be less than the GFR (not **E**). The clearance of urea is less than the clearance of inulin because it is filtered and then reabsorbed, but we cannot determine from the information given what the clearance of "any substance" will be in relation to urea (not **A**). It could be less than, greater than, or equal to the clearance of urea.

22. **As tubular fluid passes along the ascending limb of the loop of Henle:**
   A. osmolarity increases
   B. water is always reabsorbed
   C. urea concentration increases more than 3-fold
   D. in the presence of ADH, water is reabsorbed
   E. chloride is reabsorbed

   Answer = E. Along the ascending limb of the loop of Henle, Na and Cl are reabsorbed without the concurrent reabsorption of water; the ascending limb is impermeable to water even in the presence of ADH. Hence, osmolality decreases (not **A**), and water is not reabsorbed (not **B** or **D**). Because water is not reabsorbed and the ascending limb is relatively impermeable to urea, very little change in urea concentration occurs (not **C**).

Questions 23–24. A patient has a pH of 7.49 and an arterial P_{CO_2} of 50 mm Hg. Using these data, answer questions 23 and 24.

23. **The HCO_3^- concentration is:**
   A. 40 mM
   B. 37 mM
   C. 30 mM
   D. 46 mM
   E. 16 mM

   Answer = B. The Henderson-Hasselbach equation for HCO_3^- can be solved using a pocket calculator. The H_2CO_3 concentration is equal to 0.03 × the P_{CO_2} (50 mm Hg) = 1.5 mM; at a pH of 7.49 the log ratio of the HCO_3^-/ H_2CO_3 = 1.39 (7.49 minus the pK of 6.1) or 24.55 = x/1.5; x = 24.55 × 1.5 = 36.8 mM HCO_3^-) or 37 mM.

24. **What type of acid/base disturbance does this patient have?**
   A. acute respiratory alkalosis
   B. chronic respiratory alkalosis
   C. chronic respiratory acidosis
   D. metabolic acidosis
   E. metabolic alkalosis

Answer = E. The patient has an alkalosis (not **C** or **D**) caused by an elevated HCO_3^- level, a metabolic alkalosis (not **A** or **B**). The respiratory system is compensating for this alkalosis by decreasing alveolar ventilation to raise the P_{CO_2}, which buffers the effect that the increase in HCO_3^- has on the increase in pH. *Note:* Without the increase in P_{CO_2}, the ratio of HCO_3^- to $H_2CO_3 = 37$ mM/1.2 mM $= 30.83$, and the log of 30.83 $= 1.489$; so the arterial pH would have been 6.1 $+$ 1.489 $=$ 7.589.

25. **Which of the following might be a cause of this patient's problem?**
    A.   ingestion of NaCl
    B.   increased production of ketoacids
    C.   decrease in plasma potassium
    D.   decreased aldosterone secretion
    E.   decrease in plasma angiotensin II levels

Answer = C. A decrease in plasma potassium will produce a metabolic alkalosis because of the effect that it has on the kidney to stimulate the secretion of H^+. The inappropriate secretion of H^+ leads to the formation of HCO_3^-, which produces the metabolic alkalosis. Ingestion of NaCl would cause volume expansion and a dilution of the HCO_3^- concentration, both of which would tend to produce a metabolic acidosis (not **A**). The increased production of ketoacids would cause a metabolic acidosis (not **B**). A decrease in aldosterone secretion caused by an adrenal deficiency or by a decrease in plasma angiotensin II levels would lead to a decrease in H^+ secretion and, thus, would tend to produce a metabolic acidosis (not **D** or **E**). Finally, a decrease in angiotensin II would also decrease the activity of the Na^+/H^+ exchanger in the proximal tubule and, thus, decrease the amount of bicarbonate that is reabsorbed, which would lead to a metabolic acidosis.

Questions 26–27. To answer questions 26 and 27, use the data presented in Fig. 4-1 for the renal handling of glucose.

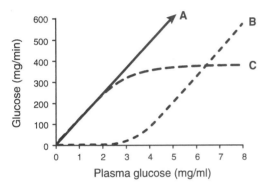

FIG. 4-1

26. **Which of the following properly identifies the three curves presented in the above figure?**
    A.   A = excretion of glucose; B = filtration of glucose; C = reabsorption of glucose
    B.   A = filtration of glucose; B = excretion of glucose; C = reabsorption of glucose
    C.   A = filtration of glucose; B = reabsorption of glucose; C = excretion of glucose
    D.   A = reabsorption of glucose; B = excretion of glucose; C = filtration of glucose
    E.   A = reabsorption of glucose; B = filtration of glucose; C = excretion of glucose

Answer = B. Glucose is freely filtered, reabsorbed by a T_{max}-limited system that leads to a high rate of urinary excretion once the T_{max} has been exceeded. Being freely filtered means that the mass per minute being filtered is directly proportional to the plasma concentration (Curve A = filtration of glucose). Since reabsorption is limited by the T_{max} for the system, reabsorption increases until the T_{max} is reached; then it plateaus (Curve B = reabsorption of glucose). Until the T_{max} is reached, little glucose appears in the urine; it then increases in proportion to the increase in filtered glucose (Curve C = excretion of glucose).

27. **When the plasma level of glucose was increased from 5 to 7 mg/ml, the:**
   A. clearance of glucose increased
   B. excretion of glucose remained constant
   C. reabsorption of glucose decreased
   D. filtered load of glucose remained constant
   E. T_{max} was finally exceeded

   Answer = A. The clearance of glucose can be calculated by determining how much glucose is being excreted when the plasma level of glucose is either 5 or 7 mg/ml (read from y-axis) and then dividing by the plasma glucose concentration (e.g., at 5 mg/ml, excretion = ~200 mg/min/5 mg/ml = 40 ml/min; while at 7 mg/ml, excretion = ~460 mg/m in/7 mg/ml = ~66 ml/min). You can also answer this question by knowing that as the plasma concentration of glucose increases, a greater percentage of the filtered load is being excreted; thus, more glucose is being cleared from the body. Furthermore, the excretion of glucose increases (not **B**); while the reabsorption of glucose remains constant (not **C**), the filtered load of glucose increases (not **D**). The T_{max} was already exceeded when plasma glucose concentration reached 5 mg/dl (not **E**).

28. **PAH is secreted by a T_{max}-limited system. When the plasma concentration of PAH is above that required for the T_{max}, any further increase in the plasma concentration of PAH will cause all of the following *EXCEPT*:**
   A. the amount of PAH secreted each minute will remain constant
   B. the excretion of PAH will increase
   C. the clearance of PAH will decrease
   D. the filtered load of PAH will increase
   E. the extraction ratio for PAH will increase

   Answer = E. *Remember you are looking for the exception.* The extraction ratio for PAH is equal to [(arterial$_{PAH}$ − renal venous$_{PAH}$/arterial$_{PAH}$]. As the concentration of PAH is increased beyond the T_{max}, the kidney will excrete a smaller and smaller fraction of the PAH delivered to it each minute; hence, the extraction ratio will decrease, not increase. The amount of PAH secreted will remain constant once the T_{max} has been exceeded (**A**). The excretion of PAH will continue to increase since the increased amount being filtered (**B**) will be excreted in the urine. The clearance of PAH will decrease (**C**) since a smaller percentage of the PAH delivered to the kidney each minute is being excreted in the urine. The filtered load of PAH will increase (**D**).

29. **After a large hemorrhage, you would expect all of the following *EXCEPT*:**
   A. increased ADH secretion
   B. increased osmolar excretion
   C. increased renin secretion
   D. decreased urine flow
   E. increased aldosterone secretion

   Answer = B. *Remember you are looking for the exception.* As plasma and extracellular volume decrease, a number of reflex pathways that tend to help restore blood volume are activated by the decrease in blood pressure and by the decrease in the stretch of the lower pressure receptors within the atria. The decrease in blood pressure, the increase in sympathetic nerve activity to the kidney (causing a decrease in GFR), and the increase in angiotensin II and aldosterone cause the kidney to decrease sodium and osmolar excretion. There is an increase in ADH secretion (**A**) and in renin secretion (**C**), which leads to an increase in aldosterone secretion (**E**). The increase in sodium reabsorption, the high level of ADH, and the decrease in GFR all contribute to the decrease in urine flow (**D**).

30. **A patient has a head injury that has damaged the medullary respiratory center. His breathing is very rapid and deep. The most likely finding upon analysis of the blood would be:**
   A. elevated pH and elevated P_{CO_2}
   B. elevated pH and low P_{CO_2}
   C. low pH and low P_{CO_2}
   D. low pH and elevated P_{CO_2}
   E. none of the above

   Answer = B. The data suggest that the patient is inappropriately hyperventilating, which should cause the P_{CO_2} to decrease. The decreased P_{CO_2} causes, in turn, an acute respiratory alkalosis (elevated pH).

Questions 31–32. Use the following data obtained from a
patient to answer questions 31 and 32.

Urine Data	Plasma Data	Renal Function
Volume $= 0.1$ liter/h	$HCO_3^- = 24$ mM	GFR $= 100$ ml/min
$HCO_3^- = 0.7$ mMol/h	pH $= 7.38$	
$NH_4^+ = 2.0$ mMol/h	$Na^+ = 138$ mM	
Titratable acid $= 3.0$ mMol/h	$K^+ = 4.1$ mM	

31. The net HCO_3^- generation for the patient was:
    A. 4.7 mMol/h
    B. 50 mMol/h
    C. 5 mMol/h
    D. 146.3 mMol/h
    E. 4.3 mMol/h

    Answer $=$ E. The amount of HCO_3^- that is generated is equal to the amount of titratable acid (3.0 mMol/h) plus
    the amount of NH_4^+ (2.0 mMol/h) excreted in the urine minus any HCO_3^- (0.7 mmol/h) that was lost from the
    body via the urine. Thus, 5.0 mmol/h $-$ 0.7 mmol/h $=$ 4.3 mmol/h.

32. How many mMol of H^+ per hour did this patient secrete?
    A. 148.3 mMol/h
    B. 4.3 mMol/h
    C. 146.3 mMol/h
    D. 150 mMol/h
    E. 5.0 mMol/h

    Answer $=$ C. The amount of H^+ secreted is equal to the amount of HCO_3^- reabsorbed [amount filtered $-$
    amount excreted (24 mM $\times$ 100 ml/min $\times$ 60 min/h $-$ mMol/h $=$ 144 mMol/h $-$ 0.7 mMol/h) $=$ 143.3 mMol/
    h] plus the amount of H^+ secreted to produce the titratable acids in the urine (3.0 mMol/h), making a total of 146.3
    mMol/h of H^+ being secreted. The NH_4^+ is excreted as the ion and, therefore, is not a H^+, but it does help to
    generate new HCO_3^-.

33. One of the consequences of the deranged metabolism in diabetes mellitus is an excessive production of acid. After
    this condition has been untreated for several days, all of the following will be observed *EXCEPT*:
    A. decreased plasma pH
    B. increased anion gap
    C. decreased plasma P_{CO_2}
    D. increased NH_4^+ excretion
    E. increased HCO_3^- excretion

    Answer $=$ E. *Remember you are looking for the exception.* What are the consequences of several days of exposure
    to a high level of ketoacid production? Plasma pH decreases (**A**), and the anion gap increases considerably because
    the HCO_3^- being used up to buffer the ketoacids is being replaced with ketates (**B**). The acidosis stimulates the
    respiratory center to hyperventilate, causing the plasma P_{CO_2} to decrease (**C**) as compensation for the metabolic
    acidosis. The excretion of NH_4^+ increases (**D**) in response to the acidosis (increases the generation of new bicarbonate
    to compensate for that lost in buffering the ketoacids being produced). The amount of HCO_3^- excreted in the urine
    should decrease (not increase) as the pH of the urine drops to very low levels.

34. Aldosterone:
    A. secretion is increased by converting enzyme inhibitors
    B. acts through basolateral membrane receptors to increase luminal membrane sodium channels
    C. increases Na^+ entry into intercalated cells along the late distal tubule and collecting duct
    D. increases the amount of Na^+/K^+ ATPase in the principal cells
    E. decreases the number of K^+ channels on the luminal membrane of the principal cells

Answer = D. Aldosterone causes several events that increase sodium reabsorption and potassium secretion; one of these is an increase in the amount of Na^+/K^+ ATPase in the principal cells. The secretion of aldosterone is determined in large part by the level of angiotensin II; hence, a converting enzyme inhibitor will decrease angiotensin II levels and, thus, lead to a decrease in aldosterone secretion (not **A**). As a steroid hormone, aldosterone does not react with a basolateral receptor but rather with cytoplasmic and nuclear receptors (not **B**) that do increase the number of luminal membrane sodium channels. The principal cells are thought to be the primary target for aldosterone, not the intercalated cells (not **C**), which are involved in H^+ secretion. No evidence indicates that aldosterone directly affects potassium channels (not **E**); if it did, one might expect an increase in K channels to account for the increase in potassium secretion.

Questions 35–38. Use the following data to answer questions 35–38. Both patients complain of intense thirst and a constant desire to urinate.

Item	Patient 1	Patient 2
Plasma osmolality	290 mOsm	280 mOsm
Urine osmolality	98 mOsm	170 mOsm
Urine volume	3 ml/min	2.2 ml/min

35. **What is the osmolar clearance for Patient 1?**

C_{osm} = _____

Answer = 1.0 ml/min. $C_{osm} = (U_{osm} \times UF)/P_{osm} = (98 \text{ mOsm} \times 3 \text{ ml/min})/290 \text{ mOsm} = 1.0 \text{ ml/min}$. This is a straightforward clearance calculation.

36. **What is the free water clearance for Patient 1?**

C_{H_2O} = _____

Answer = 2.0 ml/min. This is a special clearance equation to give us a measure of the amount of osmotically free water that is being excreted (positive values) or the amount of osmotically free water returned to the body (negative values). The equation for free water clearance is: $UF - C_{osm}$ (3.0 ml/min − 1.0 ml/min = 2.0 ml/min).

Question 37. One hour following the administration of excess antidiuretic hormone, the following data were obtained for these two patients. Use these data to answer question 37.

Item	Patient 1	Patient 2
Plasma osmolality	288 mOsm	275 mOsm
Urine osmolality	500 mOsm	700 mOsm

37. **Which of the following is true regarding the two patients?**
    A. Both patients have nephrogenic diabetes insipidus (inability of the kidney to respond to ADH).
    B. Patient 1 has nephrogenic diabetes insipidus, but Patient 2 does not have nephrogenic diabetes insipidus.
    C. The endogenous plasma ADH concentration was high in both patients before administering the ADH.
    D. Patient 2 had a higher medullary interstitial osmolality than did Patient 1.
    E. Both patients have primary diabetes insipidus (inability to make ADH).

Answer = D. Both patients responded to the administration of ADH; hence, both have kidneys that have functional receptors for ADH; i.e., they do not have nephrogenic diabetes insipidus (not **A** or **B**). We can conclude that in the presence of excess ADH the urine osmolarity will be determined by the osmolarity of the medullary interstitial fluid. We do not know whether the ADH in the plasma was high before ADH was administered (not **C**). It is likely that ADH was very low in Patient 2 because the plasma osmolarity was low. Both patients could have primary diabetes, but we cannot conclude this from the data presented up to this point (not **E**).

Question 38. Following an overnight dehydration (no water available), the following data were obtained for these two patients. Use these data to answer question 38.

Item	Patient 1	Patient 2
Plasma osmolality	315 mOsm	290 mOsm
Urine osmolality	140 mOsm	600 mOsm

38. Which of the following is true regarding the two patients?
    A.   Patient 1 has primary diabetes insipidus (inability to make ADH).
    B.   Patient 2 would benefit from receiving ADH treatment.
    C.   Patient 2 has primary diabetes insipidus (inability to make ADH).
    D.   Patient 1 should not be given ADH treatment.
    E.   Both A and B are true.

Answer = A.   Based on Patient 1's inability to respond to a water deprivation test but ability to respond to an ADH injection test, an inability to produce or secrete ADH is established. Patient 2, on the other hand, has a physiologically intact system; therefore, this patient must have a psychogenic drive to drink (not C). Giving Patient 2 ADH treatment is dangerous because the patient would continue to drink water, even though the kidneys cannot now produce the hypotonic urine that needs to be excreted. Hence, Patient 2 will become water intoxicated (not B). Patient 1 would benefit from receiving ADH treatment (not D), especially at night when the production of a concentrated urine allows sleep without the necessity of getting up every hour to empty the bladder.

39. Following 24 hours without any fluid intake, you would expect plasma osmolarity to 1, which would cause the secretion of 2, and also a(an) 3.

	1	2	3
A.	increase	more ADH	increased thirst
B.	increase	less ADH	decreased thirst
C.	decrease	less ADH	decreased thirst
D.	decrease	more ADH	increased thirst
E.	remain the same	less ADH	increased thirst

Answer = A.   Without fluid intake, water is lost from the body by evaporation (lungs) and diffusion (skin), causing the osmolarity to increase (not C, D, or E). The increase in plasma osmolarity stimulates ADH secretion (not B), causing water reabsorption by the kidney, and thirst increases.

40. An increase in plasma potassium would stimulate the secretion of 1, which would cause potassium secretion by the 2 to 3.

	1	2	3
A.	ADH	distal nephron	increase
B.	renin	proximal tubule	decrease
C.	aldosterone	distal nephron	increase
D.	renin	distal nephron	decrease
E.	aldosterone	proximal tubule	increase

Answer = C.   An increase in potassium concentration evoked by a direct action on the adrenal glomerulosa cells stimulates aldosterone secretion, which causes cells along the distal nephron to increase potassium secretion. Neither ADH nor renin is involved in mediating the effect of plasma potassium on aldosterone secretion (not A, B or D). Potassium secretion is increased along the distal nephron, not along the proximal tubule (not E).

41. Assume a normal GFR. The afferent arterial concentration of substance X = 100 mg/dl, and the efferent arterial concentration of substance X = 100 mg/dl. Substance X is most likely:
    A.   secreted by the renal tubules
    B.   metabolized by the glomerulus
    C.   not reabsorbed by the renal tubules
    D.   freely filtered
    E.   reabsorbed by the renal tubules

Answer = D. Since the efferent arteriole is a true artery, the only factor that affects its blood composition is events that occur during the passage of blood through the glomerular capillaries. When a molecule is freely filtered, then the concentration of the molecule in the filtrate is the same as in the plasma; no change in concentration occurs as the blood leaves the glomerulus (the mass delivered has decreased because blood flow is less). The glomerulus does very little to metabolically alter the composition of the blood or its constituents (not **B**). We can tell nothing about what will happen to the substance along the nephron (not **A**, **C**, or **E**) because that will affect the composition of the peritubular capillary blood, not the blood in the efferent artery.

42. **At the distal end of the proximal tubule, which of the following substances would normally have a lower concentration in tubular fluid than in the original glomerular filtrate?**
    A. urea
    B. bicarbonate
    C. hydrogen ions
    D. creatinine
    E. chloride

Answer = B. To have a lower concentration in the fluid from the distal end of the proximal tubule, a substance has to be reabsorbed at a rate greater than the rate at which sodium and water are being reabsorbed. Bicarbonate is rapidly reabsorbed by the secretion of H^+ ion, causing the HCO_3^- concentration to fall. As water is reabsorbed, the concentration of urea increases (not **A**), which establishes the concentration gradient for its passive reabsorption. Chloride concentration is higher because Cl^- accumulates in the fluid as the bicarbonate concentration is reduced (not **E**). The secretion of H^+ causes its concentration to increase (not **C**). Creatinine is not reabsorbed; in fact, there can be some secretion of creatinine, so its concentration increases (not **D**).

43. **The appearance of protein molecules in the urine depends on:**
    A. molecular size
    B. net charge on the protein
    C. reabsorption along the proximal tubule
    D. answers A and B are correct
    E. answers A, B, and C are correct

Answer = E. All three factors contribute to the normal level (very low) of protein that appears in the urine. The size barrier accounts for why most very large protein molecules do not appear in the urine; but the basement membrane is negatively charged, which impedes the filtration of proteins, which are mostly negatively charged. However, the barrier still allows ~30 mg/dl (recall that plasma protein concentration is 6,000 mg/dl or 6 g%) of protein to appear in the filtrate. That means that ~50 g of protein are filtered each day, but only 100–300 mg of protein are excreted each day. There is a T_{max} reabsorptive system for protein that reabsorbs about 30–40 mg/min or ~50 g/day. Thus, these three factors contribute to the formation of a protein-free urine.

44. **If the activity of carbonic anhydrase in the kidney is inhibited by the drug acetazolamide, which of the following would be most correct?**
    A. clearance of bicarbonate would decrease
    B. urine would become more acidic
    C. plasma bicarbonate would decrease
    D. titratable acid excretion would increase
    E. NH_4^+ excretion would increase

Answer = C. Inhibition of carbonic anhydrase will decrease the rate of H^+ formation, causing the rate of H^+ secretion along the nephron to decrease, causing bicarbonate reabsorption to be decreased. This will result in more bicarbonate being excreted, causing a decrease in plasma bicarbonate. This means that the clearance of bicarbonate will increase (not **A**). The urine will become alkaline (not **B**). There will be a decrease in both titratable acid and NH_4^+ excretion because both of these are inversely related to the pH of the urine (not **D** or **E**).

45. **If the production of creatinine by the body decreased from 1,000 mg/day to 500 mg/day and plasma creatinine decreased from 2 mg/dl to 1 mg/dl, then:**
    A. the glomerular filtration rate would decrease approximately 50%
    B. the glomerular filtration rate would approximately double
    C. no change in glomerular filtration would occur
    D. it is impossible to estimate what would happen to the glomerular filtrate from these data

Answer = C. The rate of creatinine production determines the amount that is excreted each day in the urine. The GFR determines the concentration of plasma creatinine that will exist in order for the kidney to excrete (mostly via filtration) the daily production of creatinine. If production falls by half and the plasma creatinine also falls by half, then no change in GFR has occurred; i.e., 1,000 mg/day/2 mg/dl = **500 liters/day** = 500 mg/day/1 mg/dl.

46. **The percentage of fluid reabsorbed by the proximal tubule can be increased by:**
   A. aldosterone
   B. angiotensin II
   C. an increase in peritubular capillary pressure
   D. AVP
   E. a decrease in oncotic pressure in the peritubular capillaries

Answer = B. By stimulating the Na/H exchanger in the proximal tubule, angiotensin II will enhance the rate of fluid reabsorption. Aldosterone and AVP have no known effects on the proximal tubule (not **A** or **D**). An increase in peritubular capillary pressure as well as a decrease in oncotic pressure in the peritubular capillaries will inhibit fluid uptake (not **C** or **E**), leading to an inhibition of fluid reabsorption by the proximal tubule.

47. **A patient is inadvertently given 2 liters of isotonic saline (0.9% NaCl) over a 4-h period of time. This infusion should cause an increase in:**
   A. AVP
   B. plasma oncotic pressure
   C. angiotensin II
   D. atrial natriuretic factor
   E. aldosterone

Answer = D. The administered isotonic saline will expand the extracellular compartment, leading to an increase in blood volume, causing the atria to secrete atrial natriuretic factor. The saline will also dilute the plasma protein concentration and, thus, decrease oncotic pressure (not **B**); the increase in central venous pressure will be sensed by low-pressure baroreceptors, leading to a decrease in AVP secretion (not **A**). The increase in blood volume will result in a decreased sympathetic outflow, contributing to a decrease in renin that causes angiotensin II and aldosterone to decrease (not **C** or **E**).

48. **A patient is given the drug furosemide, which blocks the $Na^+/K^+/2\ Cl^-$ cotransporter. After a few hours (drug is still effective), you would expect all of the following *EXCEPT*:**
   A. a decreased plasma volume
   B. an increase in angiotensin II
   C. an increase in potassium excretion
   D. a large volume of hypertonic urine
   E. an increase in sodium excretion

Answer = D. *Remember you are looking for the exception.* When the $Na^+/K^+/2\ Cl^-$ cotransporter is blocked, sodium reabsorption by the thick ascending limb is inhibited and the osmotic gradient established by this active transport of sodium will be destroyed, making the medullary osmolality iso-osmotic. The large volume of fluid being presented to the distal nephron will prevent urea from being concentrated along the late distal tubule and collecting duct, and the urea gradient will also be destroyed. Hence, the patient will be putting out a large volume of isotonic, not hypertonic, urine. The loss of sodium (**E**) will cause plasma volume to decrease (**A**) and renin and angiotensin II to increase (**B**). The increase in delivery of sodium and water to the distal nephron and the inhibition of potassium reabsorption along the thick ascending limb will both contribute to an increase in potassium excretion (**C**).

49. **It has been found that a nephron segment studied in a dish does not actively transport Na and is impermeable to water. This segment is the:**
   A. proximal tubule
   B. thin descending limb of Henle
   C. thin ascending limb of Henle
   D. thick ascending limb of Henle
   E. distal tubule

Answer = C. The thin ascending limb of Henle reabsorbs sodium passively because of the large concentration gradient brought about by the high interstitial urea concentration, while the fluid within the thick ascending limb is mostly NaCl. Since this segment is impermeable to water, an osmotic gradient is generated, with the ascending limb fluid being hypotonic to the adjacent interstitial fluid. The descending limb also does not actively reabsorb sodium but it is very permeable to water (not **B**). The other three segments all have active Na transport (not **A**, **D**, or **E**).

Questions 50–53. The following data were obtained in a subject. Assume that GFR is 100 ml/min throughout.

	Period 1	Period 2	Period 3	Period 4
Plasma concentration of X	100 mg/dl	200 mg/dl	300 mg/dl	400 mg/dl
Urinary X excretion	0 mg/min	20 mg/min	100 mg/min	200 mg/min

50. **The filtered load of X in period 3 was:**
   A.   3 mg/min
   B.   30 mg/min
   C.   100 mg/min
   D.   200 mg/min
   E.   300 mg/min

Answer = E. The filtered load can be determined from the GFR and the plasma concentration of glucose; thus, 100 ml/min $\times$ 300 mg/dl = 300 mg/min.

51. **The T_{max} for X was:**
   A.   100 mg/min
   B.   180 mg/min
   C.   200 mg/min
   D.   20 mg/min
   E.   cannot estimate from the above data

Answer = C. First determine how much glucose was being reabsorbed in each period to determine if a T_{max} has been obtained. Filtered load − excretion = amount reabsorbed.
   Period 1 = 100 ml/min $\times$ 100 mg/dl = 100 mg/min − 0 mg/min = 100 mg/min reabsorbed
   Period 2 = 100 ml/min $\times$ 200 mg/dl = 200 mg/min − 20 mg/min = 180 mg/min reabsorbed
   Period 3 = 100 ml/min $\times$ 300 mg/dl = 300 mg/min − 100 mg/min = 200 mg/min reabsorbed
   Period 4 = 100 ml/min $\times$ 400 mg/dl = 400 mg/min − 200 mg/min = 200 mg/min reabsorbed
Thus, for this patient the T_{max} for glucose is only 200 mg/min, with a threshold for glucose near 200 mg/dl. This is a very low value for a normal individual, but such values can be observed and cause patients to spill glucose into their urine at physiological levels of plasma glucose. In such patients, glucose in the urine does not indicate diabetes mellitus.

52. **An increase in aldosterone can affect H^+ secretion by the proximal tubule by:**
   A.   direct stimulation of the H^+/ATP pump
   B.   direct stimulation of the Na^+/H^+ exchanger
   C.   causing hypokalemia
   D.   causing hyponatremia
   E.   causing an increase in angiotensin II

Answer = C. Aldosterone has no known direct effect on the proximal tubule cells to increase H^+ secretion (not **A** or **B**). However, an increase in aldosterone will cause an increase in potassium secretion, leading to a net loss of potassium and producing hypokalemia. Hypokalemia is a factor known to stimulate H^+ secretion by the proximal tubule. An increase in aldosterone would not be expected to produce hyponatremia (it might produce a mild hypernatremia), but there is no direct relationship between hyponatremia and H^+ secretion (not **D**). An increase in angiotensin II would increase H^+ secretion via its effect on the Na^+/H^+ exchanger, but an increase in aldosterone will decrease angiotensin II (not **E**).

53. **A large increase in sympathetic nerve activity to the kidney is noted, but glomerular capillary pressure does not change (i.e., it remains at 60 mm Hg). In view of this information, you would predict that the:**
   A.   filtration fraction will increase
   B.   protein concentration in the efferent artery will decrease
   C.   Hct in the efferent arteriole will decrease
   D.   peritubular capillary pressure will increase
   E.   renal plasma flow will remain constant

Answer = A. Since glomerular capillary pressure did not change, GFR will tend to be maintained, whereas the increase in nerve activity to the kidney will cause renal blood flow to decrease (not **E**). Hence, the filtration fraction will increase. This will also cause the protein concentration and the Hct in the efferent arteriole to increase (not **B** or **C**). Because the resistance of the efferent arteriole increased and flow decreased, a decrease in peritubular capillary pressure will occur (not **D**).

Questions 54–55. A patient is aggressively treated with a diuretic for several weeks, and the following data are obtained.

Patient	Normal
Plasma Na = 130 mM	138–145 mM
Plasma Cl = 81 mM	95–105 mM
Plasma K = 2.5 mM	3.5–5.0 mM
P_{osm} = 265 mOsm	285–290 mOsm
Blood pressure = 105/65 mm Hg	120/80 mm Hg
Plasma pH = 7.52	7.40
P_{CO2} = 50 mm Hg	40 mm Hg
Plasma HCO_3 = 39 mM	22–26 mM

54. This patient has:
A. metabolic acidosis
B. acute respiratory alkalosis
C. chronic respiratory alkalosis
D. chronic respiratory acidosis
E. metabolic alkalosis

Answer = E. This patient has a metabolic alkalosis with respiratory compensation.

55. All of the following might be expected in this patient *EXCEPT*:
A. decreased extracellular volume
B. increased intracellular volume
C. increased renin secretion
D. urine pH > 7.4
E. increased H^+ secretion

Answer = D. *Remember you are looking for the exception.* In view of the history and data presented for this patient, you would expect that the patient has lost a large amount of sodium (diuretic-induced) and ingested enough water (possibly because of decreased ECV stimulating thirst) to dilute extracellular sodium and osmolality. Hence, cell volume would be increased (**B**), while extracellular volume would be decreased (**A**), which would lead to an increase in renin secretion (**C**); note the low arterial blood pressure. Since the patient has hypokalemia (diuretic-induced) and the extracellular volume is depleted, H^+ secretion (by both proximal and distal nephron segments) is stimulated (**E**), causing an excess production of HCO_3 that causes the alkalosis. Hence, this patient is secreting excessive amounts of H^+, producing an acidic urine. Only when the plasma potassium concentration and extracellular volume are restored to normal will the urine become alkaline and correct the metabolic alkalosis by excreting the excess HCO_3.

Question 56. A sample of blood is obtained from a blood vessel within the kidney of a normal individual, and the following data are obtained:

Hct	60%
Protein concentration	7.2 g%
Pressure within the vessel	35 mm Hg

56. The arterial blood of this individual has a Hct of 50% and a protein concentration of 6.0 g%. The sample was obtained from the:
A. afferent arteriole
B. glomerular capillary
C. efferent arteriole
D. peritubular capillary
E. vasa recta

Answer = C. Blood from the efferent arteriole has a higher Hct and protein concentration because it becomes concentrated as protein and RBC-free fluid are filtered across the glomerular membrane into Bowman's space. The pressure is lower than expected for the glomerular capillaries (not **B**) and higher than expected for the peritubular capillaries or vasa recta (not **D** or **E**). Blood from the afferent arteriole would have a higher pressure (not **A**), and the Hct and protein concentration would be identical to that in the arterial blood sample.

Questions 57–58. To answer questions 57 and 58, use the following laboratory data obtained in a patient.

Arterial pH	7.2
P_{CO_2}	26 mm Hg
Plasma Na	140
Plasma K	5
Plasma Cl	105

57. **What is the plasma HCO_3?**
    A. 7 mM
    B. 10 mM
    C. 14 mM
    D. 18 mM
    E. 22 mM

Answer = B. Since the pH is 7.2, the log ratio of the HCO_3/H_2CO_3 must be $7.2 - 6.1 = 1.1$. Given that the $H_2CO_3 = (26 \times 0.03 = 0.78$ mM), the $HCO_3 = \log 1.1 = HCO_3/0.78$; $12.59 = HCO_3 \times 0.78 = 9.8$ mM or **10 mM.**

58. **What is a possible cause of this patient's condition?**
    A. ingestion of HCl acid
    B. excretion of an alkaline urine
    C. ingestion of $NaHCO_3$
    D. increased production of lactic acid
    E. vomiting HCl

Answer = D. This patient has a metabolic acidosis associated with a large anion gap ([140 mM $-$ (105 mM + 10 mM)] $= 25$ mM). Hence, there must be a source of acid production or the addition of an acid that would produce an increase in the unmeasured anions. An increase in the production of lactic acid will produce such an acidosis. Both **A** and **B** will produce a metabolic acidosis, but the anion gap will be near normal (not **A** or **B**). Ingestion of $NaHCO_3$ or vomiting HCl tends to cause an alkalosis (not **C** or **E**).

59. **The H^+ ions secreted by the Na^+/H^+ exchanger in the kidney are most likely to:**
    A. combine with $HPO_4^=$
    B. combine with HCO_3^-
    C. lower tubule pH to below 6.0
    D. combine with Cl^-
    E. combine with $SO_4^=$

Answer = B. H^+ ions secreted by the Na^+/H^+ exchanger are found along the proximal tubule where most of the H^+ ions react with HCO_3^-. Because there is a limited amount of unreabsorbed $HPO_4^=$ available compared to amount of bicarbonate that is filtered, only a few mMoles of H^+ ions react with $HPO_4^=$ (not **A**). The pH of the fluid within the proximal tubule can only decrease to a pH of 6.8 (not **C**). Cl^- is the base of HCl and can only combine with H^+ ions at a pH far below that found in urine (not **C**). $SO_4^=$ is only present in low amounts and is not a good base at the pH found within the luminal fluid of the proximal nephron (not **E**).

60. **Ca^{2+} handling by the distal tubule and collecting duct involves all of the following *EXCEPT*:**
    A. a passive Ca^{2+} entry mechanism in the luminal membrane
    B. maintenance of a low intracellular Na^+ concentration by Na^+/K^+ ATPase
    C. Ca^{2+} ATPase in the basolateral cell membrane
    D. a Ca^{2+} secretory process similar to that for potassium
    E. a parathyroid hormone-sensitive reabsorptive process

Answer = D. *Remember you are looking for the exception.* Like sodium excretion, but unlike potassium excretion, calcium excretion is determined by filtration of the free calcium and then the reabsorption of the majority of the filtered load of calcium; a secretory process is not thought to be involved. Calcium enters the cells across the luminal membrane down a large electrochemical gradient via undefined passive mechanisms (**A**). One of the calcium transport processes located on the basolateral membrane is a Na^+/Ca^{2+} exchange process that utilizes the energy from the large sodium concentration gradient established by the Na^+/K^+ ATPase (**B**). Another calcium transport process is a Ca^{2+} ATPase in the basolateral cell membrane (**C**). Parathyroid hormone is known to enhance calcium reabsorption along the distal nephron and collecting duct (**E**).

61. A sample of tubular fluid was obtained by micropuncture of a segment of the nephron in a normal mammal. The fluid had an osmolarity of 900 mOsm/l and a pH of 5.5. The tubular fluid came from the:
    A.   proximal tubule
    B.   tip of the loop of Henle
    C.   upper portion of the ascending limb of the loop of Henle
    D.   papillary collecting duct
    E.   late portion of the distal tubule

    Answer = D. The high osmolarity of the sample places the location somewhere within the medulla or papilla. The second important piece of information is the acidity of the sample, which places the sample some place beyond the distal nephron. Hence, the papillary collecting duct is the best choice.

62. Relative to the plasma in the efferent arteriole, the fluid in Bowman's capsule has a:
    A.   higher glucose concentration
    B.   higher sodium concentration
    C.   higher potassium concentration
    D.   lower oncotic pressure
    E.   all of the above

    Answer = D. As fluid is filtered across the glomerular membrane into Bowman's capsule, there is little change in the concentration of small-molecular-weight molecules, such as glucose, sodium, and potassium. Hence, the concentration of these molecules is virtually the same in plasma from the efferent arteriole and fluid from Bowman's space (not **A**, **B**, or **C**). However, since the protein that generates the oncotic pressure is not freely filtered, oncotic pressure in the plasma from the efferent arteriole is very high, while Bowman's space fluid has virtually no protein and an oncotic pressure of zero.

63. Inulin is infused intravenously in a normal subject. The concentration of inulin in the plasma in the peritubular capillaries is:
    A.   zero
    B.   higher than the concentration of inulin in the fluid in Bowman's capsule
    C.   lower than the concentration of inulin in the fluid in Bowman's capsule
    D.   the same as the concentration of inulin in the fluid in Bowman's capsule

    Answer = C. Inulin is freely filtered; hence, the concentration of inulin in plasma from the efferent arteriole is the same as that in the fluid in Bowman's space. However, as fluid is reabsorbed along the nephron, the concentration of inulin in the plasma from the peritubular capillaries decreases because inulin is not reabsorbed but remains in the lumen of the nephron.

64. In a person on a very high potassium intake, the urine at the end of the ascending limb of the loop of Henle will:
    A.   contain approximately 10% of the filtered potassium
    B.   contain approximately 50% of the filtered potassium
    C.   contain approximately 100% of the filtered potassium
    D.   contain approximately 200% of the filtered potassium
    E.   have a potassium concentration higher than that of the plasma

    Answer = A. This person will be excreting an increased amount of potassium in the urine. However, the vast majority of the increase in excretion is due to an increase in the secretion of potassium along the cortical part of the distal nephron. The proximal tubule and loop of Henle continue to reabsorb potassium; hence, approximately 10% of the filtered potassium will be present at the end of the ascending limb of the loop of Henle.

65. A drug that blocks angiotensin-converting enzyme (ACE) is given to a patient. All of the following are likely to decrease *EXCEPT*:
   A. peripheral arterial resistance
   B. plasma aldosterone concentration
   C. arterial blood pressure
   D. plasma renin concentration
   E. plasma angiotensin II concentration

   Answer = D. *Remember you are looking for the exception.* The converting enzyme inhibitor blocks the formation of angiotensin II from angiotensin I. Since angiotensin II has a direct negative feedback effect on the secretion of renin by the juxtaglomerular cells, renin levels will be increased, not decreased. All of the other factors will be decreased because of the low levels of angiotensin II.

Questions 66–68. Match the following lettered sets of data with the condition (shown in questions 66–68) that best fits the data. The subjects are humans, and normal values are shown in the first row of data.

	Urine Flow (ml/min)	$[Osm]_U$ mOsm/kg	Hct %	$[Osm]_P$ mOsm/kg	$[Na]_P$ mM
Normal Values	1.0	560	46	290	142
A.	4.5	110	38	270	130
B.	4.7	100	54	310	151
C.	4.3	720	42	308	138
D.	0.4	780	54	310	151
E.	0.3	790	38	270	130

66. _____ Diabetes insipidus

   Answer = B. A patient with diabetes insipidus does not produce ADH (or will not respond to ADH) and consequently will excrete a large volume of dilute (low osmolality) urine. This will cause plasma osmolality and plasma [Na] both to be increased and may also cause some hemoconcentration, which would cause the Hct to be higher than normal.

67. _____ Diabetes mellitus

   Answer = C. A patient with diabetes mellitus excretes a large volume of urine containing excessive amounts of glucose (an osmotic particle). The glucose also contributes to an increase in plasma osmolality, but plasma sodium concentration is near normal. Until there is a marked ketonuria, the patient increases water intake enough to maintain total body water and plasma volume near normal levels.

68. _____ Inappropriate ADH secretion (SIADH)

   Answer = E. The inappropriate secretion of ADH causes the production of very concentrated urine. Any water that is ingested by the patient is retained and leads to the dilution of the [Na] and osmolality in the plasma.

69. At the end of the proximal tubule, which of the following substances would normally have a higher concentration in tubular fluid than in the original glomerular filtrate?
   A. glucose
   B. amino acids
   C. phosphate
   D. creatinine
   E. sodium

   Answer = D. Only creatinine, which is freely filtered and not reabsorbed but secreted, will have a higher concentration in the fluid at the end of the proximal tubule. All of the other substances have a transporter that reabsorbs them; thus, their concentrations are less than those found in the original glomerular filtrate, except that of sodium, which is basically not different from that found in the glomerular filtrate.

70. **If you place a patient on a low-sodium diet, you would expect a decrease in:**
   A. glucose reabsorption
   B. amino acid reabsorption
   C. hydrogen ion secretion by the proximal tubule
   D. bicarbonate reabsorption
   E. none of the above would be decreased

   Answer = E. Although all of the processes listed involve a sodium ion-dependent carrier or exchanger in their transport process, a low-sodium diet has little effect on the concentration of sodium; and, even more important, the concentration of sodium needed to drive these processes is far below the concentration of sodium found in patients under any circumstance.

71. **The major factor determining the long-term ECF volume is:**
   A. the amount of sodium retained in the ECF
   B. the ECF sodium concentration
   C. the amount of K^+ retained in the ECF
   D. the osmolality of the ECF

   Answer = A. The basis for this question is that the majority of the sodium is in the extracellular compartment; the size of the extracellular compartment is determined by how much sodium is present, assuming osmolality is kept within normal limits. Since the concentration of sodium (and osmolality) is a function of both the amount of sodium and the amount of water, it is not a predictor of the extracellular volume (not **B** or **D**). Potassium is retained primarily within the intracellular, not extracellular compartment (not **C**).

Questions 72–75. The table below gives arterial blood gas findings and pertinent electrolytes for patients with acid-base disturbances. Use these data for questions 72-75.

	P_{CO_2} mm Hg	HCO_3^- mM	pH U	Na^+	K^+ mEq/l	Cl^-	Creatinine mg/dl
Patient A	35	19	7.35	140	5.5	110	1
Patient B	40	30	7.50	140	3.0	99	4
Patient C	15	5	7.15	140	6.0	105	2
Patient D	60	30	7.32	140	5.5	99	1
Patient E	25	20	—	140	4.8	109	1

72. **The patient with metabolic acidosis consistent with uncontrolled diabetes mellitus is:**
   A. Patient A
   B. Patient B
   C. Patient C
   D. Patient D
   E. Patient E

   Answer = C. Patient C has a metabolic acidosis with a large anion gap (= 20 mM) and a slightly elevated creatinine that probably reflects the extracellular volume depletion caused by the osmotic diuresis associated with the ketoacidosis.

73. **Characterize Patient E.**
   A. metabolic acidosis without increased anion gap
   B. respiratory alkalosis, compensated
   C. metabolic acidosis with increased anion gap
   D. metabolic alkalosis, compensated
   E. respiratory acidosis, uncompensated

   Answer = B. The patient has a primary decrease in pCO_2 with some compensatory decrease in plasma bicarbonate.

74. Total H^+ secretion would be highest in which patient?
   A. Patient A
   B. Patient B
   C. Patient C
   D. Patient D
   E. Patient E

Answer = D. The patient has a primary increase in pCO_2 with a compensatory increase in plasma bicarbonate. Hence, this patient is filtering (*Note:* normal plasma creatinine indicates a normal GFR) a large quantity of bicarbonate. The amount of H^+ needed to be secreted just to reabsorb this bicarbonate is greater for this patient than for any of the other patients.

75. In a hydropenic state (water scarcity) and relative to the renal artery, the renal vein would be:
   A. the same tonicity
   B. slightly hypertonic
   C. slightly hypotonic

Answer = C. In the absence of water, the kidney will be putting out a hypertonic urine, which means that the body will be retaining water in excess of solutes; hence, the renal vein osmolality will be slightly less than that in the renal artery.

76. What are the putative events in the tubuloglomerular feedback hypothesis of renal autoregulation? (DTF = distal tubule flow; MD = macula densa; JG = juxtaglomerular apparatus; AR = afferent arteriole resistance; ER = efferent arteriole resistance.)
   A. $\downarrow$DTF$\rightarrow$ MD response$\rightarrow\uparrow$AR$\rightarrow\downarrow$GFR
   B. $\uparrow$DTF$\rightarrow\uparrow$trenin$\rightarrow\uparrow$aldosterone$\rightarrow\downarrow$GFR
   C. $\uparrow$DTF$\rightarrow$MD response$\rightarrow\uparrow$AR$\rightarrow\downarrow$GFR
   D. $\uparrow$DTF$\rightarrow$JG response$\rightarrow\uparrow$AR$\rightarrow\downarrow$GFR
   E. $\downarrow$DTF$\rightarrow$JG response$\rightarrow\uparrow$AR$\rightarrow\downarrow$GFR

Answer = C. An increase in distal tubular delivery of fluid is sensed by the macula densa, which causes an increase in afferent arteriole resistance, which decreases the GFR back to its normal level.

77. The rate of inulin excretion is dependent upon which two variables?
   A. urine flow and arterial blood pressure
   B. GFR and proximal reabsorption
   C. urine flow and plasma concentration
   D. plasma concentration and proximal secretion
   E. plasma concentration and GFR

Answer = E. Since the amount of inulin filtered at the glomerulus will equal the amount excreted in the final urine, you need to know the plasma inulin concentration and the GFR.

78. Two hours after ingestion of one liter of an unknown fluid, urine flow increased from 1 to 10 ml/min, urine osmolality decreased from 1,000 to 250 mOsmol/kg • H_2O, sodium excretion was unchanged, potassium excretion increased from 75 to 175 mEq/min, and urinary pH increased from 5.6 to 7.3. The fluid ingested was probably:
   A. water
   B. 0.15 M NaCl
   C. 0.5 M glucose
   D. 0.05 M $NaHCO_3$
   E. 0.3 M urea

Answer = D. Because urine flow increased and osmolality decreased, a hypotonic solution was probably ingested (not **B**). With urine becoming alkaline and potassium excretion increasing, a bicarbonate solution is suggested. The poorly reabsorbed bicarbonate flowing through the distal nephron accounts for the increase in potassium secretion that causes the increase in potassium excretion. Water and the isosmotic urea solution would not have altered pH or potassium excretion, whereas a hypertonic glucose solution would have produced an osmotic diuresis.

79. A 60-kg subject runs a 10-km race on a hot day. At the end of the race, plasma osmolarity is elevated to 320 mOsmol/l from a control value of 280 mOsmol/l. Assuming that total body water initially was 60% of body weight and that the subject lost only water during the race, estimate the extracellular fluid volume after the race.
   A. 24 liters
   B. 12 liters
   C. 36 liters
   D. 10.5 liters
   E. 8.5 liters

   Answer = D. The loss of volume can be estimated from the change in osmolality based on the assumption that only water was lost. Assuming that the extracellular volume is 20% of body weight, the initial value for the extracellular volume is 121 liters × 280 mOsmol/liter = 3,360 mOsm divided by the final osmolarity of 320 mOsmol/liter = 10.5 liters.

80. **Which of the following inhibits the secretion of aldosterone?**
   A. i.v. infusion of 1 liter of isotonic NaCl solution
   B. a fall in plasma osmolality
   C. an increase in plasma potassium concentration
   D. stimulation of renal nerves
   E. decrease in sodium delivery to the macula densa

   Answer = A. The infusion of isotonic saline would cause the secretion of renin to be decreased primarily via a decrease in sympathetic nerve activity to the juxtaglomerulosa cells. The decrease in renin would lead to a decrease in angiotensin II, which would cause aldosterone secretion to decrease. All of the other factors stimulate aldosterone secretion either directly (**B** and **C**) or indirectly via activation of renin (**D** and **E**).

81. **The nephron segment in which the sodium concentration in the tubular fluid is greater than that in the surrounding interstitial fluid is the:**
   A. late proximal tubule
   B. thick ascending loop of Henle
   C. medullary collecting duct
   D. thin ascending loop of Henle
   E. distal tubule

   Answer = D. Within the thin portion of the loop of Henle, the sodium concentration within the lumen is greater than that found in the surrounding interstitium. Along the thin ascending limb of the loop of Henle, it is this gradient that drives sodium reabsorption. In all of the other listed segments of the nephron, the sodium concentration is either equal to **A** or less than **B**, **C**, or **E**.

82. **All of the following will increase GFR *EXCEPT*:**
   A. constriction of the efferent arteriole
   B. a marked rise in K_f
   C. a rise in arterial pressure
   D. dilation of the afferent arteriole
   E. a fall in plasma oncotic pressure

   Answer = C. *Remember you are looking for the exception.* Because autoregulation by the kidney is associated with alterations in afferent arteriolar resistance, increases in arterial pressure above normal do not normally cause an increase in GFR. All of the other choices would either increase net filtration pressure (**A**, **D**, and **E**) or increase the filtration coefficient, which would increase GFR.

83. Two lean patients are of the same height, age, sex, and body weight. However, one of the patients has a 75% reduction in renal tissue, while the other patient has normal renal function. Each patient is then given an identical inulin infusion (i.e., the same amount in milligrams of inulin/min). Which of the following statements is true?
   A. Plasma inulin concentration would be higher in the normal patient 1 h after starting the infusion.
   B. Urine inulin concentration would be higher in the patient with the reduced renal function 1 h after starting the infusion.
   C. At the time that plasma inulin concentration is constant in both patients, the rate of inulin excretion in the urine would be equal in the two patients as well.
   D. At the time that plasma inulin concentration is constant in both patients, the clearance of inulin also would be equal.
   E. After 2 h of inulin infusion, the plasma inulin concentration of both patients would be equal.

Answer = C. The loss of renal tissue is to be interpreted as a similar loss in the number of glomeruli. Hence, one patient has a GFR that is only 1/4 of that found in the other normal patient. When inulin is infused, it will reach a steady-state level in each patient at which the rate of inulin excretion in the urine will be the same (i.e., input = output; not **B**); however, the plasma inulin concentration will be four times higher in the patient with the reduced GFR (not **A** or **E**), i.e., a reduced clearance of inulin (not **D**).

84. **Which of the following elevates the filtration fraction?**
    A. dilation of the afferent arteriole
    B. an increase in the ultrafiltration coefficient of the glomerulus
    C. dilation of the efferent arteriole
    D. a marked rise in arterial pressure
    E. an increase in tubular pressure

Answer = B. An increase in filtration fraction is caused by an increase in GFR without a similar increase in renal plasma flow. Hence, an increase in the ultrafiltration coefficient increases GFR without increasing renal plasma flow. Choices **C** and **E** both will decrease net filtration pressure and, thus, decrease GFR and the filtration coefficient. An increase in arterial pressure will have little effect on the filtration fraction since both GFR and renal blood flow are autoregulated (not **D**). Afferent arteriolar dilation will increase both GFR and renal blood flow and probably have little effect on the filtration fraction (not **A**).

Questions 85–88. Use the following data to answer questions 85–88.

    Urine flow = 1 ml/min
    Urine sodium concentration = 75 mMol/l
    Urine inulin concentration = 100 mg/ml
    Urine potassium concentration = 200 mMol/l
    Plasma sodium concentration = 150 mMol/l
    Plasma potassium concentration = 5 mMol/l
    Plasma inulin concentration = 1 mg/ml

85. **The amount of sodium filtered at the glomerulus is:**
    A. 15 mMol/min
    B. 75 mMol/min
    C. 7500 mMol/min
    D. 100 ml/min
    E. 2 ml/min

Answer = A. First, determine GFR, which is equal to the clearance of inulin = $([I]_U \times$ urine flow$)/[I]_{P1}$ = 100 mg/min/1 mg/ml = 100 ml/min. The filtered load of sodium is GFR $\times [Na]_{P1}$ = 100 ml/min $\times$ 150 mMol/l (150 μMol/ml) = 15 mMol/min.

86. **What percentage of the filtered potassium is excreted in the urine?**
    A. 25.7%
    B. 40%
    C. 60%
    D. 100%
    E. 20%

Answer = B. First calculate the filtered load of potassium, which = GFR $\times [K]_{P1}$ = 500 μMol/min; then calculate the amount excreted = Urine flow $\times [K]_U$ = 200 μMol/min. The percentage of filtered potassium (500 μMol/min) that was excreted (200 μMol/min) = 40%.

87. **The renal clearance of sodium is:**
    A. 1 ml/min
    B. 100 ml/min
    C. 75 μMol/min
    D. 150 mMol/min
    E. 0.5 ml/min

Answer = E. The clearance of sodium is simply (urine flow $\times$ [Na]$_U$)/[Na]$_{Pl}$ = 75 μMol/min/150 μMol/ml = 0.5 ml/min

88. **The net rate of tubular reabsorption of potassium is:**
    A. 100 μMol/min
    B. 500 μMol/min
    C. 300 μMol/min
    D. 200 μMol/min
    E. 50 μMol/min

    Answer = C. Since the filtered load of potassium = 500 μMol/min and 200 μMol/min are excreted in the urine, then 300 μMol/min = the net amount of potassium reabsorption.

89. **A 25-year old patient presents in the walk-in clinic with polydipsia and polyuria (5 liters/day of dilute urine, 50–100 mOsm/kg water, Sp. Gr. = 1.002–1.005). The initial diagnosis is diabetes insipidus. Which one of the following observations is consistent with this diagnosis?**
    A. a concentrated urine is elaborated in response to an i.v. infusion of hypertonic saline
    B. a concentrated urine is produced in response to an infusion of hypotonic saline
    C. a concentrated urine is produced after i.v. vasopressin
    D. a concentrated urine is voided upon overnight restriction of fluid intake
    E. both A and C of the above choices are correct

    Answer = C. If the patient has primary diabetes insipidus, he cannot secrete vasopressin but he can respond to vasopressin; hence, the patient should respond to an i.v. infusion of vasopressin. He should not be able to produce a concentrated urine following either a hypertonic infusion (not **A** or **E**) or an overnight restriction of fluid (not **D**). A hypotonic infusion will never lead to the production of a concentrated urine (not **B**).

90. **Patients with cirrhosis of the liver typically exhibit edema formation. Which of the following must occur in order to establish this edema?**
    A. increased cell membrane K$^+$ permeability
    B. increased plasma oncotic pressure
    C. decreased plasma renin activity
    D. Na$^+$ retention
    E. stimulation of ADH release

    Answer = D. The basic cause of the edema is an elevated hydrostatic pressure in the hepatic circulation, but for there to be a large and detectable amount of edema present in the abdomen, the kidneys must retain sodium for several days to accumulate the excess sodium and water. There is not enough interstitial fluid or plasma stored in the body to allow for the accumulation of a significant volume of edematous fluid within the abdomen. The sodium retention is, in part, due to an increase in renin–angiotensin II-aldosterone secretion (not **C**). Neither increased plasma oncotic pressure nor cell membrane K$^+$ permeability is a cause of edema (not **A** or **B**).

91. **Three patients have been diagnosed with severe chronic renal failure. These patients all exhibit plasma creatinine concentrations exceeding 6 mg/dl, hematocrits less than 38%, and plasma potassium concentrations between 4.3 and 5.8 mEq/l. Assuming a normal diet and physical activity for each of these patients, you would expect their creatinine excretion rates to be:**
    A. widely disparate
    B. similar to normal GFR
    C. less than those of normal individuals
    D. greater than those of normal individuals
    E. similar to those of normal individuals

    Answer = E. Even these patients will reach a steady-state plasma creatinine concentration (much higher than that of normal individuals; not **C**) at which the normal daily production of creatinine is filtered and then excreted into the urine (not **A** or **D**). Choice **B** is not related to the urinary excretion of creatinine.

92. **In a normal subject, 24 h of water deprivation results in:**
   A. an osmolality of the tubular fluid at the end of the thick ascending loop of Henle equal to that of the plasma
   B. increased urea reabsorption in the papillary collecting duct
   C. increased osmolality of the cortical interstitium
   D. decreased osmolality of the papillary interstitium
   E. none of the above

   Answer = B. The clearance of urea is the lowest (i.e., highest rate of reabsorption) when the urine flow is slow and a concentrated urine is being excreted. During water deprivation, ADH causes a very high level of water and urea permeability along the medullary collecting duct, which produces the very high interstitial osmolality within the papillary interstitium (not **D**). Water deprivation has little effect on the osmolality of the fluid that leaves the thick ascending limb, which is always hypotonic (not **A**). There will be little change in the osmolality of the cortical interstitium since it remains iso-osmotic to arterial plasma (not **C**).

93. **Sodium in the proximal tubule:**
   A. is reabsorbed exclusively through the paracellular pathway
   B. moves from lumen to cell actively against a concentration gradient
   C. is transported across the basolateral cell membrane actively by a Na^+/K^+ ATPase
   D. is reabsorbed exclusively by cotransport with glucose
   E. is reabsorbed exclusively by counter-transport with hydrogen ions

   Answer = C. The active transport step in the reabsorption of sodium occurs across the basolateral cell membrane by the Na^+/K^+ ATPase. Although paracellular reabsorption of sodium occurs, it is not the exclusive mechanism (not **A**). Sodium enters the cells down its electrochemical gradient (not **B**) via a variety of processes, including cotransport, exchange, and channels (not **D** or **E**).

94. **A compound that has a renal clearance 25 times that of creatinine is probably:**
   A. only filtered at the glomerulus
   B. only secreted by the nephron
   C. both filtered and secreted
   D. synthesized by the nephron and secreted
   E. filtered, secreted and reabsorbed

   Answer = D. Since approximately 20% of the renal plasma flow is filtered, the maximum clearance that a substance can have is five times that of the marker for glomerular filtration (inulin or creatinine) (not **A**, **B**, **C** or **E**) unless that substance is synthesized by the tubular cells lining the nephron.

95. **All of the following have an established transport T_m EXCEPT:**
   A. glucose
   B. sodium
   C. albumin
   D. para-aminohippuric acid (PAH)
   E. lactate

   Answer = B. *Remember you are looking for the exception.* Sodium has never been shown to have a transport maximum (*not* **B**), even though it is transported by the sodium pump; the capacity of the pump for moving sodium apparently exceeds the highest load that the nephron ever sees. All of the other substances have been shown to have T_m.

1. **Gastrointestinal hormones are:**
    A.   steroids
    B.   released into the lumen of the GI tract
    C.   destroyed in their passage through the liver
    D.   found in endocrine cells distributed over wide areas of mucosa
    E.   members of either one or the other of two chemically related families

    Answer = D.   Unlike many endocrine tissues, the hormone-secreting cells of the GI tract are not discretely localized but are distributed over wide areas of mucosa. They are mostly peptide in nature (not **A**) and are released into the bloodstream (not **B**), where most must successfully pass through the liver to affect the target tissue (not **C**). There are now considered to be more than two families (not **E**).

2. **Members of the secretin family of peptides:**
    A.   act either as hormones or neurocrines
    B.   contain fragments possessing full biological activity
    C.   stimulate gastric acid secretion
    D.   function physiologically as paracrines
    E.   can be released by distention of the stomach

    Answer = A.   All GI hormones are also found in nerves throughout the GI tract. Members of the secretin family are peptides that require all of their amino acids for activity (not **B**). These hormones primarily stimulate the pancreatic secretion of bicarbonate (not **C**) and are released in response to acidification (not **E**) of the duodenum. They do not function as paracrines (not **D**).

3. **A substance released from nerves that stimulates contraction of the ileocecal sphincter is likely to be:**
    A.   VIP (vasoactive intestinal peptide)
    B.   GRP (gastrin-releasing peptide)
    C.   one of the enkephalins
    D.   peptide YY
    E.   motilin

    Answer = C.   Enkephalins are thought to mediate the contraction of the ileocecal sphincter, which helps to explain the well-known antidiarrheal properties of opiates. VIP (not **A**) is a vasorelaxant, GRP (not **B**) is a gastric neurocrine, peptide YY (not **D**) is a neurocrine that is not localized at the ileocecal sphincter, and motilin (not **E**) is primarily considered to be the hormone responsible for initiating the migrating motility complex.

4. **A muscle cell that has no striations and has a ratio of thin to thick filaments of 15:1 most likely would be found in the:**
    A.   external anal sphincter
    B.   lower esophageal sphincter
    C.   pharynx
    D.   tongue
    E.   upper esophageal sphincter

    Answer = B.   Only the lower esophageal sphincter is composed of smooth muscles; all of the other muscles listed are striated muscles.

5. **A lesion results in loss of primary peristaltic contractions of the pharynx and esophagus; however, secondary peristalsis of the lower esophagus still occurs upon distention of the esophageal body. The lesion most likely is in the:**
    A.   cortical region of the brain
    B.   cricopharyngeal muscle (upper esophageal sphincter)
    C.   enteric nerves
    D.   nucleus ambiguus
    E.   pharyngeal muscle

Answer = D. Since the peristalsis in the pharynx and upper esophagus is under voluntary control and involves striated muscle, any disturbance of the swallowing center (not **A**) will prevent swallowing and the initial peristaltic wave in the upper esophagus from being initiated; but the lower esophagus is under the control of the enteric nerves (not **C**). A defect in either the cricopharyngeal muscle (not **B**) or the pharyngeal muscle (not **E**) will not prevent a peristaltic wave from being initiated by the striated muscle of the upper esophagus.

6. A catheter that monitors pressure at its tip is inserted through the nose and passed an unknown distance. The catheter records a pressure between swallows that is subatmospheric and that decreases during inspiration and increases during expiration. The catheter tip is most likely in the:
    A.   upper esophageal sphincter
    B.   esophageal body above the diaphragm
    C.   esophageal body below the diaphragm
    D.   lower esophageal sphincter
    E.   orad region of the stomach

Answer = B. The pressure pattern is that of the thoracic cavity: negative pressure at rest that becomes more negative upon contraction of the diaphragm and intercostal muscles. Sites **C–E** are below the diaphragm and would have a positive pressure upon inspiration. The upper esophageal sphincter is outside the thoracic cavity and would be somewhat insensitive to respiratory motions (not **A**).

7. In fasting subjects, the period of intense contractions of the MMC (migrating motility complex), when compared to the period of minimal contractions, is characterized by:
    A.   a decrease in the apparent propagation velocity of control slow waves
    B.   a decrease in the frequency of duodenal slow waves
    C.   an increase in the amplitude of antral slow waves
    D.   an increase in the frequency of antral slow waves
    E.   the occurrence of slow waves in the orad stomach

Answer = C. These contractions originate in the midportion (not **E**) of the stomach and are characterized by a wave of both increasing velocity (not **A**) and amplitude but no change in frequency (not **B** or **D**).

8. Which of the following solutions would empty most rapidly from the stomach?
    A.   100 mN HCl
    B.   water
    C.   isotonic starch
    D.   hypertonic NaCl
    E.   isotonic NaCl

Answer = E. Isotonic saline empties most rapidly. Abnormal osmolality, acidic pH, and food stuff all reduce the rate of gastric emptying.

9. A region of the intestine contracts weakly upon stimulation of its extrinsic nerves. Distention of the region elicits a peristaltic reflex, but with weak contractions. Slow wave activity is absent. These findings suggest a disorder of the:

    A.   enteric nerves
    B.   parasympathetic nerves
    C.   release of CCK
    D.   smooth muscle cells
    E.   sympathetic nerves

Answer = D. The absence of slow waves, which are an inherent characteristic of the smooth muscle cells of the small intestine, indicates a smooth muscle cell defect. Although enteric nerves may play a role in initiating a contraction, the strength of the contraction and the presence of slow waves are a function of the muscle cells.

10. Intraluminal pressure is monitored from a region of the colon that exhibits a relatively constant resting pressure of about 20 mm Hg. When an adjacent region of colon is distended, resting pressure falls to near 0 and then increases slowly back toward 20 mm Hg, even though the distention persists. The region being monitored is most likely the:
    A.   ileocecal sphincter
    B.   ascending colon
    C.   transverse colon
    D.   internal anal sphincter
    E.   external anal sphincter

Answer = D. The internal anal sphincter relaxes when the rectum is distended and then accommodates by gradually restoring its tone. The ileocecal sphincter will relax when the ileum is distended but contracts when the colon is distended (not **A**). The pressures in the colon are those associated with peristaltic contractions (not **B** or **C**), whereas the external sphincter is primarily under voluntary control (not **E**).

11. Compared to fluid in a salivary gland acinus, the fluid at the duct opening in the mouth will have a:
   A.   lower concentration of K^+
   B.   higher concentration of water
   C.   higher concentration of Na^+
   D.   higher concentration of Cl^-
   E.   lower pH

Answer = B. As saliva flows down the duct, Na and Cl are reabsorbed (not **C** or **D**), which lowers the osmolality of the saliva. Furthermore, the potassium (not **A**) and bicarbonate concentrations (raise pH; not **E**) are elevated.

12. A substance found in saliva that increases blood flow to the salivary glands is:
   A.   kallikrein
   B.   bradykinin
   C.   lactoferrin
   D.   lysozyme
   E.   acetylcholine

Answer = A. Kallikrein is released into the saliva and converts a plasma protein into bradykinin (in the plasma; not **B**), which is a potent vasodilator.

13. Salivary amylase:
   A.   digests starch into glucose units
   B.   is an endopeptidase
   C.   is activated by low gastric pH
   D.   is essential for normal starch digestion
   E.   remains active in unmixed contents of the orad stomach

Answer = E. α-amylase (not **B**) remains active in the orad stomach as long as the pH is not too acidic, which could inactivate the amylase (not **C**). It does not, however, break starch down to simple sugars (not **A**). Although it can digest up to 75% of the starch, the total absence of salivary amylase has no major effect on starch digestion since the pancreatic amylases can digest all of the starch present in the small intestines (not **D**).

14. A cell isolated from the gastric mucosa contains granules localized between its nucleus and the basal membrane. That cell is most likely a:
   A.   parietal cell
   B.   gastrin cell
   C.   chief or peptic cell
   D.   mucous neck cell
   E.   surface epithelial cell

Answer = B. Since gastrin is a hormone that is secreted into the bloodstream, granules containing gastrin are located near the basal cell membrane. **A**, **C**, and **D** secrete their products into the lumen of the gut, and the epithelial cells should have few granules (**E**).

15. During the interdigestive phase, a subject is injected with a dose of histamine that is sufficient to stimulate acid secretion. Compared to the period before stimulation:
   A.   the potential difference across the gastric mucosa will be less
   B.   the pH of the gastric venous blood will be less
   C.   the concentration of Na^+ in the gastric juice will be greater
   D.   there will be more tubulovesicles in the parietal cells
   E.   none of the above

Answer = A. As the H^+ are secreted, the potential difference will change from about -80 mV to about -30 mV. The pH of the venous blood will actually become alkaline (not **B**). As the H^+ concentration increases, the sodium concentration of gastric juice decreases (not **C**) and the amount of tubulovesicles in the parietal cells decreases (not **D**).

16. **Following the stimulation of gastric secretion, the concentration of H^+ in gastric juice increases because:**
    A. the volume of secretion from the parietal cells increases
    B. the concentration of H^+ being secreted by the parietal cells increases
    C. the gastric mucosal barrier tightens and prevents a loss of H^+
    D. the nonparietal component of gastric secretion is inhibited
    E. H^+ is exchanged for Na^+ as the juice moves up the gastric gland

    Answer = A. The primary reason for the increase in H^+ concentration is the increase in the volume of fluid secreted by the parietal cells. The H^+ concentration of the parietal secretion remains at ~150 mEq/liter (not **B**). The mucosal barrier is not directly altered by stimulation of gastric secretion (not **C**). The nonparietal component of gastric secretion does not change (not **D**). The exchange of H^+ for Na^+ occurs at very low rates of gastric secretion and tends to reduce the acidity of the gastric juice (not **E**).

17. **Enterokinase is directly responsible for the activation of:**
    A. carboxypeptidase A
    B. enterokinase
    C. colipase
    D. trypsin
    E. all of the above

    Answer = D. Enterokinase is a brush border enzyme responsible for converting trypsinogen to trypsin. Trypsin is then the primary enzyme that converts the proenzyme or profactor into the active products (**A**, **B**, **C**, and, in fact, **D**). Hence, it is indirectly, not directly, involved in all of the listed products.

18. **Histamine-2 (H_2) receptor blockers, such as cimetidine, inhibit the acid secretory response to:**
    A. histamine and gastrin but not acetylcholine
    B. histamine but not gastrin
    C. the stimuli present during the cephalic phase
    D. somatostatin
    E. none of the above

    Answer = C. As histamine potentiates the effects of both gastrin and ACh in the cephalic phase of acid secretion, cimetidine will inhibit the acid secretory response of all of these factors. Recall that somatostatin is a paracrine inhibitory factor (**D**).

19. **Each of the following is decreased by vagotomy *EXCEPT*:**
    A. receptive relaxation of the orad stomach
    B. pepsin secretion in response to a meal
    C. gastrin release in response to distention
    D. gastrin release in response to luminal amino acids
    E. pancreatic secretion in response to fat and amino acids in the duodenum

    Answer = D. *Remember you are looking for the exception.* Amino acids directly stimulate the G cells to release gastrin, while all of the others involve, in part, a vagal reflex.

20. **During the gastric phase of acid secretion, each of the following occurs *EXCEPT*:**
    A. acetylcholine directly stimulates the parietal cells
    B. acetylcholine releases gastrin from the G cells
    C. GRP releases gastrin from the G cells
    D. histamine potentiates the effect of acetylcholine on the parietal cells
    E. digested protein directly stimulates the parietal cells

    Answer = E. *Remember you are looking for the exception.* Digested protein directly stimulates the G cells to release gastrin, which in turns stimulates the parietal cells to secrete acid.

21. **Each of the following is inhibited by ouabain (blocks Na^+/K^+ ATPase) *EXCEPT*:**
    A. diarrhea caused by cholera toxin
    B. diarrhea caused by lactose intolerance
    C. intestinal Na^+ uptake by diffusion through membrane channels
    D. intestinal glucose uptake
    E. K^+ secretion in the colon

Answer = B. *Remember you are looking for the exception.* The inability of lactose to be digested causes the accumulation of osmotic particles within the lumen that traps water. The resultant diarrhea is independent of Na^+/K^+ ATPase activity. Many functions of intestinal cells are, however, linked to the movement of sodium down its electrochemical gradient established by the Na^+/K^+ ATPase that maintains the intracellular sodium concentration at very low levels. The increase in Cl^- secretion caused by cholera toxin stimulation of cAMP (activation of mucosal membrane Cl^- channels) is prevented by ouabain since chloride influx depends on the sodium pump's maintaining a low intracellular sodium concentration. Hence, the Na/Cl^- cotransporter, which moves Cl^- into the cell to be secreted at the mucosal surface, cannot function (**A**). If the sodium concentration inside the cell is not maintained at a low level, there will be no electrochemical gradient for the passive entry of sodium through any membrane channel (**C**) or for glucose uptake (**D**). Without the Na^+/K^+ ATPase, potassium will not be pumped into the cell; hence, the passive secretion of potassium will be blocked (**E**).

22. **Acidification of the antral mucosa will not reduce serum gastrin in patients with:**
    A.   pernicious anemia
    B.   duodenal ulcer (normal peptic ulcer)
    C.   atrophic gastritis
    D.   Zollinger-Ellison syndrome
    E.   gastric cancer

    Answer = D.   In patients with a gastrinoma (Zollinger-Ellison syndrome) that pathologically secretes gastrin, the normal negative feedback effects of antral acidification that inhibit gastrin secretion do not occur. In all of the other conditions, acidification will result in an inhibition of gastrin secretion.

23. **Pancreatic enzymes are:**
    A.   all secreted as inactive proenzymes
    B.   all secreted by acinar cells
    C.   synthesized in response to a secretory stimulus
    D.   secreted from condensing vacuoles
    E.   important for only protein digestion

    Answer = B.   Pancreatic enzymes are all secreted from the zymogen granules (not **D**) of the acinar cells. They are released in response to a stimulus (not **C**) as either an active enzyme or an inactive precursor (not just **A**). Proteases, lipases, and amylases are all part of the enzymatic cocktail secreted by the pancreas (not just **E**).

24. **Which of the following combination of agents will produce the highest rate of pancreatic bicarbonate secretion?**
    A.   secretin plus histamine
    B.   cholecystokinin plus acetylcholine
    C.   gastrin plus vagal stimulation
    D.   secretin plus vagal stimulation
    E.   cholecystokinin plus phenylalanine in the duodenum

    Answer = D.   Maximal rates of pancreatic bicarbonate secretion occur in the presence of low levels of secretin (not **B**, **C** or **E**) interacting with ACh and CCK (not **A**).

25. **Compared to hepatic bile, gallbladder bile will differ in that its:**
    A.   bile salt concentration will be less
    B.   cholesterol to bile salt ratio will be greater
    C.   osmolality will be greater
    D.   phospholipid concentration will be less
    E.   sodium concentration will be greater

    Answer = E.   Because the bile salts bind sodium and trap it, much of the sodium is osmotically inactive and its high concentration reflects the anionic nature of the bile salts. Within the gallbladder, bile is concentrated via the active reabsorption of Na^+, Cl^-, and HCO_3^-, with water following in an isosmotic manner (not **C**). Hence, the organic constituents are greatly concentrated (not **A**); bile salt and phospholipid (not **D**) concentrations will be much greater; hence, the sodium concentration will be very high. With both cholesterol and bile salts being concentrated within the gallbladder, the cholesterol:bile salt ratio will not be greater (not **B**).

26. **Bile acid A has less solubility in intestinal fluid than bile acid B. Compared to bile acid B, bile acid A is more likely to be:**
   A.   a primary bile acid
   B.   a trihydroxy rather than dihydroxy bile acid
   C.   absorbed passively in the jejunum
   D.   conjugated
   E.   deoxycholic rather than lithocholic acid

Answer = C.   The basis of this question is the solubility characteristic of the bile acids and salts. The more hydroxyl groups present on the bile acids, the more soluble they are in intestinal fluids. Bile acid A is less soluble (more lipophilic) and, hence, more likely to be passively reabsorbed. The primary bile acids have more hydroxyl groups than the secondary (**A**), and cholic acid is the most soluble (trihydroxy; **B**). Conjugated bile acids become bile salts of glycine or taurine and are more water soluble (**D**). Deoxycholic acid has two hydroxy groups compared to only one for lithocholic acid (**E**).

27. **Removal of the distal ileum will increase bile acid:**
   A.   levels in hepatic venous blood
   B.   levels in the portal vein
   C.   secretion by hepatocytes
   D.   storage in the gallbladder
   E.   synthesis by hepatocytes

Answer = E.   Since bile acids are actively reabsorbed along the distal ileum, the removal of this segment greatly decreases the recirculation of bile acids back to the liver and leads to an increase in the synthesis of bile acids via the disinhibition of 7-α-hydroxylase, the rate-limiting enzyme for bile acid synthesis from cholesterol. Since the absorption of bile acids is decreased, the bile acid level in the portal vein (not **B**) will decrease. The decrease in delivery and the active uptake of bile acids by the hepatocytes will minimize the loss of bile acids into the hepatic vein (not **A**). No increase in secretion will occur because the largest source of hepatic bile acid has been lost (not **C**); but, by increasing synthesis, secretion can be maintained (not **D**). Furthermore, the volume of bile within the gallbladder is also influenced by factors other than the volume of bile being produced by the liver.

28. **Colipase:**
   A.   is secreted as an inactive enzyme
   B.   hydrolyzes the 2′-ester linkage of triglycerides
   C.   binds to fat digestion products
   D.   binds to pancreatic lipase
   E.   is a constituent of micelles

Answer = D.   Colipase binds to pancreatic lipase and helps the pancreatic lipase digest triglycerides by displacing a bile salt micelle from the interface and exposing the pancreatic lipase so that it can act. It is secreted as procolipase, but it is not an enzyme (not **A**) and, hence, does not cause hydrolysis (not **B**). It binds to pancreatic lipase, not to digestion products (not **C**). Although by binding to a bile salt on the surface of the micelle it helps position the pancreatic lipase near to the micelle, it is not a constituent of the micelle (not **E**).

29. **Which of the following is an integral part of the intestinal brush border membrane?**
   A.   carboxypeptidase A
   B.   enterokinase
   C.   colipase
   D.   elastase
   E.   amylase

Answer = B.   Enterokinase is a brush border enzyme responsible for converting trypsinogen to trypsin. Carboxypeptidase A (**A**) and elastase (**D**) are enzymes formed within the lumen by the action of trypsin on proenzymes, as is colipase (**C**), which is not an enzyme. Amylases are secreted into the saliva or pancreatic juices (**E**).

30. The addition of glucose to the lumen of an intestinal segment is found to increase the potential difference across the mucosa. The addition of compound X to the lumen decreases the absorption of glucose but causes a further increase in the potential difference. Compound X is most likely:
    A. an amino acid
    B. fructose
    C. galactose
    D. palmitic acid
    E. glycerol

    Answer = C. One sugar transporter transports both glucose and galactose; hence, these sugars compete with each other. Since the Na^+:glucose/galactose transporter is electrogenic, the increasingly negative luminal potential (increasing potential difference) as substance X was added indicates that there was an increase in an electrogenic process. The decrease in glucose transport implies that substance X must compete with glucose. Amino acids are absorbed by an electrogenic process, but there is no competition between amino acids and glucose (not **A**). Fructose is absorbed by passive facilitated diffusion and is not electrogenic (not **B**). Glycerol and palmitic acid are passively absorbed by a nonelectrogenic process that does not compete with the transport of sugars (not **D** or **E**).

31. If the intestinal absorption of 10 mMol of glycine were compared to the absorption of 5 mMol of the dipeptide glycylglycine:
    A. the concentration of glycine in the blood would increase at the same rate in each case
    B. the concentration of dipeptide in the blood would increase at half the rate of that of the free amino acid
    C. the concentration of glycine in the blood would increase faster when the dipeptide was being absorbed
    D. the concentration of glycine in the blood would increase faster when the free amino acid was being absorbed
    E. the dipeptide, if added at the same time as free glycine, would decrease the absorption of the free amino acid

    Answer = C. The dipeptide is taken up faster than the peptide, is rapidly converted to the peptide inside the cell, and, like the absorbed peptide, leaves via facilitated diffusion. Hence, the concentration of glycine in the blood would increase more (not **B** or **D**) following 5 mMol of glycylglycine than following 10 mMol of glycine (not **A**). Since the uptake processes for dipeptides are different from that involved with the peptide, there is no competition (not **E**)

32. Fatty acid binding proteins:
    A. directly aid in the uptake of fatty acids and monoglycerides by the brush border
    B. transport fatty acids to chylomicrons
    C. are cofactors in the resynthesis of triglycerides
    D. preferentially bind medium-chain fatty acids
    E. transport fatty acids to the smooth endoplasmic reticulum

    Answer = E. The primary action of the fatty acid binding proteins is serving as a cytosolic carrier from the membrane area to the smooth endoplasmic reticulum. They are not located in the membrane but are cytosolic (not **A**) and do not directly transport fatty acids to chylomicrons (not **B**); they are not directly involved in the resynthesis of triglycerides (not **C**). Finally, they preferentially bind long-chain, not medium-chain, fatty acids (not **D**).

33. The major mechanism for the uptake of Na^+ in the colon is:
    A. exchange with H^+
    B. cotransport with Cl^-
    C. cotransport with organic solutes
    D. primary active transport
    E. diffusion through membrane channels

    Answer = E. In the colon, the primary mechanism for sodium entry is aldosterone-sensitive sodium channels. Primary active transport is the mechanism for transporting sodium from the cell to the interstitial fluid (**D**). The small intestinal absorptive villus primarily uses the mechanisms in choices **A**, **B**, and **C**.

Questions 34–37: Matching. Each choice may be used once, more than once, or not at all.
    A. histamine
    B. acetylcholine
    C. gastrin
    D. secretin
    E. bombesin (GRP)

34. **Inhibits gastric acid secretion:**

Answer = D. All of the other factors stimulate or result in the stimulation of the parietal cells.

35. **Amino acid derivative released from ECL cells:**

Answer = A. Histamine is a derivative of the amino acid histidine.

36. **Stimulates the growth of the oxyntic gland mucosa:**

Answer = C. Gastrin stimulates the growth of the oxyntic gland mucosa; recall that secretin stimulates the growth of the exocrine pancreas.

37. **Acts as a paracrine:**

Answer = A. Histamine is the only agent in the above list that acts as a paracrine. ACh is a neurotransmitter, whereas the other three are hormones.

38. **Swallowing:**
    A.   initiates primary esophageal peristalsis
    B.   is entirely voluntary
    C.   is primarily controlled by feedback via the sympathetic system
    D.   is initiated by receptors on the tongue
    E.   can occur in the absence of any material to be swallowed

Answer = A. Although we can voluntarily initiate a swallow by pushing a small amount of saliva (not **E**) into the back of the throat, the presence of the saliva stimulates the large number of receptors lining the pharynx (not **D**) that send input to the swallow center via the vagus nerve (not **B**). The swallow center then initiates a primary esophageal peristaltic wave via the vagus nerve (not **C**).

39. **The esophageal muscle immediately above the diaphragm:**
    A.   receives vagal input directly
    B.   relaxes as a bolus approaches
    C.   is tonically contracted
    D.   is normally flaccid between swallows so that the pressure inside is less than atmospheric
    E.   generates secondary peristaltic waves in response to hormones released by material distending it

Answer = D. Except at the two sphincters, the muscles of the esophagus are relaxed between peristaltic waves; hence, the pressure reflects the surrounding pressure, which will be negative above the diaphragm and positive below the diaphragm. The muscle remains relaxed (not **B** or **C**) until the bolus passes, at which time it contracts and pushes the bolus downward. Secondary peristaltic waves are induced by local distention (not **E**). The vagus nerve only directly innervates the striated muscle of the upper esophagus (not **A**); the remainder of the smooth muscles receive indirect vagal innervation via interneurons.

40. **Intact vagal innervation is required for each of the following *EXCEPT*:**
    A.   receptive relaxation of the stomach
    B.   peristalsis in the lower third of the esophagus
    C.   stimulation of acid secretion by food in the mouth
    D.   a portion of gastrin release stimulated by distending the stomach
    E.   pancreatic secretion during the cephalic phase of digestion

Answer = B. *Remember you are looking for the exception.* Only the secondary peristaltic wave in the lower esophagus can occur without an intact vagus. Both receptive relaxation (**A**) and gastrin release induced by distention of the stomach (**D**) require a vagovagal reflex. Similarly, the cephalic portion (**C** and **E**) of the digestive response requires an intact vagus nerve.

41. **The rate of gastric emptying of a test meal is increased by:**
    A. increasing the fat content of the meal
    B. increasing the volume of the meal
    C. increasing the size of the food particles in the meal
    D. making the meal hypotonic
    E. decreasing the pH of the meal from 7.0 to 4.0

    Answer = B. Recall that the greater the volume in the stomach, the faster the rate of emptying. The precise mechanism for this response has not been clearly established but is probably an intrinsic property of the stomach. A variety of factors can reduce the rate of gastric emptying, such as the fat content (**A**), presence of large particles (**C**), any deviation from isotonicity (**D**), and acidic fluid (**E**); all of these factors are thought to be sensed by receptors located in the duodenal mucosa that trigger neuronal and hormonal processes that inhibit gastric motility.

42. **Slow waves of the small intestine:**
    A. trigger contractions
    B. always contain spike potentials
    C. are produced with a lower frequency proximally than distally
    D. occur at approximately 90-min intervals
    E. set the maximal frequency of small intestinal contractions

    Answer = E. Slow waves of basal electrical activity are an inherent characteristic of the small intestine, and their frequency sets the frequency at which contractions can occur. The 5- to 15-mV slow waves do not always produce a spike potential (not **B**), but spike potentials must occur for there to be a contraction (not **A**). Their frequency decreases as you move distally (not **C**), from ~12/min in the duodenum to 8/min in the terminal ileum. Migrating motility complexes (not **D**) occur every 90 min in the unfed state.

43. **During fasting, the predominant motility activity of the small intestine is:**
    A. receptive relaxation
    B. segmentation
    C. brief sporadic contractions interrupted periodically by migrating motility complexes
    D. strong peristaltic contractions repeated over the length of the gut at frequencies of 11 to 12 cycles per min
    E. periods of quiet followed by mass movements

    Answer = C. Except for the migrating motility complexes that occur approximately every 90 min, the fasting small intestine is subject to brief sporadic contractions. Receptive relaxation occurs in the stomach, not the small intestine (not **A**). Segmentation, not large peristaltic contractions (**D**), is the predominant activity in the small intestine following feeding (not **B**). Choice **E** is more appropriate for the large intestine.

44. **Propulsion of colonic contents into the rectum:**
    A. is caused by a migrating motility complex
    B. causes an involuntary contraction of the external anal sphincter
    C. initiates defecation
    D. is voluntary
    E. causes the internal anal sphincter to relax

    Answer = E. Fecal material enters the rectum primarily because of peristaltic mass movements that occur two or three times a day. As the rectum is distended, it causes the internal sphincter to relax, whereas the external sphincter remains contracted unless voluntarily allowed to relax (not **B** or **C**). The migrating motility complex moves material from the duodenum to the ileocecal sphincter (not **A**). The peristaltic movements that push fecal material into the rectum are totally involuntary (not **D**).

45. **Salivary secretion:**
    A. is produced at high volumes relative to the mass of the glands
    B. is usually hypertonic
    C. is primarily regulated by hormones
    D. is inhibited by sympathetic stimulation
    E. has a lower concentration of Na^+ as the rate of flow increases

Answer = A. Saliva can be produced in very large amounts by the secretion of NaCl into the acinus of the gland, with water following to produce an isotonic solution that passes down the duct where Na and Cl are reabsorbed in excess of the secretion of potassium, producing the final hypotonic saliva. Regulation of the rate of salivary secretion is almost entirely via the parasympathetic and sympathetic nervous system (not **C** or **D**). Although saliva is always hypotonic (not **B**) to plasma, as the flow rate increases, both the tonicity and sodium concentration of saliva increase and approach that of plasma (not **E**).

46. **Stimulation of the parasympathetic nerves to the salivary glands results in each of the following EXCEPT:**
    A. increased output of saliva
    B. increased growth of the glands
    C. contraction of the myoepithelial cells
    D. increased metabolism of the glands
    E. vasoconstriction of the blood vessels to the glands

    Answer = E. *Remember you are looking for the exception.* Parasympathetic stimulation of the salivary gland stimulates the active secretion of saliva, which increases the output and metabolism of the gland. It also stimulates myoepithelial cells to contract and, hence, prevents distention of the acinus and propels saliva into the mouth. In addition, parasympathetic stimulation also stimulates growth and increases blood flow to the gland (*not* **E**).

47. **As a fasted individual begins eating, each of the following occurs within the parietal cells EXCEPT:**
    A. increased H^+/K^+ ATPase activity
    B. increased activity of carbonic anhydrase
    C. increased number of tubulovesicles
    D. increased ATP production by mitochondria
    E. increased area devoted to intracellular canaliculus

    Answer = C. *Remember you are looking for the exception.* Within a few minutes of being stimulated, the tubulovesicles are disappearing (*not* **C**) and the intracellular canaliculus network is expanding (**E**). Stimulation results in the activation of both the H^+/K^+ ATPase (**A**) and carbonic anhydrase (**B**) and in an increase in the production of ATP (**D**).

48. **According to the two-component hypothesis, the Na^+ concentration in gastric secretion decreases with the rate of secretion because:**
    A. the concentration of H^+ being secreted from the parietal cells increases
    B. the nonoxyntic component of secretion is stimulated
    C. the volume of the oxyntic component increases
    D. the secretion of Na^+ is inhibited
    E. the Na^+ is exchanged for K^+

    Answer = C. The nonoxyntic component of gastric secretion is secreted continually at a slow rate. When the gland is stimulated to secrete, the parietal cells increase the volume at which they secrete their 150-mM HCl component. This causes the concentration of sodium to decrease as the parietal component dilutes the nonoxyntic component. The parietal cells always secrete a high H^+ concentration solution (not **A**), whereas the nonoxyntic component remains constant (not **B** or **D**). There is some H^+ exchange for Na^+ (not **E**), especially at slow rates of secretion; but the primary event is H^+ exchange for K^+.

49. **Acidification of the gastric antrum to pH 1.0:**
    A. stimulates secretin release
    B. inhibits acid secretion by releasing enterogastrones
    C. inhibits acid secretion via a vagovagal reflex
    D. inhibits gastrin release by releasing bombesin
    E. inhibits gastrin release by releasing somatostatin

    Answer = E. Acidification of the antrum causes the release of somatostatin, which acts as a paracrine to inhibit gastrin release and to directly inhibit H^+ secretion by the parietal cells. **A–D** are incorrect. Secretin (**A**) and enterogastrones (**B**) are released from the duodenum. Bombesin (**D**) is released from vagal nerves and, like the vagovagal reflex (**C**), is important for stimulation of gastrin secretion in response to stretch.

50. **Between meals, when the stomach is empty of food:**
   A.   it contains a large volume of juice with an approximate pH of 5
   B.   gastrin release is inhibited by a strongly acidic solution
   C.   it contains a small volume of gastric juice with a pH near neutrality
   D.   bombesin acts on the parietal cells to inhibit secretion
   E.   it secretes large volumes of weakly acidic juice

Answer = B. Between meals, the lack of food buffers allows the pH of the gastric content to become very acidic (not **A**, **C**, or **E**), which causes the inhibition of gastrin secretion and the suppression of the rate of volume of acidic parietal cell secretion (not **A**). Bomebesin (GRP, gastrin-releasing peptide) is a stimulus, not an inhibitory factor (not **D**).

51. **During the cephalic phase:**
   A.   secretin stimulates pepsin secretion
   B.   CCK stimulates pancreatic enzyme secretion
   C.   ACh stimulates the G cells to release gastrin
   D.   bombesin stimulates parietal cell secretion
   E.   ACh stimulates pancreatic enzyme secretion

Answer = E. Pancreatic secretion, especially of the enzymatic component, is stimulated via the release of ACh from the vagal innervation of acinar cells. Secretin (**A**) and CCK (**B**) are released during the intestinal phase. Secretin primarily stimulates the aqueous component; although CCK does stimulate the enzymatic component of pancreatic secretion, it does so during the intestinal phase. ACh (**C**) and bombesin (GRP; **D**) are released during the cephalic phase, but ACh affects the parietal cells and bombesin stimulates the G cells.

52. **Acidification of the duodenal mucosa to pH <4.0:**
   A.   stimulates pancreatic bicarbonate secretion
   B.   inhibits pepsinogen secretion
   C.   stimulates G cells to release gastric acid
   D.   inhibits bile production
   E.   stimulates gastric emptying

Answer = A. The primary response to acidic fluid in the duodenum is the stimulation of secretin, which stimulates the aqueous component of the pancreas (which is rich in HCO_3); but it also stimulates pepsinogen secretion (not **B**). G cells release gastrin (not **C**). Acids do cause some release of CCK, which would stimulate bile production (not **D**) and contribute to the inhibition (not **E**) of gastric emptying, which is also inhibited by intrinsic reflexes that respond to acid in the duodenum.

53. **Maximal rates of pancreatic bicarbonate secretion in response to a meal in humans are due to:**
   A.   the effects of small amounts of secretin being potentiated by ACh and CCK
   B.   large amounts of secretin released from the duodenal mucosa
   C.   VIP acting on the ductule cells
   D.   potentiation between CCK and ACh released from vagovagal reflexes
   E.   potentiation between small amounts of secretin and gastrin

Answer = A. During a normal meal, the duodenal pH does not drop enough to maximally stimulate the secretion of secretin (not **B**); nevertheless, because of the simultaneous presence of ACh and CCK, maximal rates of bicarbonate secretion are reached. Vagovagal reflexes cannot potentiate the effect of ACh since they are one and the same mediator (not **D**). In humans, there is no evidence that gastrin affects pancreatic secretin of bicarbonate (not **E**). Although when injected into the bloodstream, VIP can mimic the effects of secretin, it is not released into the bloodstream; hence, it is not normally a factor in the response to a meal in humans (not **C**).

54. **In the absence of enterokinase, one would also expect a decrease in the activity of:**
   A.   pepsin
   B.   lipase
   C.   chymotrypsin
   D.   amylase
   E.   sucrase

Answer = C. The membrane-bound enterokinase acts on trypsinogen to form trypsin. Hence, chymotrypsin will decrease because less trypsin will be available to convert chymotrypsinogen to the active enzyme. None of the other enzymes is activated by the action of trypsin.

55. **Conjugation of cholic acid to glycine:**
    A. makes it less soluble in water
    B. increases its secretion from the liver
    C. ensures that it will be reabsorbed from the gut
    D. lowers its pK
    E. converts it to a secondary bile acid

    Answer = D. Conjugation actually reduces the amount of cholic acid secreted into the bile (not **B**) but has little effect on its absorption, since much of it will be deconjugated within the GI tract (not **C**).

56. **Ileal resection:**
    A. decreases the proportion of primary bile acids in bile
    B. increases the synthesis of bile acids by the liver
    C. increases the volume (production) of bile
    D. will not affect the absorption of dietary fat
    E. decreases the fecal excretion of bile salts

    Answer = B. Since the active reabsorption of bile acids occurs in the terminal ileum, the decrease in the enterohepatic recirculation of bile salts will stimulate bile acid synthesis as more bile acids are lost in the feces (not **E**). Since there will be less recirculation of secondary bile acids formed by the action of bacteria on the primary bile salts, a higher portion of primary bile acids will be in the bile (not **A**). Furthermore, without the recirculation of bile acids, a smaller volume of bile that is derived only from synthesis of new bile acids is produced (not **C**), and fat absorption is often affected (not **D**).

57. **Which of the following is water soluble?**
    A. oleic acid (C18)
    B. vitamin A
    C. cholesterol
    D. cholic acid
    E. bilirubin glucuronide

    Answer = E. Bilirubin glucuronide is a water-soluble product of the hepatocytes. All of the other listed factors are hydrophobic and, hence, water insoluble.

58. **Gallbladder contraction is stimulated by:**
    A. fat digestion products in the duodenum
    B. bile acids returning to the liver in the portal circulation
    C. secretin
    D. glucose in the duodenum
    E. osmotic concentration of the solutes within the gallbladder

    Answer = A. Fat digestion products in the duodenum stimulate the release of CCK, which causes contraction of the gallbladder and relaxation of the sphincter of Oddi.

59. **Exhaustive digestion of starch by pancreatic amylase produces:**
    A. glucose alone
    B. maltose and glucose
    C. maltose, maltotriose, and α-limit dextrins
    D. maltose, maltotriose, and galactose
    E. sucrose alone

    Answer = C. Amylase breaks starch down to maltose, maltotriose and α-limit dextrins. These products are then acted upon by α-dextrinases, maltases, and sucrases to yield simple sugars.

60. **Colipase:**
    A. digests triglycerides
    B. converts prolipase to active lipase
    C. is a brush border enzyme
    D. prevents the inactivation of lipase by bile salts
    E. binds to absorbed fatty acids, transporting them to the smooth endoplasmic reticulum for resynthesis into triglycerides

Answer = D. Colipase is a protein, not an enzyme (not **A**, **B**, or **C**), that binds to lipase (not **E**) and displaces a bile salt micelle from the interface, allowing the lipase to work. It also binds to a bile salt micelle, keeping the lipase and the micelle close together.

61. **In the small intestine, Na^+ is absorbed by each of the following processes *EXCEPT*:**
    A. by diffusion
    B. by being coupled to amino acid absorption
    C. by being coupled to galactose absorption
    D. by being coupled to the transport of H^+ in the opposite direction
    E. by being coupled to the absorption of HCO_3^-

    Answer = E. *Remember you are looking for the exception.* Sodium is reabsorbed by a number of processes that are located on the luminal cell membrane and even in passive pathways between the epithelial cells. At present, there is no evidence for a Na^+-coupled HCO_3^- transport process. All of the other processes or mechanisms have been shown to exist.

62. **Diarrhea might be expected to result in each of the following *EXCEPT*:**
    A. dehydration
    B. metabolic acidosis
    C. decreased frequency of respiration
    D. hypokalemia
    E. decreased mean circulatory filling pressure

    Answer = C. *Remember you are looking for the exception.* Diarrhea is normally associated with the loss of a large volume of alkaline fluid with a high concentration of potassium that causes dehydration (**A** and **E**), metabolic acidosis (**B**) with its compensatory increase in respiration , and hypokalemia (**D**).

63. **Of the 8–10 liters of water that enters the GI tract each day:**
    A. the majority comes from food and drink in the diet
    B. most is absorbed in the small intestine
    C. most is absorbed in the large intestine
    D. approximately 4 liters enters the large intestine
    E. most is absorbed by an active transport mechanism

    Answer = B. The small intestine reabsorbs most (~80%) of the fluid that enters the GI tract each day, leaving only about 1–2 liters (not **C** or **D**) that enters the colon. Most of this fluid is derived from secretions along the GI tract (not **A**). Water is absorbed passively (not **E**) down the osmotic gradient established by the active transport of sodium.

64. **A patient with a total absence of gastric parietal cells would have:**
    A. lower than normal serum gastrin
    B. normal digestion and absorption of dietary protein
    C. impaired digestion of starch
    D. normal absorption of vitamin B_{12}
    E. normal levels of pepsin activity

    Answer = B. The parietal cells secrete both H^+ and intrinsic factor, which is required for the reabsorption of vitamin B_{12} (not **D**). Without them, there is an elevated level of gastrin (not **A**), since the normal feedback inhibition of gastric acid secretion has been interrupted. Even though acidification helps in the digestion of proteins, it is not essential; and the proteases within the small intestine can handle the dietary sodium intake. Acidification plays no significant role in the digestion of starch (not **C**). Lack of the normal acidic stimulation of secretin from the duodenum will cause the secretion of pepsinogen to be decreased (not **E**).

65. **Patients with a congenital absence of one of the amino acid carriers do not become deficient in that amino acid due to the fact that:**
    A. the amino acid is absorbed by passive diffusion
    B. the amino acid can make use of other carriers
    C. the amino acid is absorbed by facilitated diffusion
    D. peptides containing the amino acid are absorbed by different carriers
    E. the amino acid is an essential amino acid

Answer = D. Because small peptides are reabsorbed by unique carriers, the loss of a single specific (not **B**) amino acid carrier (not **A**) will not result in a patient's becoming deficient in that amino acid. Facilitated diffusion of that amino acid will be depressed, but that is not what prevents the patient from becoming amino acid-deficient (not **C**). Choice **E** is irrelevant.

66. Following a thorough examination of a patient with chronic (several days) severe diarrhea, you would expect to find:

    A.   increased serum pH
    B.   decreased mean systemic (circulatory) filling pressure
    C.   hyperkalemia
    D.   decreased frequency of breathing
    E.   decreased heart rate

Answer = B. Since diarrheal discharge contains large amounts of HCO_3, Na, and K, the patient loses a significant amount of fluid, causing a depletion of the extracellular volume that leads to a decrease in the mean systemic (circulatory) filling pressure (**B**). The loss of fluid causes activation of volume receptors, which leads to an increase in heart rate (not **E**) and activation of the sympathetic nervous system. The loss of potassium causes the patient to develop hypokalemia (not **C**). The patient will also develop a metabolic acidosis due to the loss of an alkalotic fluid (not **A**), leading to a compensatory hyperventilation (not **D**).

67. Each of the following is true about active glucose absorption by enterocytes *EXCEPT*:
    A.   it is dependent on cotransport with Na^+
    B.   it is dependent on the activity of the Na^+/K^+ ATPase in the basolateral cell membrane
    C.   it is inhibited by hypoxia
    D.   it will decrease the transepithelial electrical potential difference
    E.   it will be inhibited by galactose

Answer = D. *Remember you are looking for the exception.* Glucose is cotransported by a sodium-dependent carrier (**A**) that also transports galactose (**E**). Because the cotransport is electrogenic in nature, stimulation of glucose transport increases (***not*** **D**) the transepithelial potential difference across the gastric mucosa. The sodium gradient maintained by the activity of the Na^+/K^+ ATPase is essential (**B**) and is dependent on a normal supply of O_2 (**C**).

Questions 68–70. Gastric emptying of three solutions was measured under three different conditions. These solutions were added to the empty stomach without any salivary contamination.

    Solutions   *Conditions*
    1. isotonic saline   1. normal—control
    2. isotonic starch   2. pancreatic secretion inhibited
    3. hypertonic glucose   3. surgical bypass of the proximal 50% of the small intestine with anastomosis of the pylorus to the proximal ileum

For each of the following statements, answer A if it is true, B if it is false.

68. In condition 1, solutions 1 and 3 will empty from the stomach at the same rates.

Answer = B (False). An isotonic solution of NaCl is the most rapidly emptied solution. Gastric emptying is affected by receptors in the duodenum that can reflexively inhibit gastric motility. Factors such as osmolality, pH, or lipid content slow emptying. Hence, hypertonic glucose would inhibit gastric emptying.

69. In condition 2, solutions 1 and 2 will empty from the stomach at the same rate.

Answer = A (True). In the absence of amylase, starch will not be broken down; hence, it will not become hypertonic, and the two solutions should empty at the same rate.

70.   In condition 3, all three solutions will empty at the same rate.

Answer = A (True). Since the receptors are being bypassed, there will be no reflexive inhibition of gastric emptying.

71.   **Administration of a drug that blocks the H^+/K^+ ATPase of the parietal cells of a secreting stomach will:**
        A.   have no effect on the volume of secretion
        B.   increase the concentration of H^+ in the secretion
        C.   decrease the concentration of Na^+ in the secretion
        D.   decrease the pH of the gastric venous blood
        E.   decrease the potential difference across the stomach

Answer = D. Since the active secretion of hydrogen ions into the lumen causes the secretion of bicarbonate into the venous blood, blocking the secretion of H^+ will decrease the pH of gastric venous blood. Inhibition of H^+ ion secretion (not **B**) will prevent the osmotic flow of water and, thus, will decrease the volume of secretion (not **A**). When parietal cell secretion is inhibited, the nonparietal cell secretion, a sodium-rich solution, will become a large fraction of the total secretion, thus increasing the sodium concentration (not **C**). Since H^+ ion secretion reduces the potential difference across the stomach, inhibiting it returns the potential to its normal, very negative value (not **E**).

72.   **Each of the following might be expected to be found in micelles *EXCEPT*:**
        A.   bilirubin glucuronide
        B.   cholesterol
        C.   taurolithocholic acid
        D.   lecithin
        E.   vitamin A

Answer = A. *Remember you are looking for the exception.* Compounds found in micelles will be hydrophobic; hence, the water-soluble product of bile acid glucuronidation will not be found in a micelle.

73.   **Gallbladder:**
        A.   contraction is physiologically stimulated by secretin
        B.   bile has a lower Na^+ concentration than hepatic bile
        C.   bile has a lower concentration of cholesterol than hepatic bile
        D.   contraction is stimulated by bile acids returning to the liver
        E.   bile has the same concentration of water as hepatic bile

Answer = E. Although hepatic bile and gallbladder bile have the same osmolarity, the gallbladder sodium concentration (not **B**) is higher because much of the sodium is bound to bile salts that have been concentrated along with cholesterol (not **C**). Contraction of the gallbladder is stimulated by CCK (not **A** or **D**), but secretin and bile acids do stimulate secretion of bile by the hepatocytes.

74.   **From the following list, the enzyme most essential to protein digestion is:**
        A.   elastase
        B.   enterokinase
        C. α-dextrinase
        D.   pepsin
        E.   trehalase

Answer = B. Since protein digestion can occur without any gastric digestion (not **D**), enterokinase, which activates trypsin, becomes a crucial enzyme for the digestion of proteins.

75. Micelles are necessary for the normal absorption of all of the following *EXCEPT*:
   A. vitamin K
   B. medium-chain fatty acids
   C. long-chain fatty acids
   D. long-chain monoglycerides
   E. dietary cholesterol

   Answer = B. *Remember you are looking for the exception.* Since both short-chain and medium-chain fatty acids are sufficiently water soluble, they do not require micelles for absorption. All of the other molecules are sufficiently hydrophobic to require micelles for absorption.

76. The ileocecal sphincter:
   A. relaxes when the ileum is distended
   B. relaxes when the proximal colon is distended
   C. response to ileal distention is mediated by a vagovagal reflex
   D. pressure is under hormonal control
   E. constricts when the pressure in the ileum increases

   Answer = A. When the ileum is distended or pressure within the ileum is increased (not **E**), the ileocecal sphincter relaxes, whereas it contracts when the proximal colon is distended (not **B**). Both reflexes are thought to be entirely mediated by the enteric (not **C** or **D**) nerves.

77. Receptive relaxation of the stomach:
   A. is abolished by vagotomy
   B. is triggered by relaxation of the lower esophageal sphincter
   C. occurs primarily in the antrum
   D. results in large increases in intragastric pressure following a meal
   E. depends entirely on the enteric nervous system

   Answer = A. Receptive relaxation, which decreases the pressure following the addition of food stuff (not **D**), requires an intact vagus nerve for both the afferent and efferent limb of this reflex (not **E**) and is activated by stretching of the orad (not **C**) stomach (not **B**).

78. The main function of the colon is to absorb:
   A. vitamins
   B. water
   C. fats
   D. carbohydrates
   E. electrolytes

   Answer = B. Only 600 ml of the 7–10 liters of water that enters the small intestine reach the colon, but the colon reabsorbs all but 100 ml of this water. All of the other factors are reabsorbed by the small intestine.

79. The most likely place to find an increase in somatostatin levels following acidification of the stomach would be:
   A. small veins of the stomach
   B. gastric artery
   C. gastric lumen
   D. hepatic portal vein
   E. a pancreatic vein

   Answer = A. The D cell of the antrum releases somatostatin in response to an increase in H^+ ion concentration that then acts in a paracrine fashion to inhibit the G cells release of gastrin. Hence, only in the area very near the site of release of somatostatin will there be a detectable increase in its venous concentration.

80.   **Gastric slow waves are different from intestinal slow waves in that they:**
   A.   occur at a higher frequency
   B.   can cause muscle contractions
   C.   increase or decrease in frequency depending on the digestive state
   D.   disappear during fasting
   E.   may be associated with spike potentials

Answer = B.   Gastric slow waves, unlike intestinal slow waves, can cause muscle contraction without producing a spike potential; but both gastric and intestinal waves can have spike potential (not **E**). The gastric slow waves do not occur at a higher frequency (not **A**). These waves occur continuously (not **B**) and their frequency is not modulated (not **C**)

1. A 46-year-old man has lost innervation to both his adrenal glands; otherwise, his nervous system is intact and functioning normally, and his adrenals have adequate circulation. Late one afternoon, he receives a telephone message that one of his children has been seriously injured. Which of the following hormones will fairly quickly increase in his plasma?
   A. ACTH, cortisol, epinephrine, and norepinephrine
   B. ACTH, epinephrine, and norepinephrine
   C. ACTH, cortisol, and norepinephrine
   D. only ACTH and norepinephrine
   E. only ACTH

   Answer = C. In the absence of neural input to the medulla, the expected release of epinephrine in response to the stressful situation will not occur. But ACTH secretion will increase, leading to an increase in cortisol secretion. Also, activation of the sympathetic nervous system will increase the plasma level of norepinephrine (NE) because some of the neuronally released NE will spill over into the systemic circulation.

2. During an oral GTT (glucose tolerance test) given in the late afternoon, which of the following hepatic enzymes is stimulated by elevated concentrations of glucagon?
   A. hexokinase
   B. acetyl Co-A carboxylase
   C. phosphofructosekinase
   D. fructose 1,6-bisphosphatase
   E. pyruvate dehydrogenase

   Answer = D. At the late stages of the GTT, insulin will have had its effects and glucose levels will fall below normal, causing stimulation of glucagon. The glucagon will stimulate gluconeogenesis in the liver via a cAMP-dependent activation of protein kinase A, which converts fructose-2,6-kinase to fructose-2,6-phosphatase and leads to a decrease in the levels of fructose 2,6-bisphosphate. It is this decrease in fructose 2,6-bisphosphate that disinhibits the enzyme fructose-1,6-bisphosphate phosphatase while it results in a decrease in phosphofructosekinase (C). Acetyl Co-A carboxylase is inhibited (B), not stimulated, by glucagon. Neither hexokinase nor pyruvate dehydrogenase is affected by glucagon.

3. In males, testosterone (or DHT) stimulates all of the following *EXCEPT*:
   A. pubertal growth of the penis, which will be permanent
   B. thelarche
   C. lowering of pitch of the voice, which will be permanent
   D. hair growth on chest and face
   E. hair growth up the midline of the abdomen (linea alba)

   Answer = B. *Remember you are looking for the exception.* Testosterone causes all of the listed events except thelarche, which is the development of breasts (often the earliest sign of the beginning of puberty in females; caused primarily by estrogen).

4. Estrogen directly produces all of the following *EXCEPT*:
   A. secretion by uterine endometrial glands
   B. pituitary hypertrophy
   C. increased contractility of uterine and oviduct muscles
   D. mammary gland growth
   E. stimulation of a thin, watery secretion by cervical glands

   Answer = A. *Remember you are looking for the exception.* Secretion by the uterine endometrial glands is stimulated by progesterone, not estrogen. All of the other items are produced by estrogen.

5. MIS (MRF; anti-Müllerian factor) causes the:
    A. Wolffian ducts to develop into male internal structures
    B. Müllerian ducts to develop into female internal structures
    C. Müllerian ducts to disappear, leaving Wolffian ducts intact
    D. gonadal ridges to develop into testes instead of ovaries
    E. testes to secrete testosterone in early fetal life, inducing Wolffian ducts to develop into male external structures

Answer = C. MIS is an acronym for Müllerian inhibiting substance; MRF is an acronym for Müllerian regression factor. Although items **A, B,** and **E** are true, MIS (MRF) does not cause these structures to develop into male and female structures. Testes development from the gonadal ridge is determined by the Y-chromosome-specific testis-determining gene, not by MIS (not **D**).

6. The plasma concentration of hCG:
    A. increases steadily throughout pregnancy
    B. increases beginning about 2 months after fertilization
    C. increases beginning less than 2 weeks after fertilization
    D. peaks 4–6 months after fertilization
    E. Both C and D are correct.

Answer = C. hCG measurements are used as a pregnancy test, can be detected in plasma a few days after conception, and rise rapidly (not **B**) until a peak (not **A**) is reached by ~2 months (not **D**).

7. Erection can occur when:
    A. penile blood flow increases about 25-fold
    B. parasympathetic input to penile arterioles causes them to relax
    C. sympathetic input to penile arterioles is blocked by stimulation of an inhibitory interneuron
    D. some appropriate stimulus (such as tactile, visual, or psychological) reaches the erection center in the lower spinal cord
    E. all of the above

Answer = E. Erection is caused by a dilation of arterioles induced by efferent parasympathetic fibers arising from the erection center in the lower spinal cord. Sympathetic input will cause vasoconstriction of the penile arterioles; and, hence, blocking the vasodilation.

8. ADH secretion would be increased by all of the following *EXCEPT*:
    A. increased plasma osmolality
    B. decreased fluid intake
    C. excessive fluid loss
    D. increased water ingestion
    E. decreased ECF volume

Answer = D. *Remember you are looking for the exception.* Remember that the secretion of ADH is influenced by two factors: plasma osmolality and the neural input from volume and/or baroreceptors. An increase in plasma osmolality (**A,** and possibly due to **B** and **C**) and a decrease in extracellular volume (**B, C,** and **E**) would both stimulate ADH secretion. The ingestion of water would decrease plasma osmolality and inhibit ADH secretion.

9. An assay of serum samples from a normal woman with a history of regular 28-day cycles indicates that, during the last 12 h, there has been a peak in the serum concentration of estradiol-17β in the absence of any detectable progesterone. Which of the following can be expected to occur within 3 days?
    A. cessation of menstruation
    B. decreased basal body temperature
    C. onset of menstruation
    D. ovulation
    E. regression of the corpus luteum

Answer = D. Inspection of any textbook figure illustrating the hormonal profile throughout a normal menstrual cycle shows that ovulation is the expected event. The estradiol peak with an absence of progesterone is a late follicular event leading up to ovulation and the associated increase in basal body temperature (not **B**).

10.   **All of the following are true about growth hormone in humans *EXCEPT*:**
A.   somatostatin withdrawal is sufficient to induce GH secretion
B.   much of our daily GH secretion occurs when we first enter deep sleep
C.   integrated daily GH secretion is highest during the pubertal growth spurt
D.   only human-derived GH is clinically useful
E.   thyroid hormones increase pituitary GH synthesis

Answer = A.   *Remember you are looking for the exception.* To stimulate growth hormone secretion, there must be both an increase in GRH and a decrease in somatostatin. All of the other statements are true.

11.   **In humans, the stimulus that initiates parturition is:**
A.   increased fetal cortisol
B.   increased ratio of free progesterone to free estrogen in fetal blood
C.   increased ratio of free progesterone to free estrogen in maternal blood
D.   maternal oxytocin secretion
E.   still unknown

Answer = E.   Although items **A–D** are associated with the initiation of parturition, the precise stimulus is still not known.

12.   **PTH:**
A.   secretion increases when plasma ionized calcium ($P_{Ca^{2+}}$) increases
B.   directly stimulates osteoclasts to prevent bone resorption
C.   acts on kidney and bone to raise $P_{Ca^{2+}}$
D.   secretion is stimulated after excessive vitamin D intake
E.   acts directly on intestinal mucosa to increase Ca absorption

Answer = C.   A primary action of PTH is to act on the kidneys and bones to reabsorb calcium and to mobilize Ca^{2+}, respectively. PTH acts on the osteoblasts to mobilize calcium (not **B**). It is secreted in response to a decrease in plasma ionized calcium, which can be caused by an excessive intake of vitamin D (not **A** or **D**). PTH enhances the formation of 1,25 dihydroxy-vitamin D (not **E**), which directly stimulates calcium absorption.

13.   **All of the following are true about vitamin D *EXCEPT*:**
A.   Vitamin D is formed in three steps: first in the skin, then the liver, and then the kidney.
B.   In severe renal failure, 1,25-dihydroxy vitamin D accumulates in plasma because it cannot be excreted in the urine.
C.   PTH enhances the formation of calcitriol, the most active form of vitamin D.
D.   Vitamin D facilitates movement of Ca into and out of bone.
E.   Vitamin D facilitates intestinal Ca absorption.

Answer = B.   *Remember you are looking for the exception.* In severe renal failure, the conversion of 25-hydroxy vitamin D to 1,25-dihydroxy vitamin D fails to occur. All of the other statements are true for vitamin D.

14.   **ACTH:**
A.   is a dimer of alpha and beta subunits
B.   has a beta subunit that contains all of the ACTH-like biological activity
C.   has an alpha subunit that can produce its antigenic activity
D.   all of the above
E.   none of the above

Answer = E.   ACTH is a small single-chain peptide hormone; it has no subunits.

15.   **All of the triplets listed below are correct *EXCEPT*:**

	Pituitary Hormone	*Hypothalamic Hormone*	*Action of Hypothalamic Hormone*
A.	somatotropin	SS	decreases GH secretion
B.	prolactin	DA	decreases PRL secretion
C.	follicle-stimulating hormone	GnIH	increases FSH secretion
D.	thyrotropin	TRH	increases TSH secretion
E.	luteinizing hormone	GnRH	increases LH secretion

Answer = C.   *Remember you are looking for the exception.* GnRH, not GnIH, stimulates the release of FSH.

16. **In humans, the major circulating steroids that produce the three main types of adrenal steroid actions are:**

	Glucocorticoid	Mineralocorticoid	Adrenal Androgen
A.	cortisol	aldosterone	DHEA*
B.	cortisone	DOC**	androstenedione
C.	ACTH	cortisol	testosterone
D.	cortisol	DOC	androstenedione
E.	corticosterone	aldosterone	testosterone

*DHEA = hydroepiandrosterone ($\pm$ sulfate).
**DOC = oxycorticosterone.

Answer = A. The human adrenal makes mostly the hormones listed in **A**.

17. **Which of the following situations will result in stimulation of glucagon secretion?**
    A. decreased plasma amino acid concentration
    B. increased somatostatin secretion within the islets
    C. increased plasma glucose, especially above 70 mg/dl
    D. decreased plasma insulin when peripheral insulin resistance occurs
    E. high levels of plasma insulin in the absence of insulin resistance

Answer = E. A low level of glucose, (<70 mg/dl; not **C**) is the primary stimulus for glucagon. High levels of insulin in the absence of insulin resistance will lead to a fall in plasma glucose and, hence, an increase in glucagon secretion. An increase in amino acids is a stimulus for glucagon (not **A**). Somatostatin secretion inhibits glucagon and insulin secretion (not **B**). In the presence of insulin resistance and low levels of insulin, glucose levels will be high; and, hence, glucagon secretion will be low (not **D**).

18. **To evaluate whether the pancreas has recovered some beta cell secretory capability in an insulin-requiring type-2 diabetic (adult-onset diabetes), which of the following plasma measurements would be most useful?**
    A. insulin in a GTT
    B. C-peptide in a GTT
    C. proinsulin after injecting epinephrine
    D. insulin after stimulation with amino acids
    E. glucagon after inducing mild hypoglycemia

Answer = B. Since insulin and C-peptide are secreted in equimolar amounts by the beta cells of the pancreas, C-peptide levels would be increased if the beta cells have recovered function. Finding insulin in a patient who has been receiving insulin may not be due to the release of insulin, but rather the presence of injected insulin (not **A** or **D**). Proinsulin is not readily released; but, more important, epinephrine inhibits insulin secretion (not **C**). Glucagon (not **E**) is not released from the beta cells, but from the alpha cells of the pancreatic islets.

19. **As plasma glucose concentrations fall from normal toward those that could produce a coma, all of the following can be considered beneficial (counter-regulatory) responses EXCEPT:**
    A. decreased cognitive function
    B. decreased insulin secretion
    C. increased epinephrine secretion (SNS activation)
    D. increased glucagon secretion
    E. increased GH, ACTH, and cortisol secretion

Answer = A. *Remember you are looking for the exception.* All of the items listed are true, but a loss of cognitive function is not a beneficial response since it impedes one's ability to obtain a dietary source of glucose. All of the other situations will lead to an increase in plasma glucose concentration and, as such, serve a beneficial role.

20. **All of the following are important actions of insulin EXCEPT:**
    A. increased synthesis of lipoprotein lipase, which facilitates FA removal from circulating VLDL and chylomicrons
    B. increased synthesis of muscle protein
    C. increased synthesis of glycogen
    D. inhibition of hormone-sensitive lipase, reducing TAG (triacylglycerol) breakdown
    E. stimulation of intestinal glucose absorption

Answer = E. *Remember you are looking for the exception.* Insulin is not required for glucose absorption by the GI tract to occur.

21. **When taken orally, all of the following hormones should have biological effects on their usual target tissues, EX-CEPT:**
    A. progesterone
    B. parathyroid hormone
    C. estrogen
    D. T_3
    E. thyroxin

    Answer = B. *Remember you are looking for the exception.* Because PTH is a peptide hormone, it will be digested by the GI tract and never reach the circulation. The other hormones are either steroid- or amino acid-based and, as such, can be absorbed across the GI tract and successfully enter the circulation.

22. **Excessive secretion of GH before fusion of the epiphyseal growth plates causes:**
    A. giantism
    B. acromegaly
    C. Cushing's syndrome
    D. Addison's disease
    E. dwarfism

    Answer = A. Excessive secretion of GH will lead to giantism if the epiphyseal growth plates have not fused. After closure of the growth plates, excess GH will cause acromegaly (**B**). Cushing's syndrome and Addison's disease are diseases of the adrenal cortex, and are not caused by GH secretion (**C** and **D**). Dwarfism is caused by too little GH secretion, not too much (**E**).

23. **In males, inhibin reduces:**
    A. libido, by directly inhibiting adrenal androgen secretion
    B. testosterone synthesis, by a direct action on Leydig cells
    C. FSH secretion and, hence, spermatogenesis
    D. LH secretion and, hence, testosterone secretion
    E. all of the above

    Answer = C. Inhibin, a product of the Sertoli cells of the testis, inhibits FSH secretion, leading to a decrease in spermatogenesis. It is part of the negative feedback loop between the pituitary (FSH) and the testis. It does not affect adrenal androgen production (not **A**), testosterone production by the Leydig cells (not **B**), or LH secretion (not **D**). Testosterone, not inhibin, inhibits LH secretion.

24. **Which of the following hormones is anabolic on muscle protein at physiological concentrations, but is catabolic at very high levels?**
    A. insulin
    B. GH
    C. testosterone
    D. thyroid hormone
    E. none of the above

    Answer = D. Normal levels of thyroid hormone are essential for normal anabolic processes to occur and stimulate growth; at high levels, however, muscle protein catabolism is stimulated.

25.   Figure 6-1 depicts the response to an increased dose of a hormone.

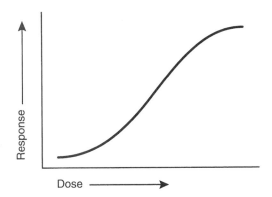

FIG. 6-1

The addition of an inhibitor that competes for the receptor to the hormone would:
    A.   lower the maximal response and shift the curve to the right
    B.   shift the curve to the left
    C.   lower the maximal response
    D.   shift the curve to the right
    E.   lower the maximal response and shift the curve to the left

Answer = D.   A competitive inhibitor will displace the natural hormone from the receptor, thus shifting the curve to the right (not B or E), i.e., requiring more natural hormone to produce the same response. Since it is a competitive inhibitor, the maximal response will not be affected (not A, C, or E).

26.   **Prolonged administration of metyrapone is likely to increase all of the following EXCEPT:**
    A.   CRH secretion
    B.   plasma glucocorticoid activity
    C.   ACTH secretion
    D.   plasma deoxycorticosterone (DOC) concentration
    E.   potassium excretion

Answer = B.   *Remember you are looking for the exception.* Metyrapone inhibits the late steps in cortisol synthesis, leading to a decrease in cortisol levels and, hence, a compensatory increase in CRH (A) and ACTH (C), which then stimulates the conversion of cholesterol by the adrenal. In the presence of metyrapone, there is an accumulation of mid-products such as DOC (D), a compound with a significant amount of mineralocorticoid activity that causes an increase in potassium excretion (E).

27.   **As its plasma concentration progressively increases, which hormone's feedback regulation can change from negative to positive and back to negative?**
    A.   GH
    B.   FSH
    C.   progesterone
    D.   estradiol
    E.   testosterone

Answer = D.   Estrogen at lower levels has a negative feedback affect on LH and FSH; at the higher levels reached at the end of the follicular phase, it has a positive burst-like effect on the secretion of LH and FSH.

28.   **In boys, the first anatomical event signaling the onset of puberty usually is:**
    A.   the appearance of some pubic hair
    B.   testicular enlargement
    C.   the beginning of the growth spurt
    D.   the appearance of some axillary hair
    E.   the presence of mature sperm in a semen analysis

Answer = B. The enlargement of the testes signals an increase in testosterone secretion, which leads to events **A, C,** and **D** and contributes to the development of mature sperm (**E**).

29. After delivery of her fourth child, a 40-year-old woman had severe hemorrhage and hypotension. She then developed Sheehan's syndrome (from postpartum necrosis of the anterior pituitary gland). She lost all normal anterior pituitary function. She doesn't want any more children, but does desire to avoid bone loss, reduce her risk of atherosclerosis, and have a satisfactory sex life (e.g., adequate lubrication by vaginal mucus glands). She does not want to nurse her latest baby. To induce relatively normal physiological function of important target tissues, you would likely treat her with all of the following *EXCEPT*:
    A. gonadotropins
    B. a glucocorticoid, given orally
    C. an estrogen
    D. oral thyroid hormone, e.g., T_4 and/or T_3
    E. progesterone

    Answer = A. *Remember you are looking for the exception.* Since the woman does not want to remain fertile, she does not need to maintain a totally normal menstrual cycle. You do want to maintain her thyroid and gluco-corticoid levels (**D** and **B**). The administration of an estrogen (**C**) and a progesterone (**E**) will help her maintain her sex life and minimize her risk for atherosclerosis and bone loss. Prolactin is not needed since she is not planning on nursing her child; gonadotropins are not needed since she does not want to maintain her fertility.

30. A 35-year-old woman desperately wants one child, but has isolated hypogonadotropic hypogonadism of hypothalamic origin (i.e., all pituitary hormones and her ovaries and reproductive tract are normal, but FSH and LH secretion are minimal). With which one of the following could you treat her to induce a normal ovulation and pregnancy?
    A. estrogen alone, given so it peaks twice each month
    B. progesterone alone, given so it peaks once each month
    C. estrogen, and perhaps progesterone, taken on a regular monthly schedule (two peaks of estrogen, one of progesterone)
    D. daily shots of equal amounts of both FSH and LH every day each month
    E. pulses of GnRH, administered every 1 to 2 h by subcutaneous pump

    Answer = E. You need to consider what is needed to correct this patient's primary problem, the hypothalamus. The pulsatile administration of GnRH will establish a normal physiological pattern of LH and FSH release, with the consequent development of the follicle. Neither estrogen (**A**) nor progesterone (**B**) nor any combination of these (**C**) will allow for the development of the follicle. Daily shots of LH and FSH will not work because, for one thing, they will not produce the spike in LH and FSH that is required for ovulation.

31. After the woman in question 30 has had her baby and nursed it until weaning, you probably would initiate long-term treatment with:
    A. daily estrogen alone, given continuously until she is 50 years old
    B. daily progesterone alone, given continuously until she is 50 years old
    C. estrogen, and perhaps progesterone, taken on a regular monthly schedule, as in combination or sequential birth control pills
    D. daily shots of a gonadotropin every 28 days: FSH for 14 days, LH for 10 days, nothing for 4 days
    E. pulses of GnRH, administered every 1 to 2 h by subcutaneous pump

    Answer = C. Since the woman has had her *one* child, you do not need to maintain her in a fertile state. The administration of an estrogen and a progesterone will help her maintain her sex life, maintain her long-term ability to become pregnant if she chooses, and minimize her risk for atherosclerosis and bone loss. It is unnecessary to administer either gonadotropins or GnRH (**D** and **E**). Neither **A** nor **B** will allow her to cycle in a normal manner.

32. After estrogen is increased for several weeks, such as in pregnancy or from taking birth control pills, what are the new steady-state plasma levels of CBG, cortisol, and ACTH, compared to before?

	Total CBG	Cortisol	Free Cortisol	ACTH
A.	↑	↑	↑	↑
B.	↑	↑	≈ same*	≈ same*
C.	≈ same*	≈ same*	↓	↑
D.	≈ same	≈ same	≈ same	≈ same
E.	↓	↓	≈ same	≈ same

*about the same, i.e., no change from pretreatment

Answer = B. Estrogen directly stimulates the production of CBG, which causes a transient decrease in free cortisol and, thus, a transient compensatory stimulation of ACTH secretion that continues until the subsequent increase in cortisol secretion saturates the CBG; the free cortisol and ACTH levels are then returned to normal.

33. During absorption of a normal meal, how do plasma insulin and glucagon concentrations change, and what effects does this have on nutrient stores, i.e., protein, glycogen, and fat?

	Plasma Insulin Concentration	Plasma Glucagon Concentration	Synthesis of Nutrient Stores	Breakdown of Nutrient Stores
A.	↓	↑	↑	↓
B.	≈ same*	↓	≈ same*	↓
C.	↑	≈ same*	↑	≈ same*
D.	↑	≈ same*	↑	↓
E.	↑	↓	↑	≈ same*

*about the same concentration or rate as before eating and absorbing a meal

Answer = D. Both the cephalic phase and the digestion-induced increase in glucose cause stimulation of the beta cells, leading to insulin secretion. However, since glucose levels are maintained near a normal or only slightly elevated level, glucagon secretion is not stimulated. The increase in insulin levels causes the deposition of glucose, fatty acids, and amino acids into various storage pools; and insulin inhibits the breakdown of these pools.

34. During nursing, oxytocin is secreted from the X but it had earlier been synthesized in the Y.

	X	Y
A.	mammary myoepithelial cells	mammary alveolar cells
B.	anterior lobe of pituitary	posterior lobe of pituitary
C.	posterior lobe of pituitary	hypothalamus
D.	intermediate lobe of pituitary	hypothalamic suckling center
E.	anterior lobe of pituitary	median eminence of hypothalamus

Answer = C. Like ADH, oxytocin is secreted from the nerve terminals in the posterior pituitary. The cell bodies, where the (pro)hormones are synthesized, are located in the hypothalamus.

35. Of the thyroxine produced by the thyroid:
    A. more than 90% is converted to biologically active triiodothyronine (T_3)
    B. at least 30% is converted to biologically inactive reverse triiodothyronine (rT_3).
    C. most is deiodinated before being secreted by the thyroid gland
    D. more than 90% is transported into the body cells as thyroxine and, as such, it binds to DNA and regulates metabolism

Answer = B. Actually, a much smaller fraction is converted to T_3 (<30%; not **A**). Most deiodination occurs in the peripheral tissues (not **C**). T_4 is converted to T_3, which then binds to DNA (not **D**).

36. When concentrations of thyroid hormones have been abnormally high for 2 to 3 months due to an overdose with T_4, then the circulating TSH concentration will:
    A. increase
    B. be subnormal but increase after a single TRH injection
    C. be subnormal and not increase after a single TRH injection
    D. remain normal and not increase after a single TRH injection
    E. remain normal and increase after a single TRH injection

Answer = C. Considering the normal feedback mechanism, you know that TSH should be depressed (not **A**, **D**, or **E**). In addition, the intracellular processes responsible for producing and releasing TSH are suppressed; and, like many systems suppressed for a period of time, they become unresponsive (not **B**) until stimulated for a period of time.

37. Thyroperoxidase functions in:
    A. iodination of thyroglobulin
    B. thyroxine's action on body cells
    C. hydrolysis of thyroglobulin
    D. release of thyroxine from thyroglobulin
    E. conversion of T_4 to T_3

Answer = A. Since tyrosine is bound by peptide linkage to thyroglobin, the iodination of these tyrosines is caused by the action of the thyroperoxidase.

38. **For a diabetic patient (Type 1) who is being successfully treated for ketoacidosis by the administration of insulin, a potassium salt also might be administered because:**
    A. insulin directly stimulates the excretion of potassium by the kidney
    B. a rapid (minutes) return of plasma pH and glucose to normal will lower the total body potassium content
    C. a rapid (minutes) return of plasma pH and glucose to normal will cause potassium to shift into the cells
    D. a rapid (minutes) return of plasma glucose to normal will cause a decrease in plasma volume

Answer = C. While suffering from DKA, patients excrete large quantities of potassium (as K-ketates) in their urine and consequently become potassium-depleted. The severe metabolic acidosis causes shifts of K out of the cells, which counteracts the negative effects of the urinary losses of K and tends to maintain plasma [K] within normal limits although the patient may be quite potassium-depleted. Insulin does not directly affect potassium secretion or excretion (**A**). The rapid return of plasma pH and glucose will cause a shift of K back into the cells (**C**), lowering the plasma [K]; but it would actually be associated with a decrease in the rate that K is being lost in the urine (decreased K-ketate excretion; not **B**). Choice **D** is true because as the glucose leaves the plasma and enters the cell, water will go with it and plasma volume will tend to decrease. However, this would be corrected by administering isotonic salts (saline or Ringer's lactate), not by giving potassium salts.

39. **The following are characteristic of steroid hormones** *EXCEPT*:
    A. they have a relatively long half-life
    B. most are bound to protein in the blood
    C. they bind to cytoplasmic receptor
    D. they are synthesized for the most part continuously
    E. their early action is on mRNA synthesis

Answer = D: *Remember you are looking for the exception.* The synthesis of steroid hormones is normally due to activation of the synthetic pathway, which at rest is fairly quiescent. The other characteristics are normal features of most steroid hormones.

40. **In a patient with untreated diabetic ketoacidosis, you would expect an increased urinary excretion of all of the following** *EXCEPT*:
    A. glucose
    B. keto-acids
    C. NH_4^+
    D. bicarbonate
    E. titratable acids

Answer = D. *Remember you are looking for the exception.* The patient should be excreting an acidic urine that has a very low pH (hence, very little bicarbonate; *not* **D**), with an increase in NH_4^+ (**C**) and titratable acid excretion (**E**). Glucose and keto-acids should also be high since the elevated blood levels of these compounds will exceed their renal T_{max} and large quantities will appear in the urine (**A** and **B**).

41. **Excessive secretion of growth hormone (GH) in prepubertal individuals can cause which of the following abnormal states?**
    A. giantism
    B. acromegaly
    C. hyperglycemia
    D. both A and C
    E. both A and B

Answer = D. As long as the sex steroids have not caused closure of the growth plates of the long bones, individuals can develop a very large stature (giantism; **A**). Acromegaly occurs with excess GH in adults (not **B**), and represents the continued growth of the jaw, hands and feet, and bones that lack growth plates. GH is diabetogenic because of its ability to mobilize FFA, decrease glucose uptake in some tissue, and increase hepatic glucose output; hence, excessive secretion of GH can be associated with hyperglycemia (**C**).

42. **Either decreased blood volume or increased plasma osmolality would be expected to increase plasma levels of:**
    A. ADH
    B. renin
    C. aldosterone
    D. both A and C
    E. none of the above

    Answer = A. Although all three hormones will be increased by a decrease in blood volume, only ADH is stimulated by an increase in osmolality. Renin may not be affected at all, whereas aldosterone might be slightly inhibited by the increase in osmolality.

43. **Cutting the preganglionic sympathetic nerves to the adrenal gland would cause:**
    A. hyponatremia, dehydration, and death
    B. increased plasma levels of angiotensin II
    C. hyperkalemia
    D. all of the above
    E. none of the above

    Answer = Answer E. Cutting the nerves to the adrenal gland will block the secretion of epinephrine but have no effect on the secretion of any of the steroid hormones. Choices **A, B,** and **C** are symptoms that might be associated with a lack of aldosterone secretion.

44. **Which of the following physiological abnormalities would you expect to cause dilutional hyponatremia?**
    A. hyposecretion of aldosterone
    B. inability to form angiotensin II
    C. hypersecretion of vasopressin
    D. all of the above
    E. A and B only

    Answer = C. Although hypersecretion of ADH and hyposecretion of aldosterone (**A**) caused either by adrenal failure or a lack of angiotensin II (**B**), will produce a hyponatremia, **A** and **B** will be associated with a loss of volume, not the retention of water, as is the case for vasopressin.

45. **Gonadectomy of a female fetus (XX genotype) during the "critical phase" of uterine life would result in the birth of an infant having:**
    A. masculinized external genitalia
    B. masculinized internal genitalia
    C. no uterus
    D. all of the above
    E. none of the above

    Answer = E. The fetus will develop into an individual with normal-appearing female genitalia. It is the presence of testosterone that masculinizes the genitalia, not the absence of estrogen. The uterus will develop to an infantile state from the Müllerian ducts in the absence of ovarian estrogen (not **C**).

46. **Following hypophysectomy, an individual's responsiveness to a fixed dose of insulin increases because of:**
    A. decreased growth hormone secretion
    B. decreased FSH secretion
    C. decreased cortisol secretion
    D. both A and C
    E. none of the above; the opening statement is false

    Answer = D. Both growth hormone and cortisol are diabetogenic; in their absence, an individual will produce less glucose, utilize more glucose peripherally and, hence, need less insulin to maintain plasma glucose levels within the desired range.

PART 6: ENDOCRINE PHYSIOLOGY

233

47. **In human females, menopause is thought to be due to:**
   A.   failure of the hypothalamus to secrete GnRH
   B.   failure of the anterior pituitary to secrete gonadotrophins
   C.   failure of the ovaries to secrete estrogen and progesterone
   D.   failure of peripheral tissues to respond to female sex hormones
   E.   none of the above

   Answer = C. It is the failure of the ovaries to produce adequate amounts of estrogen and progesterone that produces menopause. GnRH and the gonadotrophins are actually elevated (not **A** or **B**) because the negative feedback effects of estrogen and progesterone are no longer present. Women continue to respond to exogenous hormone administration (not **D**), which is why many postmenopausal women may decide to take estrogen to help them counteract the negative effects that the lack of estrogen has on the cardiovascular system and on bone density.

48. **A pituitary acidophilic adenoma would most likely be associated with:**
   A.   an elevated metabolic rate
   B.   acromegaly
   C.   hirsutism in females
   D.   osteoporosis
   E.   hyperpigmentation

   Answer = B. Acidophils are the cell types that secrete GH and prolactin; hence, a patient hypersecreting GH might be excepted to develop acromegaly.

49. **The 24-h urinary excretion of 19-carbon androgenic steroids would be lowest in:**
   A.   castrated males
   B.   castrated females
   C.   adrenalectomized males
   D.   adrenalectomized females
   E.   intact females

   Answer = D. Men and women produce similar amounts of adrenal androgenic steroids. In the absence of the adrenals, females will produce very small amounts of androgenic steroids.

50. **Consider a 21-year-old female patient presenting with the following:**
   1. hyperpigmentation
   2. blood pressure 165/105
   3. acne
   4. hypokalemia
   5. hypernatremia
   6. amenorrhea
   7. low fasting blood glucose level
   8. physical and mental fatigue
   9. enlarged clitoris
   10. chromatin positive buccal smear

   Identify the only endocrine disorder in the list below that could account for all of these symptoms and laboratory findings.
   A.   an ACTH-secreting tumor
   B.   11β-hydroxylase deficiency
   C.   absence of androgen receptors
   D.   21-hydroxylase deficiency
   E.   primary hypercortisolism

   Answer = B. The patient is a female (finding 10) with signs of excessive adrenal mineralocorticoid hormone secretion. Findings 2, 4, 5, and 8 are typical of patients with hypersecretion of mineralocorticoids (such as 11-DOC). A low fasting glucose level is typical of patients with hyposecretion of cortisol. The acne, enlarged clitoris, and amenorrhea could be due to hypersecretion of adrenal androgens. The hyperpigmentation is a key finding, suggesting that the adrenal mineralocorticoid hypersecretion is due to ACTH. An 11β-hydroxylase deficiency will cause a decrease in cortisol and corticosterone that leads to an increase in ACTH and a subsequent build-up of 11-DOC and 11-deoxycortisol (mineralocorticoids) and adrenal androgens.

51. **During normal development, adult sexual characteristics do not appear before puberty. The best explanation for this is that prior to puberty in normal development:**
   A.   the juvenile gonads lack the mechanism(s) required to secrete sex hormones
   B.   the juvenile pituitary lacks the mechanism(s) required to respond to GnRH
   C.   juvenile sex accessory structures lack the mechanism(s) required to respond to sex hormones
   D.   the juvenile hypothalamus lacks the mechanism(s) required to release GnRH appropriately
   E.   none of the above is best; they all are equally responsible

   Answer = D. As has been shown in studies of patients with either delayed or precocious puberty, it is the lack of a hypothalamic mechanism to release GnRH in a pulsatile manner that prevents the onset of puberty. If artificially induced by pulsatile doses of GnRH, sexual maturation can start at a very young age. The juvenile pituitary (gonadotrophs), gonads, and sex accessory structures all are responsive to physiologic levels of stimulating hormones, but too little of these circulate.

52. **Daily injections of testosterone into an adult male in amounts that would raise its serum level above normal for 10 days would be expected to increase:**
   A.   the size of the prostate
   B.   the rate of spermatogenesis
   C.   the mass of the testes
   D.   all of the above
   E.   none of the above

   Answer = A. The continued injection of large amounts of testosterone will cause hypertrophy of the prostate; but it will also cause a negative feedback inhibition of LH and FSH secretion, leading to a decrease in spermatogenesis (not **B**) and in the size of the testes (not **C**).

53. **Fertility in hypophysectomized adult males could be restored by appropriate administration of:**
   A.   follicle-stimulating hormone
   B.   luteinizing hormone or testosterone
   C.   prolactin
   D.   combinations of A and B
   E.   none of the above

   Answer = D. In the hypophysectomized adult male, both LH (or testosterone) and FSH are needed to restore fertility: LH to induce testosterone and FSH to restore normal spermatogenesis.

54. **Shortly after birth, a patient is found to have the following:**

   Karyotype: XX   External genitalia: feminine
   Internal genital structure: Fasting blood sugar: low
     Mullerian: normally developed   Plasma volume: expanded
     Wolffian: regressed

   This patient has:
   A. 17α-hydroxylase deficiency
   B. 11β-hydroxylase deficiency
   C.   21-hydroxylase deficiency
   D.   androgen insensitivity
   E.   gonadotropin deficiency

   Answer = B. The patient is a genetic female with female internal and external genitalia and evidence of hyposecretion of cortisol but hypersecretion of a mineralocorticoid. Choice **B** would produce a low level of glucocorticoid but a high level of 11-deoxycorticosterone and 11-deoxycortisol, steroid hormones, precursors with high levels of mineralocorticoid activity but low glucocorticoid activity.

55. **The most important reason we can survive not eating for at least 48 hours is that:**
   A. GH, thyroid hormones, catecholamines, and cortisol act in concert to promote muscle breakdown, providing more amino acids for gluconeogenesis
   B. there is increased secretion of GH, a rapidly acting, potent inhibitor of glucose utilization
   C. insulin secretion increases as plasma glucose rises on the second day
   D. once-daily secretion of cortisol stimulates synthesis of sufficient amounts of key enzymes in the liver to allow redistribution of carbon from stores to glucose
   E. once-daily secretion of glucagon stimulates muscle breakdown, providing amino acids for gluconeogenesis

   Answer = D.   It is the once-daily secretion of cortisol that puts the key hepatic enzymes into place, which allows for gluconeogenesis.

56. **Which of the following groups consists of only those hormones that regulate body metabolism primarily on a minute-by-minute basis, rather than on a long-term basis (hours-days)?**
   A. glucagon, insulin, epinephrine
   B. glucocorticoids, GH, thyroid hormones
   C. GH, glucocorticoids, glucagon
   D. TSH, catecholamines, insulin
   E. none of the above

   Answer = A.   Thyroid hormone, GH and cortisol, are much slower-acting than are glucagon, insulin, and catecholamines such as epinephrine. The effects of TSH on body metabolism are mediated via thyroid hormones and, hence, are slow (not **D**).

57. **Weakness from loss of muscle mass in prolonged hyperthyroidism occurs because high levels of thyroid hormone:**
   A. inhibit muscle protein synthesis
   B. decrease nutrient uptake from the GI tract (because they greatly increase GI motility)
   C. stimulate muscle protein degradation
   D. directly and strongly activate hepatic gluconeogenesis, drawing amino acids out of muscle
   E. decrease TSH

   Answer = C.   Although thyroid hormone is essential for normal growth and protein synthesis, at high levels it also stimulates muscle protein degradation, which leads to decreased muscle mass.

58. **Glucagon increases blood glucose concentration mainly because it:**
   A. inhibits insulin secretion
   B. enhances muscle protein degradation
   C. stimulates glycogen synthetase in the liver
   D. stimulates hepatic glycogenolysis and gluconeogenesis
   E. stimulates lipolysis in adipose tissue; the resulting increased FFA inhibits glucose utilization

   Answer = D.   Glucagon released from the pancreas affects the liver by stimulating hepatic glycogenolysis and gluconeogenesis, not glycogen synthetase (not **C**). Very little glucagon reaches peripheral tissues at a level sufficient to have a biological effect (not **A, B,** or **E**).

59. **Normally, the major fraction of triiodothyronine in the body is:**
   A. produced in the thyroid gland
   B. produced in the nonthyroid tissues of the body
   C. bound to TBG
   D. activated by iodination of di-iodothyronine
   E. formed from reverse T_3

   Answer = B. T_4 is produced and released by the thyroid and converted to T_3 by the deiodination of T_4 (not **D** or **E**) in the peripheral tissues (not **A**). T_3 is less than 50% bound to TBG (not **C**).

60. **A patient with diabetic ketoacidosis hyperventilates because:**
   A. elevated blood glucose stimulates central thirst and respiratory centers
   B. increased formation of CO_2 stimulates peripheral chemoreceptors
   C. elevated plasma H^+ ion concentration stimulates central respiratory centers
   D. the decrease in extracellular volume enhances bicarbonate reabsorption
   E. insulin directly inhibits the respiratory center

Answer = C. The metabolic acidosis is the stimulus via the effect of pH on the central chemoreceptors. Glucose does stimulate thirst, but not the respiratory centers (not **A**). If anything, there is a shift away from glucose oxidation that will cause a slight decrease in the formation of CO_2 (not **B**). A decrease in extracellular volume does enhance bicarbonate reabsorption, but does not cause hyperventilation (not **D**). Insulin does not directly affect the respiratory center (not **E**).

61. A high plasma Ca^{2+} level in the normal adult is likely to cause:
    A. bone decalcification (resorption)
    B. increased formation of $1,25(OH)_2D_3$
    C. increased formation of $24,25(OH)_2D_3$
    D. decreased secretion of calcitonin
    E. decreased urinary calcium excretion

Answer = C. A high plasma calcium level causes a decrease in PTH secretion that leads to a decrease in the formation of $1,25(OH)_2D_3$ (not **B**), with a corresponding increase in the formation of $24,25(OH)_2D_3$, and to an increase in calcium excretion (not **E**). Bone decalcification decreases as the calcium phosphate product is increased (not **A**). The elevated calcium also increases calcitonin secretion (not **D**).

62. An adult with a parathyroid gland tumor has a very elevated plasma PTH level. This person's urinary phosphate excretion is expected to X, whereas the plasma phosphate level is likely to Y.

	X	Y
A.	increase	increase
B.	increase	decrease or show no change
C.	decrease	increase or show no change
D.	decrease	decrease
E.	show no change	show no change

Answer = B. A primary increase in PTH will cause an increase in phosphate excretion, but plasma phosphate may show little change because there will also be a large mobilization of phosphate from bone that will counteract the renal losses. Bone, however, will become demineralized.

63. Which of the following factors is the most important in regulating the secretory rate of cortisol in normal humans?
    A. potassium
    B. angiotensin II
    C. cortisol
    D. sodium
    E. ionized calcium

Answer = C. Because of its negative feedback action on ACTH, cortisol is the most important regulator of cortisol secretion. The other factors have little or no effect on cortisol secretion, although several of them are important regulators of aldosterone secretion.

64. Patients with a pancreatic β-cell adenoma [a tumor that hypersecretes the hormone(s) of its cell type] would tend to have:
    A. hyperglycemia
    B. elevated growth hormone and ACTH levels
    C. glycosuria
    D. all of the above
    E. none of the above

Answer = B. Hypersecretion of insulin leads to pronounced hypoglycemia (not **A**), which leads to increases in both GH and ACTH. There is little chance for glycosuria (not **C**) to develop with the very low glucose levels.

65. Marked increases in cortisol secretion can occur within minutes after exposure to stress. The physiological mechanism involved depends upon:
    A. increased use of cortisol by peripheral tissues, leading to decreased plasma cortisol concentration
    B. increased impulses in nerve fibers from the median eminence of the hypothalamus to corticotrophin cells in the anterior pituitary
    C. increased impulses in nerve fibers from the hypothalamus to the adrenal
    D. increased release of corticotrophin-releasing hormone (CPH) from the hypothalamus
    E. none of the above

Answer = D. The increase in cortisol secretion is due to the release of CRH, which then stimulates the secretion of ACTH from the anterior pituitary.

66. **The single most important hormone regulating the rate of milk production (synthesis) in lactating females is:**
    A. oxytocin
    B. estradiol-17β
    C. FSH
    D. progesterone
    E. prolactin

    Answer = E. Milk production is determined primarily by prolactin acting on mature breasts. Oxytocin is involved in milk let-down, not synthesis.

For questions 67–71, refer to the information given below.
   You are presented with a 27-year-old patient manifesting the following symptoms:
   1. polyuria
   2. polydipsia
   3. elevated urine osmolality
   4. history of increased bone fragility
   5. hyperpigmentation
   6. easy bruisability

On the basis of these observations, you requested the laboratory tests that are listed below with their results.
Thyroxine: normal
Fasting insulin: 50% higher than expected for normal individuals

67. **In light of all other data (1–6, above), the laboratory report for insulin is probably:**
    A. correct
    B. incorrect

68. **The most reasonable diagnosis for this patient is a primary disorder of the:**
    A. pancreatic β cells
    B. neurohypophysis (posterior pituitary)
    C. adenohypophysis (anterior pituitary)
    D. thyroid
    E. adrenal cortex

69. **The gland having the primary malfunction in this case is secreting non-normal levels of its hormone:**
    A. insulin
    B. ADH
    C. ACTH
    D. thyroxine
    E. cortisol

Answer = Answers to questions 67–69. To answer the above questions, you must formulate the primary diagnosis. Symptoms 1–3 suggest hyperglycemia, which will induce an osmotic diuresis leading to polydipsia. An increase in cortisol can, by stimulating hepatic glycogenesis and gluconeogenesis, increase plasma glucose levels, whereas elevated cortisol has an anti-insulin action in the peripheral tissues. The hyperpigmentation suggests an increase in ACTH or MSH, whereas both the easy bruisability (clotting defect or a loss of subcutaneous tissue integrity) and the bone fragility (osteoporosis) are symptoms of excessive cortisol secretion. In view of the choices, the logical diagnosis for this patient is a hypersecretion of ACTH (**69 = C**) by the anterior pituitary gland (**68 = C**), which causes the increase in plasma cortisol. The elevated blood glucose levels should stimulate insulin secretion, and the resistance to insulin action caused by the markedly elevated cortisol levels will tend to prevent the insulin from bringing the glucose levels back down to normal; hence, a moderate elevation in insulin levels would be expected (**67 = A**).

70. During your early differential diagnosis, an alternative diagnostic hypothesis might have been a primary hypersecreting lesion of the:
    A. pancreatic β cells
    B. neurohypophysis
    C. adenohypophysis
    D. thyroid
    E. adrenal cortex

71. However, you ruled out this alternative diagnostic hypothesis because of the:
    A. polyuria
    B. polydipsia
    C. elevated urine osmolality
    D. history of increased bone fragility
    E. hyperpigmentation

Answer = Answers to questions 70–71. All but the hyperpigmentation symptoms (**71 = E**) are due to an elevated level of cortisol, the early alternative diagnosis (**70 = E**). Cortisol will not produce hyperpigmentation, but ACTH will because of its similarity to MSH.

72. You obtain the following data for a patient: plasma [T_4] is slightly elevated, plasma [TSH] is low, and thyroid gland size is below normal. Which of the following would best explain this set of observations?
    A. a lesion in the anterior pituitary gland that prevents secretion of TSH
    B. the patient is taking a drug that blocks the ability of the thyroid gland to synthesize thyroid hormone
    C. the patient is taking thyroid extract
    D. plasma levels of the thyroid hormone carrier protein are elevated
    E. a lesion in the hypothalamus that prevents secretion of TRH

Answer = C. Administration of thyroid extract could easily cause a slight increase in T_4. The increase in T_4 levels will lead to a decrease in TSH levels and, consequently, to a smaller thyroid gland. A primary decrease in TSH (not **A**) would cause the T_4 levels to be decreased. If thyroid hormone synthesis were blocked (not **B**), TSH and thyroid gland size would increase. If a carrier protein level were elevated (not **D**), there would be an increase in total hormone levels and transient increases, but not a sustained decrease in TSH or gland size. If TRH were blocked (not **E**), T_4 as well as TSH and gland size would decrease.

73. A sudden increase in the plasma concentration of a hormone binding protein would:
    A. decrease the response to the hormone
    B. increase the response to the hormone
    C. have no effect on the response to the hormone
    D. increase the amount of hormone free in the plasma
    E. decrease the release of the hormone from the endocrine gland

Answer = A. With more binding protein available, the response to either injected or physiologically released hormone will be decreased, since much of the hormone will be bound and less will be free (not **D**). The decrease in free hormone levels would stimulate the release of hormone (not **E**) to bring the plasma level of free hormone back to normal.

74. All of the following are consistent with a diagnosis of hypopituitarism *EXCEPT*:
    A. decreased cortisol response to an ACTH stimulation test
    B. frankly elevated FSH and LH with hypogonadism
    C. decreased ACTH response to CRH
    D. low TSH with very low free and total thyroxine levels
    E. very low IGF-1 levels

Answer = B. *Remember you are looking for the exception.* In the absence of the pituitary hormones due to an unresponsive pituitary gland (**C**), there will be a decreased secretion of ACTH, LH, FSH (*not* **B**), TSH, and GH that will be associated with a decrease in the size and responsiveness (**A**) of the glands and/or the amount of hormone being secreted (**D**) by the target glands. Furthermore, factors that are stimulated by the pituitary hormones (eg, the hepatic production of IGF-1) will also be decreased (**E**).

75. **All of the following are true about a typical adult patient with acromegaly EXCEPT:**
   A.   the patient is usually at least 1 foot taller than predicted
   B.   the patient usually has a pituitary tumor
   C.   the patient usually has elevated IGF-1 levels
   D.   the patient often has insulin insensitivity
   E.   the patient often has organomegaly

   Answer = A. *Remember you are looking for the exception.* Since acromegaly is an adult onset problem, the excessive secretion of growth hormone does not result in additional long bone growth; hence, individuals with acromegaly lie within the normal range of height. All of the other points are logical for patients with acromegaly.

76. **The pubertal growth spurt usually starts at a younger age in females. The most logical explanation is that:**
   A.   males have higher levels of growth hormone at puberty
   B.   pubertal increase in gonadal function occurs at a younger age in females
   C.   the pubertal increase in testosterone is greater in males compared to the pubertal increase in progesterone in females
   D.   the GHRH nuclei in the hypothalamus of males are less sensitive to glucocorticoid negative feedback
   E.   epiphyseal fusion occurs earlier in males

   Answer = B. The growth spurt starts because the activation of LH and FSH secretion occurs earlier in females than it does in males. The development of ovarian function and the accompanying increase in estradiol secretion enhance the secretion of growth hormone; hence, the growth spurt is started earlier in females than in males. The other factors are either incorrect (**E**) and/or irrelevant (not **A, C,** or **D**).

77. **A patient has been taking health food pills containing ten times the normal dose of T_3. All of the following findings are likely to occur in this patient EXCEPT:**
   A.   increased oxygen consumption
   B.   increased body temperature
   C.   suppressed TSH
   D.   increased appetite
   E.   elevated plasma T_4

   Answer = E. *Remember you are looking for the exception.* Since T_3 is the active hormone derived from the peripheral conversion of T_4, you would expect a negative feedback response leading to a decrease in TSH secretion (**C**), which will cause the secretion of T_4 to decrease (*not* **E**). The other factors are all stimulated by the diet-induced increase in T_3 (**A, B,** and **D**).

78. **Compared to a 25-year-old woman, a 75-year-old woman would be expected to have:**
   A.   lower urinary excretion of estrogen, progesterone, and gonadotropins
   B.   higher plasma progesterone, but lower plasma estrogen concentrations
   C.   lower plasma progesterone, but higher plasma estrogen concentrations
   D.   lower plasma gonadotropins, estrogen, and progesterone concentrations
   E.   higher plasma gonadotropins, but lower plasma estrogen and progesterone

   Answer = E. It is the failure of the ovaries to produce enough estrogen and progesterone that causes menopause. The lack of estrogen and progesterone results in there being no feedback inhibition of the secretion of the gonadotropins. The level of gonadotropins is therefore increased.

79. **If both adrenal glands of a person are severely damaged by tuberculosis, which of the following hormones will increase in the blood?**
   A.   aldosterone
   B.   ACTH
   C.   corticosterone
   D.   cortisol
   E.   all of the above

   Answer = B. The lack of cortisol and corticosterone leads to an increase in ACTH secretion because the normal negative feedback signals do not exist. Aldosterone levels would decrease, which would also tend to cause renin and angiotensin II levels to be elevated in this patient.

80. The plasma concentration of which of the following hormones will increase following successful transplantation of the pituitary underneath the kidney capsule?
   A.   growth hormone
   B.   somatostatin
   C.   prolactin
   D.   TSH
   E.   ACTH

   Answer = C.   The only pituitary hormone that is controlled mainly by the release of an inhibitory factor is prolactin; hence, the transplanted pituitary gland will secrete increased amounts of prolactin and decrease the amounts of the other listed hormones.

81. Rational initial treatment of newly diagnosed panhypopituitarism in an 8-year-old boy would likely include all of the following *EXCEPT:*
   A.   GH
   B.   testosterone
   C.   a glucocorticoid
   D. T_4
   E.   ADH

   Answer = B.   *Remember you are looking for the exception.* It would not be necessary to treat an 8-year-old boy with testosterone since a normal boy that age has low levels of testosterone. When the boy grows and approaches the age of puberty, the administration of testosterone would then be considered to help him develop a normal male phenotype.

82. Increased secretion from the adrenal medulla will cause all of the following *EXCEPT:*
   A.   constriction of airways in the lungs
   B.   decreased insulin secretion
   C.   increased metabolic rate
   D.   increased muscle tension
   E.   increased lipolysis

   Answer = A.   *Remember you are looking for the exception.* An increase is plasma epinephrine levels will cause everything listed above except constriction of the airways. Catecholamines, acting via β_2 receptors, cause relaxation of bronchial smooth muscle; the decreased airways resistance makes breathing easier.

83. Excessive secretion of DOC or aldosterone will promote all of the following *EXCEPT:*
   A.   Na retention, but only for about two weeks
   B.   K excretion
   C.   blood pressure elevation
   D.   production of adrenal androgens
   E.   weight gain

   Answer = D.   *Remember you are looking for the exception.* Neither DOC nor aldosterone can be converted to androgens. All of the other symptoms are logically produced by the excess production of a mineralocorticoid.

84. Which of the following would be a reasonable treatment for a person from whom Chvostek's and Trousseau's signs can be elicited after provocation by a thorough physician?
   A.   tablets containing thyroid hormone
   B.   increased dietary iodide
   C.   PTU and beta-blocking drugs
   D.   parathyroidectomy (avoiding thyroidectomy)
   E.   greatly increased dietary vitamin D and Ca

   Answer = E.   These symptoms are caused by severe hypocalcemia, not a thyroid problem (not **A, B,** or **C**); hence, you need to increase plasma calcium levels. Choice E should cause plasma calcium levels to increase, while parathyroidectomy (not **D**) will cause hypocalcemia, not hypercalcemia.

85. **An absolute or relative increase in which of the following hormones contributes to the hyperglycemia of diabetes?**
    A. cortisol
    B. glucagon
    C. epinephrine
    D. All of the above are correct.
    E. Only A and C are correct.

Answer = D. When a patient develops symptoms of volume depletion due to the loss of extracellular fluid, both cortisol and epinephrine secretion are increased. Relative to insulin, glucagon tends to be increased in diabetes, primarily due to the decreased insulin but also due to the elevated amino acid levels and increased catecholamines, which stimulate glucagon secretion.

86. **All of the following help reduce testicular temperature *EXCEPT*:**
    A. contraction of cremasteric muscle during sexual arousal
    B. countercurrent heat exchange in the pampiniform plexus
    C. sweat glands in the scrotum
    D. lowering of scrotum and testes in hot environments
    E. numerous folds in the scrotum

Answer = A: *Remember you are looking for the exception.* Contraction of the cremasteric muscles during sexual arousal raises the testes near the abdomen and actually tends to warm, not cool, the testicles; however, it does serve to protect the testes. All of the other choices help lower testicular temperature.

87. **Sertoli cells perform all of the following *EXCEPT*:**
    A. synthesize testosterone when stimulated by LH
    B. nourish developing spermatozoa
    C. synthesize androgen binding protein (ABP)
    D. provide the physical "blood–testis barrier" at their tight junctions
    E. produce fluid that pushes mature sperm toward the epididymis

Answer = A. *Remember you are looking for the exception.* Testosterone is synthesized by the Leydig cells, not the Sertoli cells. The other listed functions are performed by the Sertoli cells.

88. **Removal of the right testis at age 5 weeks in a 46-XY fetus will lead to:**
    A. sterility in adulthood
    B. bilateral cryptorchidism
    C. bilateral failure of the Wolffian ducts to develop into male internal structures
    D. failure of the Müllerian ducts to regress on the right side only
    E. failure to develop masculine external genitalia during gestation

Answer = D. The loss of the right testis at age 5 weeks removes the Sertoli cells that release Müllerian regression factor (MRF) and the Leydig cells that secrete testosterone. The lack of MRF (which acts locally) from the right testis will cause the Müllerian duct to remain on the right side in males. However, testosterone secreted by the left testis will promote development of the male structures on both sides of the body.

89. **Progesterone does all of the following *EXCEPT*:**
    A. increase basal body temperature
    B. synergize with estradiol to inhibit LH secretion
    C. convert the endometrium to a secretory state
    D. make cervical mucus thin and watery
    E. decrease myometrial contractility

Answer = D. *Remember you are looking for the exception.* Progesterone makes the cervical mucus secretion thick and sticky, hard to penetrate (*not* D). All of the other actions listed (A, B, C, and E) are caused by progesterone.

90. **Variation in the length of a menstrual cycle is determined primarily by variation in the:**
    A. length of the luteal phase
    B. time between the mid-cycle FSH surge and ovulation
    C. frequency that a woman has (protected) sexual intercourse
    D. length of menstruation
    E. length of the follicular phase

    Answer = E. The length of the follicular phase is the most variable. The luteal phase is fairly constant at about 14 days. The time between the mid-cycle surge and ovulation is quite short (not **B**). Menstruation is part of the follicular phase.

91. **Three hours after nursing, a mother hears her baby cry. This is likely to elicit which of the following?**
    A. secretion of oxytocin
    B. secretion of prolactin
    C. milk ejection ("let-down")
    D. all of the above.
    E. A and C only

    Answer = E. Secretion of prolactin is stimulated by suckling (not **B**) and not by the sights and sounds of the baby. A mother hearing her child will increase the secretion of oxytocin, which causes milk let-down. Oxytocin secretion is provoked by both exteroceptive stimuli and suckling.

92. **The predominant type of biological activity of hMG is that of:**
    A. progesterone
    B. estrogen
    C. LH
    D. FSH
    E. None of the above is correct.

    Answer = D. hMG is an acronym for human menopausal gonadotropin. It is extracted from urine of postmenopausal women who have elevated levels of gonadotropins, LH, and especially FSH. The predominant biological activity of this extract is FSH-like; and, hence, hMG can be used to promote follicular development in subfertile women.

93. **The initial increase in estrogen in a 10-year-old female produces:**
    A. menarche
    B. the first ovulation
    C. thelarche
    D. adrenarche
    E. epiphyseal closure

    Answer = C. One of the first effects of the pubertal increase in estrogen is the initial development of the breasts ("breast budding" or thelarche).

94. **If plasma calcium suddenly falls from 11.0 to 8.0 mg/dl in an otherwise normal child, all of the following will occur EXCEPT:**
    A. increased plasma PTH, which increases renal tubular calcium reabsorption
    B. increased plasma PTH, which stimulates conversion of cholecalciferol to $24,25\text{-}(OH)_2$-vitamin D_3 in the liver
    C. increased plasma PTH, which stimulates bone resorption
    D. increased plasma PTH, which decreases renal tubular phosphate reabsorption
    E. decreased plasma CT, which reduces the previous inhibition of bone resorption by CT

    Answer = B. *Remember you are looking for the exception.* First, the plasma concentration of PTH will increase (**A, B, C,** and **D**), while the plasma calcitonin level will decrease (**E**). The increase in PTH will lead to enhanced calcium reabsorption along the distal nephron of the kidney (**A**) and to bone resorption (**C**), while decreasing renal phosphate reabsorption (**D**). Reduction in CT will decease its inhibition of bone reabsorption (**E**). Conversion of cholecalciferol to 25-OH-vitamin D occurs in the kidney, not the liver (*not* **B**) which is indirectly stimulated by an increase in PTH via an increase in $1,25(OH)_2$-vitamin D_3.

95. **The maximum effect of a single oral dose of thyroid hormone on the human body is produced:**
    A. between 15 min and 2 h after ingestion
    B. between 2 and 10 h after ingestion
    C. on the fourth day after ingestion
    D. during the second month after ingestion
    E. never, because it is ineffective orally

    Answer = C. It requires several days for thyroid hormone to act fully. Therefore, it will take several days for the patient to begin to feel any beneficial effects of the treatment and several days for the patient to feel any effect of not taking the thyroid hormone.

96. **In a patient with diabetes mellitus who has ketoacidosis, you would probably find all of the following *EXCEPT*:**
    A. increased plasma renin
    B. increased plasma aldosterone
    C. contracted intracellular volume
    D. expanded extracellular volume
    E. hyperpnea

    Answer = D. *Remember you are looking for the exception.* By the time your patient has metabolic acidosis leading to hyperpnea (**E**), the plasma level of glucose and ketates is markedly elevated (plasma osmolarity is increased) and a marked osmotic diuresis is established. The elevated plasma osmolality and the loss of potassium salts contribute to a contraction of the intracellular volume, especially in insulin-sensitive tissues (**C**). This diuresis causes the loss of significant quantities of sodium; hence, plasma and extracellular volume are contracted (***not* D**). The contraction of the plasma volume leads to reflex increases in renin and, hence, aldosterone (**A** and **B**).

97. **In a patient who is being treated for diabetic ketoacidosis, a calcium salt might be administered because:**
    A. insulin directly stimulates renal calcium excretion
    B. a rapid return of plasma pH to normal will lower total plasma calcium concentration
    C. a rapid return of plasma pH to normal will lower the plasma ionized calcium concentration
    D. a rapid return of plasma glucose concentration will cause a decrease in plasma volume
    E. insulin directly inhibits the entry of calcium into fat cells

    Answer = C. As the patient begins to respond and metabolic processes revert back toward normal, the patient's metabolic acidosis will begin to subside and arterial pH will decease back to normal. This relative alkalization will not affect total calcium concentration (not **B**), but will decrease the ionized fraction of plasma Ca. Insulin is not a major regulator of calcium metabolism (not **A** or **E**). A rapid entry of glucose into the cells will cause a shift of water into the cells, causing a decrease in plasma volume; this may need to be treated by the administration of isotonic saline, but not by the administration of a calcium salt (not **D**).

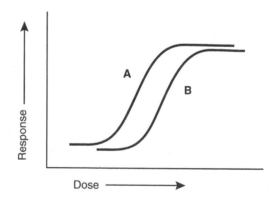

FIG. 6-2

98. **In the above figure, the change from curve A to curve B in the responses to increasing doses of a hormone could have been caused by:**
    A. an increase in the number of hormone receptors on the target cells
    B. a decrease in the number of the hormone receptors on the target cells
    C. an increase in the number of target cells
    D. a decrease in the number of target cells
    E. the presence of a noncompetitive inhibitor of the hormone

Answer = B. Shifting from curve A to B indicates that it takes more hormone (dose) to produce the same response but that the response can be obtained. This suggest that there are fewer hormone receptors on the target cells than were previously there under condition A. If the number of target cells had increased or decreased, the response maximum would have increased or decreased, whereas a noncompetitive inhibitor of the hormone would have decreased the maximum response. A competitive inhibitor (not listed) could also have produced the observed shift in the dose-response curve.

For questions 99–104, refer to the data in the box below.

You are confronted with a 19-year-old patient with a positive (sex chromatin) buccal smear and manifesting the following physical findings:

A.   delayed puberty, primary amenorrhea, absence of pubic and axillary hair, and failure of breast development
B.   dark complexion
C.   fasting hypoglycemia
D.   decreased basal metabolic rate
E.   juvenile, but otherwise apparently normal, female external genitalia

99.   The observation that is least likely to be related to the basic problem in this patient is:
A.   delayed puberty, primary amenorrhea, absence of pubic and axillary hair, and failure of breast development
B.   dark complexion
C.   fasting hypoglycemia
D.   decreased basal metabolic rate
E.   juvenile, but otherwise apparently normal, female external genitalia

Answer = B. Dark complexion is not a symptom, but an individual characteristic. The other physical findings suggest abnormal processes related to the normal development of this individual.

100.   The remaining observations are most completely explained by a primary malfunction of the:
A.   adrenal cortex
B.   ovary
C.   testis
D.   anterior pituitary
E.   thyroid

Answer = D. The variety of problems that this patient has suggests that the defect has to be one that can affect several endocrine systems. Hence, the anterior pituitary gland is the most logical choice from the above list. Several of the symptoms, however, can be related to a lack of hormones being produced by the adrenal, ovary, and thyroid glands.

101.   An exploratory laparotomy performed in this patient would reveal the presence of:
A.   testis and male internal genital structures
B.   testis and female internal genital structures
C.   ovaries and male internal genital structures
D.   ovaries and female internal genital structures
E.   none of the above

Answer = D. This is a genetically female patient (positive sex chromatin, buccal smear). Since the problem is with the pituitary, she should have a normal sexual differentiation.

102.   The fasting hypoglycemia noted in this patient would best be explained by a lesion that has directly impaired the cells that secrete the hormone(s):
A.   ACTH
B.   cortisol
C.   growth hormone
D.   A and C are correct.
E.   A, B, and C are all correct.

Answer = D. The fasting hypoglycemia could be the direct effect of a decrease in both ACTH (secondary decrease in cortisol; not **B** or **E**) and growth hormone.

PART 6: ENDOCRINE PHYSIOLOGY   245

103. To correct only the low basal metabolic rate, the most reasonable therapy would be oral administration of replacement doses of:
   A. TSH
   B. cortisol
   C. thyroid hormone
   D. ACTH
   E. estradiol

Answer = C. Since thyroid hormone can be taken orally and is well tolerated, it rather than TSH (injections) would be the most reasonable therapy.

104. In order to induce the phenotypic morphological changes of puberty in this patient, the most reasonable therapy would be administration of:
   A. TSH
   B. testosterone
   C. estradiol-17β
   D. progesterone
   E. FSH

Answer = C. Since you want to induce the phenotypic morphological changes, estrogen levels need to be increased. The simple administration of an estrogen, like estradiol-17β, would result in the patient's developing into a more mature female phenotype. FSH therapy is difficult, and by itself will not cause a sustained secretion of estrogen unless given with LH in a pulsatile manner.

105. All of the following patients would have normal or elevated C-peptide levels EXCEPT:
   A. a patient with early Type II diabetes
   B. a normal subject in the fed state
   C. a normal subject after an oral glucose load
   D. a patient with Type I diabetes receiving recombinant human insulin injections
   E. a patient with severe Cushing's syndrome

Answer = D. *Remember you are looking for the exception.* Since C-peptide is cosecreted with insulin by the beta-cells of the pancreas, in any situation in which there is a normal or elevated rate of insulin secretion (**A, B, C,** or **E**) there will also be a normal or elevated level of C-peptide. When purified insulin is administered, no C-peptide is present, and you would expect a very low C-peptide level (*not* **D**).

106. A female patient can produce androgens from the ovaries. However, she is unable to synthesize estradiol within the ovary. The most likely explanation is that:
   A. the patient has panhypopituitarism
   B. theca cell function is abnormally low
   C. granulosa cell function is abnormally low
   D. the patient has an adrenal tumor secreting cortisol
   E. the patient has a pituitary tumor overproducing the α-subunit of FSH

Answer = C. The granulosa cells use androstenedione and testosterone produced by the theca cells to produce estradiol (not **B**). A low level of androgen is associated with panhypopituitarism because both the ovarian and adrenal sources of androgen are suppressed (not **A**). An adrenal tumor secreting cortisol would not likely affect estradiol secretion (not **D**). FSH secretion stimulates the conversion of testosterone to estradiol (not **E**).

Questions 107–110. Match the phrases below to the situations in questions 107–110. Note that a phrase may be selected once, more than once, or not at all.
   A. conversion of cholesterol to pregnenolone
   B. conversion of progesterone to 17-OH pregnenolone
   C. conversion of progesterone to 17-OH progesterone
   D. conversion of pregnenolone to progesterone
   E. conversion of 11-deoxycorticosterone to aldosterone

107. Occurs only in the zona fasciculata/reticularis:

Answer = C. The conversion of progesterone to 17-OH progesterone is carried out in the fasciculata but not in the glomerulosa.

108. Occurs only in the zona glomerulosa:

Answer = E. The formation of aldosterone from 11-deoxycorticosterone is the unique function of the adrenal glomerulosa cells.

109. Catalyzed by 3β-hydroxysteroid dehydrogenase:

Answer = D. The conversion of pregnenolone to progesterone is catalyzed by 3β-hydroxysteroid dehydrogenase, which is located in both zones.

110. Rate-limiting first step of steroidogenesis:

Answer = A. In all steroid-producing cells, the rate-limiting step is the initial conversion of cholesterol to pregnenolone.

Questions 111–114. Match the phrases below with the situations given in questions 111–114. Use each answer (phrase) only once.
   A. conversion of 7-dehydrocholesterol to cholecalciferol (vitamin D_3)
   B. conversion of 25-hydroxycholecalciferol to $24,25(OH)_2D_3$
   C. conversion of 25-hydroxycholecalciferol to $1,25(OH)_2D_3$
   D. conversion of cholecalciferol to 25-hydroxycholecalciferol

111. Increased by UV light:

Answer = A. UV light converts 7-dehydrocholesterol to cholecalciferol in the skin.

112. Stimulated by $1,25(OH)_2D_3$:

Answer = B. When production of $1,25(OH)_2D_3$ is high, it induces the formation of $24,25(OH)_2D_3$ from 25-hydroxycholecalciferol, preventing overproduction of the most active form of vitamin D: $1,25(OH)_2$-vitamin D_3.

113. Stimulated by PTH:

Answer = C. PTH stimulates the conversion of 25-hydroxycholecalciferol to $1,25(OH)_2D_3$ in the kidneys.

114. Occurs primarily in the liver:

Answer = D. The liver is the site at which cholecalciferol is converted to 25-hydroxycholecalciferol.

Questions 115–118. Match the phrases below with the situations given in questions 115–118. Use each answer (phrase) only once.
   A. primary hyperparathyroidism
   B. secondary hyperparathyroidism
   C. primary hypoparathyroidism
   D. vitamin D intoxication

115. Characterized by elevated plasma PTH and low plasma calcium:

Answer = B. In secondary hyperparathyroidism, the low level of calcium stimulates the secretion of PTH.

116. **Characterized by elevated plasma PTH and elevated plasma calcium:**

Answer = A. In primary hyperparathyroidism, pathological hypersecretion of PTH leads to an increase in plasma free calcium levels.

117. **Characterized by low plasma PTH and elevated plasma calcium:**

Answer = D. Vitamin D intoxication leads to an enhanced rate of calcium uptake by the GI tract, which results in hypercalcemia and the inhibition of PTH secretion.

118. **Characterized by low plasma PTH and low plasma calcium:**

Answer = C. If the parathyroid glands cannot secrete PTH, then PTH levels will be low; this in turn will result in a fall in the plasma level of calcium.

Questions 119–121. Match the words below to the situations given in questions 119–121.
  A. increased
  B. decreased
  C. unchanged

119. **Plasma LH concentration at day 10 of the menstrual cycle as compared to day 6:**

Answer = C. Only at the very end of the follicular phase (~ day 14) does LH secretion start to surge. During most of the follicular phase, LH is very low.

120. **Plasma progesterone in mid-luteal phase as compared to mid-follicular phase:**

Answer = A. There is a mid-luteal increase of progesterone secretion, whereas during the follicular phase of the cycle, progesterone levels are very low.

121. **Plasma estradiol at day 1 of the menstrual cycle as compared to mid-luteal phase:**

Answer = B. Estradiol levels are at their lowest levels at the beginning of the menstrual cycle (day 1); estradiol levels increase twice—in the late follicular phase and again in the middle of the luteal phase.

Questions 122–125. Match the phrases below to the situations given in questions 122–125. A phrase may be used once or not at all.
  A. elevated plasma ACTH; decreased plasma cortisol
  B. low plasma ACTH; elevated urine free cortisol
  C. high normal plasma ACTH; elevated plasma cortisol; augmented petrosal sinus ACTH gradient after CRH injection
  D. very high plasma ACTH and cortisol; no petrosal sinus gradient for ACTH
  E. low plasma ACTH and subnormal cortisol response to ACTH

122. Ectopic ACTH syndrome:

Answer = D. Since there is an ectopic source of ACTH, the anterior pituitary, which is being inhibited by the elevated cortisol levels, will not secrete ACTH. Hence, there will be no petrosal sinus gradient for ACTH.

123. Hypopituitarism:

Answer = E. Since there is a defect in the ability of the pituitary to secrete ACTH (low levels of ACTH), the adrenal will atrophy over time and become unresponsive to the acute administration of ACTH.

124. **Primary adrenal insufficiency:**

Answer = A. Since there is an inability to produce cortisol, there will be a significant increase in CRF and, hence, ACTH secretion.

125. **ACTH-independent Cushing's syndrome (adrenal tumor):**

Answer = B. When there is an ACTH-independent increase in cortisol secretion, then the ACTH level will be inhibited by the normal feedback action of cortisol; but there will be an elevated level of cortisol in the blood and, hence, in the urine.

126. **A pharmacological dose of dexamethasone (8 mg/day), a potent glucocorticoid, was administered to a patient with Cushing's syndrome (elevated circulating cortisol and ACTH levels). Dexamethasone did not alter the patient's circulating cortisol level. From your knowledge of pituitary-adrenal function, this observation is consistent with:**
   A. normal adrenal function
   B. a tumor of the adenohypophysis
   C. a cortisol-secreting tumor of the adrenal cortex
   D. an extrasellar tumor that produces a substance with ACTH activity(ectopic ACTH)
   E. None of the above choices is correct.

Answer = D. Dexamethasone is not causing the expected decrease in ACTH secretion that should lead to a decrease in plasma cortisol level (not **A**). This observation is most consistent with an extrasellar tumor secreting a substance that has ACTH activity but is not subject to feedback inhibition. A tumor of the adenohypophysis may still be expected to respond to the negative feedback effects of the administration of excess amounts of a glucocorticoid (not **B**). Since ACTH is elevated, an adrenal tumor (not **C**) is not a possibility.

127. **Prolactin plays an important role in the endocrine regulation of lactation. Despite increased prolactin secretion during pregnancy, little milk production occurs until after parturition because:**
   A. plasma cortisol levels are suppressed
   B. secretion of oxytocin does not occur
   C. the neuroendocrine reflex brought about by suckling has not yet occurred
   D. there are high circulating levels of estrogen
   E. there are high circulating levels of placental lactogen

Answer = D. The high levels of estrogen suppress milk production until after parturition.

128. **Which of the following acts as a prohormone?**
   A. vasopressin
   B. aldosterone
   C. luteinizing hormone
   D. testosterone
   E. triiodothyronine (T_3)

Answer = D. Testosterone is converted in the periphery to dihydrotestosterone, a very active androgen. Vasopressin, aldosterone, and LH are hormones that act directly on target tissues (not **A, B,** or **C**). T_3 is the active form of thyroid hormone and is derived from T_4, which can be considered the prohormone.

Questions 129–132. Match the phrases below with the situations given in questions 129–132.
   A. increase in ACTH in a normal subject
   B. decrease in ACTH in a normal subject

129. **Administration of metyrapone, an inhibitor of 11β-hydroxylase:**

Answer = A. Metyrapone inhibits adrenal steroid synthesis; hence, the normal feedback inhibition is lost and ACTH secretion will increase.

130. **Administration of a competitive antagonist of the CRH receptor:**

Answer = B. A competitive antagonist of the CRH receptor will prevent CRH from stimulating the secretion of ACTH.

131. **Administration of a potent glucocorticoid agonist:**

Answer = B. Any glucocorticoid will cause a decrease in ACTH secretion due to the normal negative feedback process.

132. **Administration of the glucocorticoid receptor antagonist RU486:**

Answer = A. Blocking the glucocorticoid receptor will be sensed as a lack of glucocorticoids and result in a stimulation of ACTH.

133. **Directly or indirectly, increased cortisol secretion in the late stages of diabetic ketoacidosis (DKA) reduces:**
   A. the metabolic acidosis
   B. insulin's effectiveness
   C. the impaired insulin secretion
   D. gluconeogenesis
   E. mobilization of depot fat

Answer = B. Cortisol, especially at the high levels that are present in patients in the late stages of DKA, impairs insulin effectiveness by virtue of its ability to promote gluconeogenesis (not **D**) and decrease glucose utilization in peripheral tissues. Cortisol does not reduce the metabolic acidosis (not **A**) but increases it by increasing ketones, lactate, and pyruvate levels (metabolic acids). Cortisol has no major effect on the secretion of insulin (not **C**), and it mobilizes fat (not **E**).

134. **The hypothalamus releases factors that directly do all of the following EXCEPT:**
   A. increase the production of milk
   B. increase the secretion of parathyroid hormone
   C. facilitate ovulation
   D. increase cortisol secretion
   E. facilitate the growth of long bones

Answer = B. *Remember you are looking for the exception.* Parathyroid hormone is not controlled by the hypothalamic pituitary axis (*not* **B**), but by the plasma concentration of calcium. Prolactin (**A**), LH and FSH (**C**), ACTH (**D**), and growth hormone (**E**) are all part of the hypothalamic pituitary axis.

135. **In the adolescent girl, progesterone in the absence of estrogen causes:**
   A. growth and development of the uterus
   B. growth and development of the breasts
   C. closure of the epiphyses of long bones
   D. deposition of subcutaneous fat to hips and thighs
   E. none of the above changes

Answer = E. All of the above effects (**A–D**) require simultaneous or previous exposure to estrogen.

136. **In a healthy 30-year-old woman with a menstrual cycle of 26 days:**
   A. injection of estrogen will increase the size of the ovaries
   B. the proliferative phase of the uterus is caused by estrogen derived from the Graafian follicle
   C. menstruation is caused by progesterone from the corpus luteum
   D. estradiol concentration begins to fall prior to ovulation and continues to decrease until menstruation
   E. the highest plasma levels of FSH are associated with the start of menstruation

Answer = B. Estrogen released by the follicle does induce the proliferative phase of the uterus. Injection of estrogen will decrease the release of FSH and, hence, decrease the size of the ovaries (not **A**). Menstruation occurs when the corpus luteum stops making progesterone (not **C**). After ovulation, the corpus luteum is formed, and it causes the luteal rise in estrogen secretion (not **D**). The highest levels of FSH are associated with ovulation, not the start of menstruation (not **E**).

137. **After implantation has occurred, the first missed period in a healthy female is caused by the fact that:**
   A.   the corpus luteum degenerates
   B.   a trophoblast is formed that secretes estrogen and progesterone
   C.   a trophoblast is formed that secretes gonadotropins
   D.   the ovaries decrease their production of estrogen and progesterone
   E.   the placenta releases enough estrogen and progesterone to prevent menstruation

Answer = C.   The trophoblast that is formed releases human chorionic gonadotropin (HCG)—not estrogen and progesterone (not **B**)—that facilitates the growth of the corpus luteum (not **A**), which continues to release estrogen and progesterone (not **D**). In time, the placenta will produce enough estrogen and progesterone to maintain pregnancy; but this will not occur immediately after implantation.

1. **The peripheral receptive field is defined as the spatial area on the receptor surface:**
   A. that increases first-order afferent nerve activity when stimulated with an adequate stimulus
   B. comprising the excitatory "on-center" area
   C. with the lowest absolute threshold to the adequate stimulus
   D. that evokes any change in neural activity when stimulated with an adequate stimulus
   E. containing all of the receptors of the branches of a first-order afferent

   Answer = D. The peripheral receptive field is the entire (not **B**) spatial area on the receptor surface that elicits either an increase or decrease (not **A**) in afferent nerve activity when stimulated with an adequate stimulus, independent of threshold (not **C**). Receptive fields of higher-order afferent nerves are often determined by the convergence of several sensory units (not **E**).

2. **The "pattern" code of sensory information:**
   A. compares the relative action potential frequency evoked from the center and the surround portions of a receptive field
   B. proposes that the sensation evoked by afferent stimulation depends primarily upon the specific nerves stimulated
   C. depends upon the relative activation of several afferents with different response sensitivities
   D. contributes to the coding of stimulus intensity
   E. is based upon the law of specific nerve energies

   Answer = C. The "pattern" encoding of information depends upon the relative activation of a population of afferent nerves. To encode different sensations in the same nerve population, receptors and afferent nerves must respond to several stimuli representing different sensations (not **B** or **E**). Pattern responses are usually associated with encoding stimulus quality, not intensity (not **D**).

3. **Phasic (rapidly adapting) receptors:**
   A. generally respond best to changes in stimulus strength
   B. discharge continuously with stimulation of constant intensity
   C. primarily encode the intensity of a stimulus
   D. encode both rate of change and stimulus magnitude
   E. encode information regarding pain and joint position

   Answer = A. Rapidly adapting receptors respond best to the onset of stimulus and/or changes in stimulus strength and cease responding when the stimulus becomes constant (not **B**). Therefore, they encode rate of change of a stimulus, and not absolute intensity (not **C** or **D**). Pain and joint position are encoded by slowly adapting (tonic) receptors (not **E**).

4. **The law of specific nerve energies states that:**
   A. a perceived sensation depends upon the type of energy stimulating the afferent receptor
   B. perceived sensation depends solely upon the afferent nerve stimulated
   C. a sensation is perceived to originate in a specific location regardless of where in the afferent chain the stimulus is applied
   D. magnitude is encoded by action potential frequency in afferent nerves
   E. all afferent nerves of a given modality terminate in the same cortical region

   Answer = B. The law of specific nerve energies states that the sensation evoked depends solely upon the nerve stimulated, regardless of the nature of the stimulus (not **A**), and is different from the law of projection (not **C**). The law of specific nerve energies relates to quality coding, not stimulus magnitude (not **D**), and is not related to cortical projection (not **E**).

5. The anterior spinothalamic and lateral spinothalamic tracts carry information about:
   A. fine touch and pressure
   B. vibration
   C. joint position
   D. slight skin movement
   E. pain

   Answer = E. Information related to **A, B, C,** and **D** are transmitted in the dorsal column system.

6. Each of the following contributes to the adaptation characteristics of rapidly adapting, somatic pressure receptors *EXCEPT:*
   A. presence or absence of a tissue capsule
   B. elasticity of the tissue surrounding the receptor
   C. physical characteristics of capsule enclosing the receptor
   D. the threshold of receptor membrane tissue distortion needed for depolarization

   Answer = D. *Remember you are looking for the exception.* The presence of a tissue capsule, its physical characteristics, and the elasticity of the tissue surrounding the receptor all determine whether receptor membrane distortion is maintained during constant stimulation. Relief of the receptor membrane distortion reduces excitation in the afferent nerve. In order to have adaptation of a receptor, the stimulus must be above threshold.

7. The visual abnormality resulting from uneven curvature of the cornea in different planes is called:
   A. astigmatism
   B. myopia
   C. hyperopia
   D. emmetropia
   E. presbyopia

   Answer = A. Myopia (long eyeball) results from excess curvature of the cornea in all planes (not **B**); hyperopia (short eyeball) results from insufficient curvature of the cornea in all planes or (not **C**); emmetropia is normal vision, in which the axial and focal lengths of the eye are equal (not **D**); and presbyopia is loss of near-point vision with age (not **E**).

8. Glaucoma results from:
   A. decreased intraocular pressure
   B. vascular hypertrophy in the retina
   C. intraocular hemorrhage
   D. blockade of the canal of Schlemm
   E. accumulation of denatured proteins on the lens

   Answer = D. Glaucoma is characterized by increased intraocular pressure (not **A**) resulting from blockade of the canal of Schlemm, which drains ocular fluid from the eyeball. Increases in intraocular pressure do not induce hemorrhage or vascular hypertrophy (not **B** or **C**). Coagulation of denatured proteins in the lens results in cataracts (not **E**).

9. Substances that stimulate peripheral chemoreceptors that encode pain sensation include all of the following *EXCEPT:*
   A. serotonin
   B. histamine
   C. potassium
   D. enkephalin
   E. proteolytic enzymes

   Answer = D. *Remember you are looking for the exception.* All of the substances except enkephalin (**A, B, C,** and **E**) have been shown to excite free-nerve endings that signal pain. Opioids, including enkephalin, are involved in the reduction of pain sensation through actions in the central nervous system.

10. Sensations of sharp, pricking pain are mediated via:
   A.   most sensory receptors subjected to sudden, intense stimulation
   B.   specialized free nerve endings of A-delta nerve fibers
   C.   specialized encapsulated nerve endings of "C" fibers
   D.   specialized free nerve endings of "C" fibers
   E.   specialized encapsulated nerve endings of A-delta fibers

   Answer = B.   Pain results from stimulation of free nerve endings (not C or E) that transduce only painful stimuli (not A) and is carried by A-delta and small, unmyelinated "C" fibers. Sharp pain is carried in more rapidly conducting A-delta nerve fibers, whereas dull aching pain is conducted in the slower conducting "C" nerve fibers (not D).

11. Precise topographic representation of fine touch/pressure information is:
   A.   present throughout the spinothalamic system
   B.   present for visceral sensation
   C.   lost in the somatosensory cortex
   D.   present throughout the dorsal column system
   E.   not present in the medulla, but regained in the cortex

   Answer = D.   Fine touch/pressure information is not carried in the spinothalamic system (not A). In addition, pain/temperature sensation, which is carried in the spinothalamic system, and visceral information are not characterized by precise topographical representation in the CNS (not A or B). However, touch/pressure information, which is carried in the dorsal column system, has precise topographical organization throughout the afferent system (not C or E).

12. The anterolateral system in the spinal cord:
   A.   carries pain information originating on the contralateral side of the body
   B.   decussates in the medial lemniscus so that second-order afferents terminate in the contralateral thalamus
   C.   has first-order afferents that synapse in the ipsilateral medulla
   D.   carries fine touch/pressure information originating on the ipsilateral side of the body
   E.   has first-order afferents that do not synapse until they reach the thalamus

   Answer = A.   The first-order afferents in the anterolateral (i.e., spinothalamic) system, which carry pain and temperature information (not D), synapse and decussate in the spinal cord (not B, C, or D). Second-order (not E) afferent nerves in the anterolateral system synapse in the thalamus.

13. The most likely site of direct interaction between afferent and efferent sensory systems that modulate pain sensation is the:
   A.   sensory nerve endings transducing pain
   B.   anterior commissure of the spinal cord
   C.   substantia gelatinosa
   D.   periaqueductal grey region
   E.   thalamus

   Answer = C.   First-order pain afferents and descending corticofugal fibers from higher brain centers that respond to painful stimulation synapse on enkephalinergic interneurons in the substantia gelatinosa of the spinal cord.

14. Nerve fibers that carry information that is perceived consciously as visceral pain enter the spinal cord with the:
   A.   sympathetic nerves
   B.   parasympathetic nerves
   C.   cutaneous nerves
   D.   cranial nerves

   Answer = A.   Although nerve cell bodies of afferent nerves that transmit pain sensation from the viscera are located in the dorsal root ganglia, the nerve fibers travel with the sympathetic nerves, not the cutaneous nerves (not C). Parasympathetic and cranial nerves also carry afferent information, but these nerves do not appear to transmit visceral pain (not B or D).

15. A positive lens with a refractive power of 10 diopters focuses parallel light rays behind the center of the lens:
    A.   0.1 cm
    B.   1 cm
    C.   10 cm
    D.   100 cm
    E.   1,000 cm

Answer = C. Refractive power in diopters = 1/focal length (meters). A lens with a refractive power of 10 diopters would focus parallel light rays $10 = 1/x$ m; $x = 0.1$ m $= 10$ cm.

16. Which portion of the eye provides the greatest amount of light refraction?
    A.   the anterior surface of the cornea
    B.   the posterior surface of the cornea
    C.   the anterior surface of the crystalline lens
    D.   the posterior surface of the crystalline lens
    E.   the aqueous humor

Answer = A. The anterior surface of the cornea provides $+48.2$ diopters of refraction, whereas the posterior surface provides -5.9 diopters (not B), the anterior surface of the lens 5.0 diopters (not C), and the posterior surface of the lens 8.3 diopters (not D). The aqueous humor does not refract light (not E).

17. Presbyopia results from:
    A.   insufficient refraction by the anterior cornea
    B.   insufficient refractive capability of the lens
    C.   maintenance of the lens in an oval shape
    D.   fatigue of the zonule fibers (suspensory ligaments)
    E.   development of cataracts

Answer = B. The loss of near-point vision (presbyopia) develops with aging and is not a result of defects in the optical apparatus (not A) or increased diffusion of light prior to stimulating the retina (not E). Gradual loss of accommodation develops as the lens becomes increasingly stiff and loses the ability to assume a more oval shape (not C) when tension is reduced on the zonule fibers (not D).

18. The correct lens combination for an individual with myopia and presbyopia would be bifocals with a:
    A.   combination lens on top and a negative lens on the bottom
    B.   combination lens on top and a positive lens on the bottom
    C.   positive lens on top and a negative lens on the bottom
    D.   negative lens on top and a negative lens on the bottom
    E.   negative lens on top and a positive lens on the bottom

Answer = E. Myopia (near-sightedness) results from excessive refraction of parallel light rays from distant objects. Therefore, to correct far vision, a diffusing, or negative, lens is required (not A, B, or C). Presbyopia is loss of near vision due to reduced refractive ability of the lens with age. Therefore, correction of near vision requires a converging, or positive lens (not D).

19. The outer layer of the retina, including the outer segments of the rods and cones, obtains nutrition primarily from:

    A.   blood vessels coursing through the retina
    B.   the cornea
    C.   the schlera
    D.   the choroid
    E.   the pigmented layer

Answer = D. Divisions of the retinal artery supply the inner retinal surface. However, the outer segments of the inverted receptor cells do not receive a preponderance of nutrients or oxygen from this vascular source (not A), but rather by diffusion from the highly vascularized choroid. The cornea (not B), schlera (not C), and pigmented layer (not E) do not supply nutrients to the outer segment of the rods and cones.

20. **11-cis retinal:**
    A. exists only in the light
    B. is found only in rods
    C. converts to all-trans retinal in the dark
    D. spontaneously binds to both scotopsin and photopsin
    E. does not bind with scotopsin

Answer = D. This isomeric form of retinal exists only in the dark (not **A**) and isomerizes to all trans-retinal when stimulated by light (not **C**). This form of retinal is present in both rods and cones (not **B**) and binds to both scotopsin (rod opsin) and the photopsins (cone opsins) (not **E**).

21. **When light strikes the outer segment of a rod:**
    A. the receptor cell depolarizes
    B. action potentials are generated in the first and second-order afferents
    C. 11-cis retinal isomerizes to all-trans retinal
    D. diffusion of sodium ions out of the inner segment of the receptor increases
    E. binding of retinal to photopsin increases

Answer = C. Visual receptor cells hyperpolarize when stimulated (not **A**), which results from decreased sodium reabsorption in the outer segment (not **D**) following the dissociation of retinal and photopsin (not **E**). Furthermore, the first action potentials in the visual afferent system occur in the third-order, ganglion cells (not **B**).

22. **When a visual stimulus is continually focused on a specific population of receptor cells:**
    A. the perceived stimulus intensity increases
    B. there is adaptation mediated by the lateral geniculate body
    C. ganglion cells become facilitated
    D. the amount of lateral inhibition increases in the inhibitory surround
    E. the perceived image will fade and disappear

Answer = E. When a stimulus is maintained on the same population of receptor cells, the image disappears (not **A**) due to receptor cell fatigue (not **B**), which decreases ganglion cell activity (not **C**) and is independent of lateral geniculate adaptation (not **D**). This does not normally occur because of the constant, small eye movements that continually change the population of stimulated receptor cells.

23. **Color vision is coded by:**
    A. rods
    B. activation of color-specific receptor cells that are responsive to wavelengths representing each color perceived
    C. differential responses in ganglion cells that depend upon the wavelength of the stimulus
    D. differential spectral sensitivity of receptors mediating "scotopic" and "photopic" vision
    E. the concentration of rhodopsin present in the cones

Answer = C. Chromatic vision is encoded by three populations of cones (not **A**), each sensitive to a range of wavelengths representing several colors (not **B**) and containing a specific photopigment. Rods, which contain rhodopsin (not **E**) and mediate achromatic vision (not **D**), do not contribute to color vision. This trichromatic encoding is translated into a response pattern in color-sensitive ganglion cells characterized by opposite responses, ie, excitation or inhibition to the specific color combinations of red-green and yellow-blue.

24. **A point of light from the right visual field will stimulate receptors:**
    A. on the nasal side of the left eye
    B. on the temporal side of the right eye
    C. in the right eye that have terminal projections in the contralateral visual cortex
    D. in the right eye that have terminal projections in the ipsilateral visual cortex
    E. in the right and left eyes that have terminal projections in the ipsilateral visual cortex

Answer = C. Stimuli from the right visual field activate receptors on the temporal side of the left eye (not **A**) and the nasal side of the right eye (not **B**). Afferents from the nasal sides of both eyes decussate in the optic chiasm and project to the contralateral side of the brain, whereas afferents from the temporal receptors project ipsilaterally (not **E**). Therefore, stimulation of the receptors of the right eye (nasal) would activate afferents projecting to the contralateral side of the brain (not **D**).

25. **The impedance mismatch between sound pressure waves traveling through air and through the cochlear fluid is compensated for by:**
   A.   a decrease in the force of the pressure stimulus resulting from the leverage exerted during vibration of the tympanic membrane
   B.   an increase in the force of the pressure stimulus resulting from the configuration of the ossicles
   C.   an increase in the amplitude of the pressure stimulus due to contraction of the tensor tympanic muscle
   D.   a decrease in the amplitude of the pressure stimulus due to the relative sizes of the tympanic membrane and the oval window
   E.   concentration of the sound pressure stimulus by the pinna

   Answer = B. The lever action of the tympanic membrane and the size difference between the tympanic membrane and the oval window both increase the force of the pressure stimulus transmitted to the cochlea (not **A** or **D**). Contraction of the tensor tympanic muscle would decrease the stimulus (not **C**), and the pinna does not alter the amplitude of the sound pressure stimulus (not **E**).

26. **Stimulation of the tensor tympanis and the stapedius muscles:**
   A.   diminishes the amplitude of sound pressure stimuli entering the cochlea
   B.   occurs during auditory stimulation with low-amplitude stimuli
   C.   compensates for the impedance mismatch between air and cochlear fluid
   D.   increases the amplitude of the basilar membrane wave envelope
   D.   is initiated by bone conduction

   Answer = A. Contraction of these muscles is induced by presentation of high-amplitude (not **B**) sound pressure stimuli through air or bone conduction (not **E**). Stimulation of these muscles decreases the energy of the sound stimulus (not **C** or **D**) and serves to protect the cochlear cells from potentially injurious stimulation.

27. **A sound pressure stimulus of 60 dB is ___ times larger than a sound pressure stimulus of 30 dB.**
   A.   2
   B.   10
   C.   20
   D.   100
   E.   1,000

   Answer = E. One decibel equals 0.1 log unit of sound pressure energy. Therefore, 30 dB equals 3 log units or a 1,000 times greater energy level.

28. **When the point of maximal displacement of the basilar membrane is close to the oval window, it indicates that the:**

   A.   stimulating frequency is high
   B.   stimulating frequency is low
   C.   stimulus is very loud
   D.   stimulus is near the detection threshold for audition
   E.   stimulus was transferred to the cochlea by bone conduction

   Answer = A. Stimuli applied to the cochlea through the ossicles or through bone conduction both stimulate the basilar membrane in the same manner (not **E**). The point of maximal displacement on the basilar membrane is primarily determined by stimulus frequency and not by stimulus amplitude (not **C** or **D**). As the frequency of the stimulus increases, the point of maximum displacement on the basilar membrane moves closer to the oval window (not **B**).

29. **The endocochlear potential is:**
   A.   generated in the endolymph by stimulation of the auditory receptor cells
   B.   an electrical potential difference between the scala tympani and scala vestibuli
   C.   maintained by the tectorial membrane
   D.   created by the initiation of a traveling wave along the basilar membrane
   E.   an electrical potential difference between the perilymph and the endolymph

   Answer = E. The endocochlear potential is the potential difference between the perilymph in the scala tympani and vestibuli and the endolymph in the scala media (not **B**). This potential difference results from the high concentration of potassium ions in the endolymph, which is maintained by Reissner's membrane (not **C**) and is independent of stimulation (not **A** or **D**).

30. **Gustatory receptor cells are different from olfactory receptor cells because they:**
   A. hyperpolarize when stimulated
   B. are rapidly adapting chemoreceptors
   C. have chemical binding sites on their cell bodies
   D. are depolarized by stimuli representing a single primary taste
   E. are separate receptor cells that make synaptic contact with the first-order afferent nerve fibers

   Answer = E. Both gustatory and olfactory receptor cells depolarize (not **A**) when an appropriate stimulus is applied to chemical binding sites located on cilia projecting from the cell body (not **C**). Furthermore, both are "phasic-tonic" type receptors, exhibiting continued excitation with continuous stimulus presentation (not **B**), and generally respond to chemical stimuli representing more than one basic taste or odor (not **D**).

31. **Directional sensitivity of single receptor cells in the vestibular system:**
   A. is present because the receptor cells have a high degree of spontaneous activity
   B. accounts for the similarity of first-order afferent responses from contralateral semicircular canals during rotational acceleration
   C. is present only in receptor cells located on the ampular crest
   D. is independent of reflex activation of efferent inhibitory neurons
   E. is independent of CNS integration of afferent activity originating in the semicircular canals and otolith organs

   Answer = A. All vestibular hair cells exhibit directionally specific responses (not **C**), and rotational acceleration results in opposite responses from contralateral canals (not **B**). Central integration can alter responses of individual vestibular cells through efferent innervation (not **D** or **E**). Each cell can hyperpolarize or depolarize, depending upon which direction the kinocilia-stereocilia are bent, and thus increase or decrease the high spontaneous discharge rate in receptor cells.

32. **The rate of change of length of intrafusal muscle fibers is detected by X afferent fibers from nuclear Y fibers and can be modified by efferent activity in gamma Z nerve fibers.**

	X	Y	Z
A.	primary	chain	dynamic
B.	primary	bag	dynamic
C.	secondary	chain	static
D.	secondary	bag	dynamic
E.	primary	chain	static

   Answer = B. Primary afferent stretch receptors are particularly responsive to rate of change in muscle length (not **C** or **D**). Whereas nuclear chain intrafusal muscle fibers are innervated by both primary and secondary stretch receptors, nuclear bag fibers are innervated only by primary afferent fibers (not **A** or **E**). Finally, activation of gamma dynamic efferent motor neurons selectively sensitizes the response to changing muscle length (not **C** or **E**).

33. **During a normal voluntary muscle movement, the:**
   A. gamma motor system is not activated
   B. extrafusal muscle fibers shorten, whereas the intrafusal fibers do not
   C. intrafusal fibers provide the main contractile force for movement of the joint
   D. intrafusal and extrafusal fibers both shorten
   E. contraction of the intrafusal fibers inhibits the stretch reflex

   Answer = D. During voluntary muscle contraction, both the alpha and the gamma motor systems are activated (not **A**) to shorten both the extrafusal and intrafusal muscle fibers (not **B**). While only the extrafusal muscle fibers provide the force for joint movement (not **C**), shortening of the intrafusal muscle fibers maintains sensitivity of the stretch reflex while the muscle is shortening (not **E**).

34. **Increased tension on Golgi tendon organs:**
   A. produces inhibition of the gamma motor system
   B. produces adaptation of the stretch reflex
   C. enhances the strength of the stretch receptor response
   D. excites spinal interneurons that inhibit extrafusal muscle fiber activity
   E. sensitizes the "load reflex" (i.e., enhanced gamma motor neuron activity as a muscle contracts against a load)

   Answer = D. Activation of Golgi tendon organs excites inhibitory interneurons in the spinal cord, which decrease activity in alpha-motor neurons innervating extrafusal muscle fibers (not **A** or **C**), which decreases the strength of the stretch reflex (not **B**) and the load reflex (not **E**).

35. **Parkinson's disease is characterized by:**
    A. decreased dopamine in the putamen and caudate nucleus
    B. lesions of the pyramidal decussation
    C. lesions located in the motor cortex
    D. lesions of the cerebellum
    E. excitation of the basal ganglia

Answer = A. Loss of the dopamine-mediated inhibitory influences of the basal ganglia on motor function (not **B**, **C**, **D**, or **E**) results in symptoms characteristic of Parkinson's disease.

36. **All of the following are characteristics of the blood–brain barrier _EXCEPT_:**
    A. tight junctions of endothelial cells
    B. glial foot processes
    C. increased mitochondria in capillary endothelial cells
    D. reduced permeability of high-molecular-weight substances
    E. reduced permeability of lipid soluble substances

Answer = E. _Remember you are looking for the exception._ Endothelial cells of brain capillaries are characterized by an increased number of mitochondria (**C**) and tight junctions (**A**), which decrease permeability to high-molecular-weight substances (**D**), but not to lipophilic substances (_not E_). In addition, glial cells in the brain have processes that circle brain capillaries and decrease the perivascular space, thus reducing the extracellular space available for diffusion (**B**). However, lipophilic substances, which pass through endothelial cells, are permeable.

37. **Cerebrospinal fluid is absorbed from the brain through the:**
    A. choroid plexus
    B. arachnoid villi
    C. Foramen of Monro
    D. fenestrae in cerebral capillaries
    E. cerebral aqueduct

Answer = B. CSF is produced in the choroid plexi (not **A**) and courses through the ventricular system, which includes the foramen of Monro (not **C**) that connects the lateral ventricles to the third ventricle and the cerebral aqueduct, which connects the third and fourth cerebral ventricles (not **E**). Brain capillaries do not have fenestrae (not **D**).

38. **Activation of the cross-extensor reflex:**
    A. stimulates the ipsilateral extensor
    B. inhibits the ipsilateral flexor
    C. stimulates the contralateral flexor
    D. inhibits the contralateral extensor
    E. stimulates the contralateral extensor

Answer = E. The cross extensor reflex supports the body as a limb is reflexively withdrawn from an injurious stimulus. This reflex stimulates the ipsilateral flexor (not **B**), inhibits the ipsilateral extensor (not **A**), stimulates the contralateral extensor (not **D**), and inhibits the contralateral flexor (not **C**).

39. **Each of the following is important in encoding constant stimulus magnitude _EXCEPT_:**
    A. the size of the receptive field of the stimulated afferent
    B. the size of the receptor potential generated by stimulation
    C. the number of afferents activated by the stimulus
    D. the thresholds of the activated afferents
    E. the adaptation characteristic (i.e., phasic or tonic) of the stimulated afferents

Answer = A. _Remember you are looking for the exception._ The size of the receptor potential is related to the magnitude of the stimulus (**B**) and the number of action potentials in the first-order afferent nerve, but not directly to the size of the receptive field (_not A_). Furthermore, in many sensory systems, the stimulated area on the receptor surface increases with stronger stimuli, thus increasing the number of afferent fibers activated (**C**), and activates nerve fibers with higher thresholds (**D**). Finally, constant stimulus magnitude is not signaled by a phasic receptor that completely adapts during continuous stimulation of constant magnitude (**E**).

40. **The receptive field of a first-order cutaneous afferent is characterized by:**
   A. constant threshold for stimulation across the receptive field
   B. innervation by multiple sensory units of the same type
   C. evoking both excitatory and inhibitory responses in the afferent nerve
   D. modality specificity
   E. encoding of several cutaneous sensations

   Answer = D. Each receptive field of a first-order afferent is innervated by only one afferent of a given type (not **B**), which has a lower threshold for stimulation in the center of the field (not **A**). Stimulation of the receptive field produces a single response in the first-order afferent (not **C**) and encodes a single sensation (not **E**).

41. **All cutaneous receptors are characterized by:**
   A. histological specificity of stimulus encoding
   B. physiological specificity of stimulus encoding
   C. ability to encode multiple cutaneous sensations
   D. rapid adaptation
   E. encapsulated nerve endings

   Answer = B. Cutaneous receptors are either encapsulated or free nerve endings (not **E**) and can be either slowly or rapidly adapting (not **D**). Separate free nerve endings can encode different sensations, i.e., temperature or pressure; but each individual receptor encodes only a single sensation (not **A** or **C**). Therefore, these cutaneous receptors demonstrate physiological specificity; each individual receptor can encode only a single sensation, but not histological specificity, as different receptors of the same anatomical class encode different sensations.

42. **The tissue lamina surrounding the nerve ending of a Pacinian corpuscle:**
   A. dampens receptor membrane distortion during stimulus onset
   B. changes the response pattern of the receptor from phasic–tonic to phasic
   C. is necessary for generation of the receptor potential
   D. prevents afferent activation during removal of the stimulus
   E. is necessary for encoding constant stimulus magnitude

   Answer = B. The capsule surrounding the Pacinian corpuscle transmits the pressure stimulus to the receptor membrane with great fidelity (not **A**) as long as the stimulus is changing. After the stimulus stops changing, the capsule redistributes to relieve the membrane tissue distortion on the receptor membrane, so the receptor cannot signal constant stimulus magnitude (not **E**). Upon removal of the stimulus, the capsule returns to its normal shape, distorting the receptor membrane and stimulating afferent activity (not **D**). Stimulating the receptor membrane when the capsule has been removed does not prevent the receptor potential (not **C**), but changes the adaptation characteristics.

43. **According to the gate control theory of pain, enkephalin, an endogenous opioid, inhibits pain sensation by:**
   A. facilitation of second-order touch-pressure afferent nerves
   B. postsynaptic inhibition of third-order afferent pain nerves
   C. presynaptic inhibition at first-order afferent pain nerve terminals
   D. inhibition of enkephalin interneurons in the substantia gelatinosa
   E. competing for receptor sites on the peripheral pain receptor

   Answer = C. Stimulation (not **D**) of enkephalinergic neurons in the spinal cord (not **E**) leads to presynaptic and postsynaptic inhibition of second-order (not **B**) neurons transmitting pain information (not **A**).

44. **First-order afferent nerve fibers from visceral pain receptors:**
   A. do not synapse in the substantia gelatinosa
   B. travel with cutaneous afferent nerves originating in the same dermatomal segments as the organ of innervation
   C. have cell bodies in sympathetic ganglia
   D. are topographically organized
   E. densely innervate visceral organs

   Answer = A. The visceral organs are sparsely innervated (not **E**) by pain afferents whose axons travel with the sympathetic nerves (not **B**) but have cell bodies located in the dorsal root ganglia (not **C**). Finally, pain sensation in general does not exhibit precise topographical organization (not **D**).

45. **When the axial length of the eyeball is shorter than the focal length of the optical apparatus:**
    A. the eye is myopic
    B. the eye is presbyopic
    C. the eye is emmetropic
    D. vision can be corrected by a negative lens
    E. parallel light rays are focused posterior to the retina

    Answer = E. In the myopic eye, the focal length is less than the axial length of the eye, and parallel light rays focus anterior to the retina (not **A**); the eye can be corrected with a negative lens (not **D**). In the emmetropic eye, the focal length equals the axial length of the eye, and parallel light rays focus on the retina (not **C**). Presbyopia is reduced near vision due to loss of lens flexibility with age and does not relate to axial and focal length of the eye (not **B**).

46. **When you are viewing a near object:**
    A. parasympathetic activity to the ocular apparatus increases
    B. the tension of ocular zonular fibers increases
    C. sympathetic activity to iris musculature increases
    D. the crystalline lens flattens
    E. the ciliary muscles relax

    Answer = A. Parasympathetic activation causes ciliary muscle contraction (not **E**), reducing tension on the ocular zonular fibers (not **B**) supporting the crystalline lens, allowing the lens to assume a more oval shape (not **D**), which increases refraction. Parasympathetic activation also causes pupillary constriction (not **C**) when viewing a near object.

47. **Hyperopia results from:**
    A. parallel light rays being focused anterior to the retina
    B. maintenance of the lens in its most oval shape
    C. the axial length of the eye exceeding the focal length
    D. insufficient refractive capability of the optical apparatus
    E. excess curvature of the cornea

    Answer = D. Myopia results when parallel light rays focus anterior to the retina (not **A**) and is induced by excessive curvature of the cornea (not **E**) or the axial length of the eye exceeding the focal length (not **C**). An oval lens increases the refraction of parallel light rays (not **B**).

48. **The X luminosity curve represents Y cell function derived from the Z eye.**

	X	Y	Z
A.	photopic	rod	light-adapted
B.	scotopic	rod	dark-adapted
C.	scotopic	cone	light-adapted
D.	photopic	cone	dark-adapted
E.	scotopic	cone	dark-adapted

    Answer = B. The photopic luminosity curve represents responses of cones (not A) and is derived by testing the light-adapted (not **D**) eye. The scotopic luminosity curve represents rod function (not **C** or **E**) and is derived by testing the dark-adapted (not **C**) eye.

49. **Neural convergence is the principal mechanism for:**
    A. color weakness
    B. foveal resolution
    C. monocular detection of depth
    D. visual feature detection
    E. the "photopic" luminosity curve

    Answer = D. Color weakness results from reduced cone function (not **A**), and foveal resolution is characterized by a lack of neural convergence (not **B**). Monocular depth perception relies upon size constancy and juxtaposition of stimuli (not **C**), and the luminosity curves represent wave length sensitivity of rods and cones (not **E**).

50. **Auditory pitch is encoded by the:**
   A. frequency of basilar membrane oscillation at high frequencies (>1,000 Hz)
   B. point of maximal displacement of the basilar membrane at low frequencies (<100 Hz)
   C. frequency of oscillation of basilar membrane at low frequencies (<100 Hz)
   D. frequency of action potentials in the auditory nerve at all frequencies
   E. pattern of neural activity in a population of nerves at all frequencies

   Answer = C. Low-frequency stimulation and high-frequency stimulation produce different patterns of movement of the basilar membrane and, thus, different patterns of receptor cell stimulation (not **D** or **E**). Low-frequency auditory stimuli initiate movement of large portions of the basilar membrane in synchrony with the stimulating frequency (not **A**), whereas higher frequencies produce a more specific point of maximal displacement (not **B**) along the membrane, which is frequency-dependent and moves closer to the oval window as the frequency increases.

51. **Outer hair cells of the cochlea do each of the following _EXCEPT_:**
   A. provide 95% of afferent neurons in the auditory portion of the VIIIth cranial nerve
   B. contract
   C. modify basilar membrane movement
   D. modify inner hair cell response
   E. outnumber inner hair cells

   Answer = A. _Remember you are looking for the exception._ The outer hair cells outnumber the inner hair cells (**E**) but provide only 5–10% of the afferent neurons of the auditory portion of the VIIIth cranial nerve (_not_ **A**). The outer hair cells can contract (**B**) and modify the movement of the basilar membrane (**C**) relative to the tectoral membrane and, therefore, alter the stimulation of the inner hair cells (**D**).

52. **Rotation of the head to the left in the horizontal plane:**
   A. increases activity in the vestibular portion of the left VIIIth nerve
   B. increases activity in the vestibular portion of the right VIIIth nerve
   C. bends the kinocilia in the right horizontal canal away from the stereocilia
   D. bends the kinocilia in the left horizontal canal toward the stereocilia
   E. has no effect on the neural activity in the right VIIIth nerve

   Answer = A. Rotation alters neural activity in the vestibular portions of both the left and right VIIIth nerves (not **E**). The movement of fluid in the semicircular canals is slower than the movement of the bony labyrinth due to inertial forces. The action of the fluid against the ampular crest bends the cilia of the hair cells in the left canal away from the kinocilium (not **D**), thus depolarizing the cells and increasing afferent discharge in the left VIIIth nerve. However, the cilia in the right canal are bent toward the kinocilium (not **C**), resulting in hyperpolarization and decreased activity in the right VIIIth nerve (not **B**).

53. **Olfactory and gustatory receptor cells:**
   A. are the sites for complete adaptation of taste and smell sensation
   B. are narrowly tuned and respond only to stimuli that represent one or two basic odors and tastes
   C. are depolarized by specific chemicals binding to protein receptors located on their cell bodies
   D. are both bipolar neurons
   E. are slowly adapting, phasic–tonic receptors

   Answer = E. Most olfactory and gustatory receptor cells respond to stimuli representing several sensations (not **B**), following binding of chemicals to binding sites located on cilia projecting from the cell bodies (not **C**). Unlike the bipolar olfactory cells (not **D**), gustatory receptor cells are specialized cells that synapse with the first-order afferent nerves. Both receptor cells are phasic–tonic type receptors that exhibit a steady-state response for extended periods during stimulation (not **A**).

54. **When gamma-motor neuron discharge increases simultaneously with alpha-motor neuron discharge, the:**
   A. activity of primary spindle afferents is inhibited
   B. contraction of the muscle is prolonged
   C. activity of secondary spindle afferents is inhibited
   D. activity of primary spindle afferents is less than that observed with alpha-motor neuron stimulation alone
   E. activity of primary spindle afferents is greater than that observed with alpha-motor neuron stimulation alone

Answer = E. Alpha-gamma coactivation maintains stretch on the muscle spindle afferents during shortening of the muscle. Therefore, activity in both the primary (not **A** or **D**) and secondary (not **C**) spindle afferents is maintained even though the muscle is shortening. This does not directly affect the temporal characteristics of the muscle contraction (not **B**).

55. **Increasing tension in innervated skeletal muscle eventually causes relaxation of the extrafusal muscle fibers because of:**
    A. alpha-motor neuron fatigue
    B. inhibition of afferent input from primary muscle spindle receptors
    C. stimulation of afferent input from secondary muscle spindle receptors
    D. stimulation of afferent activity from Golgi tendon organs
    E. inhibition of afferent activity from Golgi tendon organs

Answer = D. With increasing tension, stimulation of Golgi tendon organs increases (not **E**), which activates inhibitory interneurons in the spinal cord that directly inhibit alpha-motor neurons (not **A**) and cause muscle relaxation despite continued afferent stimulation from the stretch receptors (not **B** or **C**).

56. **For a person with both astigmatism and presbyopia, the lens combination yielding the best vision would be:**
    A. a positive lens for far vision and a positive lens for near vision
    B. a combination lens for far vision and a positive lens for near vision
    C. a negative (nonrefracting) lens for far vision and a positive lens for near vision
    D. a combination lens for far vision and a negative lens for near vision
    E. a positive lens for far vision and a negative lens for near vision

Answer = B. Due to uneven curvature of the cornea, a combination lens is required to correct far vision (not **A**, **C**, or **E**), whereas a positive lens is required to compensate for the loss of accommodation due to aging (presbyopia) (not **D** or **E**).

57. **The following events occur when rods are stimulated by light. Select the proper sequence.**
    1. **production of phosphodiesterase**
    2. **isomerization of retinal**
    3. **decreased intracellular cGMP**
    4. **receptor hyperpolarization**
    5. **closure of sodium channels in the outer segment**
    A. 3, 4, 5, 2, 1
    B. 2, 3, 1, 4, 5
    C. 1, 3, 2, 5, 4
    D. 1, 2, 3, 5, 4
    E. 2, 1, 3, 5, 4

Answer = E. Light energy causes the isomerization of retinal, which increases production of phosphodiesterase, resulting in hydrolization of cGMP. Reduced cGMP causes the sodium channels in the outer segment to close, decreasing sodium reabsorption, which hyperpolarizes the receptor cell (not **A**, **B**, **C**, or **D**).

58. **Mechanisms of visual accommodation include:**
    A. increased tension on suspensory ligaments of the lens
    B. a decrease in the curvature of the lens
    C. pupillary dilation
    D. contraction of the ciliary muscle
    E. activation of sympathetic nerve fibers to the iris

Answer = D. A blurred image on the retina evokes reflex activation of the parasympathetic nervous system (not **E**), which decreases pupillary diameter (not **C**) and contracts the ciliary muscle. Ciliary muscle contraction relieves the tension on the suspensory ligaments (not **A**) that maintain the lens in a flattened shape. When the ligament tension is reduced, the lens assumes a more oval shape (not **B**), which increases refraction.

59. **All of the following are adaptations of the fovea** *EXCEPT:*
   A.   increased rhodopsin concentration
   B.   increased cone density
   C.   increased melanin concentration in the pigmented layer
   D.   the presence of cylindrically shaped cones
   E.   the fibers of the receptor cells are splayed radially

   Answer = A. *Remember you are looking for the exception.* The fovea contains only cones (**B**), which are more cylindrical than in other parts of the retina (**D**). Since there are no rods in the fovea, there is no rhodopsin (*not* **A**). The neural projections from these receptors project laterally to reduce interference of light transmission to the receptors (**E**). Furthermore, the pigmented layer contains high concentrations of melanin to increase absorption of stray light rays (**C**).

60. **Activation of the parasympathetic nervous system innervating the optical apparatus:**
   A.   induces accommodation
   B.   causes pupillary dilation
   C.   causes ciliary muscle relaxation
   D.   flattens the lens
   E.   decreases refraction of the optical apparatus

   Answer = A. Parasympathetic activation produces pupillary constriction (not **B**), contraction of the ciliary muscle (not **C**), and a more oval lens (not **D**). These responses combine to increase the refraction of the optical apparatus (not **E**) and, therefore, focus light from near objects.

61. **Opposite responses in visual ganglion cells to specific pairs of wavelengths demonstrate:**
   A.   the Purkinje shift
   B.   feature detection
   C.   the difference between scotopic and photopic vision
   D.   the presence of three distinct populations of cones
   E.   opponent processing of color sensation

   Answer = E. The Purkinje shift is the difference in wavelength sensitivity of rods (scotopic vision) and cones (photopic vision) (not **A** or **C**). Feature detection is selective sensitivity to patterns of illumination such as bars and slits of light (not **B**). Color is initially encoded by three populations of cones (not **D**) and is transformed into opposite responses in ganglion cells to specific color combinations (red-green and yellow-blue).

62. **Receptors located on the temporal side of the left eye are activated by stimuli in the** *X* **visual field and project to the** *Y* **side of the brain.**

	X	*Y*
A.	right	contralateral
B.	left	ipsilateral
C.	right	ipsilateral
D.	left	contralateral
E.	right	ipsilateral and contralateral

   Answer = C. Receptors on the temporal side of the left eye are stimulated by light originating in the right (not **B** or **D**) visual field and project exclusively to the ipsilateral (not **A**, **D**, or **E**) visual cortex.

63. **The sacculus and the utricle:**
   A.   have hair cells arranged with kinocilia oriented toward the striola
   B.   are stimulated by fluid forces bending the ampullary crest
   C.   have hair cells embedded in the cupula
   D.   respond to rotational acceleration
   E.   do not contain otoliths

   Answer = A. The sacculus and utricle contain vestibular receptors that respond to gravity and linear acceleration (not **D**), due to the presence of otoliths (not **E**). The semicircular canals contain vestibular receptors that respond to rotational acceleration and are embedded in the cupula (not **C**) on the ampular crest (not **B**).

64. **Adaptation of gustatory sensation occurs because:**
    A. stimulant molecules transiently depolarize receptor cells
    B. gustatory receptors are phasic receptors
    C. of lateral inhibitory connections between receptor cells
    D. of central nervous system interactions
    E. of concurrent activation of tactile afferents from the tongue

    Answer = D. Gustatory receptors are phasic–tonic receptors (not **B**) that remain depolarized for extended periods of stimulation (not **A**) and are not affected by concurrent stimulation of other gustatory (not **C**) or tactile receptors (not **E**).

65. **Stimulation of the gamma X fibers contracts the Y muscle fibers, which enhances the Z response to muscle stretch.**

	X	*Y*	*Z*
A.	dynamic	bag	phasic
B.	dynamic	chain	phasic
C.	static	bag	tonic
D.	dynamic	chain	tonic
E.	static	bag	phasic

    Answer = A. Since only nuclear bag fibers signal the dynamic portion of the response to muscle stretch, stimulation of gamma motor neurons that contract these intrafusal muscle fibers (not **B** or **D**) would increase the phasic portion of the response to muscle stretch (not **C** or **D**). Gamma motor neurons that selectively increase the phasic portion of the stretch response are termed ''gamma dynamic fibers'' (not **E**).

66. **Activation of Golgi tendon organs:**
    A. stimulates alpha-motor neurons
    B. excites inhibitory interneurons in the spinal cord
    C. enhances the strength of the stretch reflex
    D. decreases muscle stretch
    E. induces reflex muscle contraction

    Answer = B. Stimulation of Golgi tendon organs stimulates inhibitory interneurons in the spinal cord to inhibit alpha-motor neurons (not **A**), inhibits the stretch reflex (not **C**), reduces muscle contraction (not **E**), and results in increasing muscle length (not **D**).

67. **Activation of the basal ganglia:**
    A. induces rigidity
    B. excites the reticular formation
    C. decreases muscle tone throughout the body
    D. increases intention tremor
    E. produces symptoms characteristic of Parkinson's disease

    Answer = C. The basal ganglia dampen activation of the motor system and inhibit the reticular formation (not **B**). Inhibition of basal ganglia increases muscle tone (not **A**), induces tremor (not **D**), inhibits the excitatory influence of the reticular formation, and evokes symptoms of Parkinson's disease (not **E**).

68. **Cerebrospinal fluid is produced by the:**
    A. choroid plexus
    B. arachnoid villi
    C. brain capillary endothelium
    D. fenestrae of cerebral capillaries
    E. circumventricular organs

    Answer = A. Cerebrospinal fluid is made by the choroid plexus in the lateral, third, and fourth cerebral ventricles.

69. **Adaptation to a sensory stimulus is defined as:**
    A. inhibition of sensation when another stimulus is applied to an adjacent area on the receptive field
    B. diminished sensation when a stimulus is repeatedly administered
    C. a diminished sensation when a stimulus is continually administered
    D. failure to perceive a stimulus when attention is directed to another matter
    E. increased sensitivity to stimulation during continued application of a stimulus

Answer = C. Decreased sensation during stimulation of adjacent areas is lateral inhibition (not **A**); decreased response to repeated stimulus presentations is habituation (not **B**); and increased sensitivity during repeated presentations is facilitation (not **E**). Attention directed at another stimulus is not adaptation (not **D**).

70. **First-order A-delta afferents from free nerve endings primarily:**
    A. ascend the spinal cord and synapse in the nucleus gracilis or nucleus cuneatus
    B. synapse on second-order afferents that ascend the ipsilateral side of the spinal cord
    C. synapse on second-order nerve fibers that cross to the contralateral side of the brain in the medial lemniscus
    D. are the longest neurons in the human nervous system
    E. synapse in the spinal cord on second-order afferents that cross to the contralateral side of the cord

    Answer = E. These afferent neurons transmit pain sensation, synapse upon entering the spinal cord (not **A**), cross the midline (not **C**), and ascend on the contralateral side of the cord (not **B**) to the thalamus (not **A**). Due to the synapse in the spinal cord, these neurons are not as long as the cutaneous afferents, which do not synapse until they reach the medulla (not **D**).

71. **Removal of the tissue capsule surrounding the nerve ending of a Pacinian corpuscle:**
    A. eliminates the amplifying effect of the capsule on weak pressure stimuli
    B. enhances the magnitude of the receptor potential
    C. changes the receptor response pattern from purely phasic to phasic– tonic
    D. decreases action potential frequency in the first-order afferent to a given pressure stimulus
    E. blocks generation of the receptor potential

    Answer = C. The tissue capsule transmits the stimulus to the receptor membrane with great fidelity (not **A** or **B**). The capsule does not decrease the receptor potential (not **E**) or action potential frequency in the first-order afferent (not **D**).

72. **Sensations of dull, aching pain are mediated via:**
    A. most receptors during continuous, high-intensity stimulation
    B. encapsulated nerve endings of A-delta fibers
    C. free nerve endings of C-type fibers
    D. encapsulated nerve endings of C-type fibers
    E. free nerve endings of both C- and A-delta fibers

    Answer = C. Pain is transmitted by A-delta and small unmyelinated ``C'' fibers originating from specialized free nerve endings (not **A**, **B**, or **D**). Sharp, pricking pain is mediated by free nerve endings and A-delta fibers, whereas dull aching pain is transmitted by small ``C'' fibers (not **E**).

73. **The decrease in sensation resulting from continuous presentation of a sensory stimulus is termed:**
    A. adaptation
    B. deprivation
    C. facilitation
    D. habituation
    E. accommodation

    Answer = A. Deprivation is reduction or elimination of sensory input (not **B**); facilitation is an increased response (not **C**); habituation is a decreased response during sequential stimulus presentations (not **D**); and accommodation is optical adjustments to bring near objects into focus (not **E**).

74. **Axons in the fasciculus cuneatus:**
    A. contain second-order afferents from temperature receptors of the lower limbs
    B. decussate in the medial lemniscus
    C. carry touch/pressure sensation from the upper limbs
    D. synapse in the contralateral nucleus cuneatus
    E. carry somatic information from receptors in the face

    Answer = C. The fasciculus cuneatus is part of the dorsal column system containing axons of first-order afferents (not **A**), mediating touch/pressure (not **A**) information from the upper limbs. These afferents course from the receptors to synapse in the ipsilateral medulla (not **D**). The second-order afferents in this system cross the midline in the medial lemniscus (not **B**). Cutaneous information from the face is carried in the trigeminal nerve (not **E**).

266   SECTION II: QUESTIONS AND ANSWERS

75. **All axons of the lateral corticospinal tract:**
    A. represent the "final common pathway" of skeletal motor movement
    B. mediate reflex, involuntary movements
    C. descend ipsilaterally from the brain to the spinal cord
    D. originate exclusively from the pyramidal cells of Betz of the precentral gyrus
    E. form the pyramidal decussation

    Answer = E. The axons that comprise the lateral corticospinal tract are derived from cell bodies in the precentral gyrus, the postcentral gyrus, and other areas of the cortex (not **D**), which cross the midline in the medulla (not **C**) and stimulate alpha-motor neurons in the spinal cord, which comprises the "final common pathway" (not **A**) to initiate and complete voluntary, controlled movements (not **B**).

76. **Unilateral lesion of the internal capsule would result in:**
    A. chronic spastic paralysis on the contralateral side of the body
    B. chronic flaccid paralysis on the contralateral side of the body
    C. flaccid paralysis on the ipsilateral side of the body
    D. loss of spinally mediated reflexes such as the patellar tendon reflex
    E. loss of the Babinski reflex

    Answer = A. Following acute flaccid paralysis, chronic spastic paralysis results from loss of upper motor neurons when the lower (alpha) motor neurons remain intact (not **B** or **C**). Since the majority of the motor axons coursing through the internal capsule decussate in the medulla, the primary effect would be on the contralateral side of the body from the lesion (not **C**). Furthermore, spinally mediated reflexes such as the stretch reflex and the Babinski response are exaggerated (not **D** or **E**) following lesion of upper motor neurons.

77. **All of the following are characteristic of cerebellar damage** *EXCEPT:*
    A. improper muscle coordination
    B. increased muscle tone
    C. intention tremor
    D. cannot rapidly alternate pronation and supination
    E. failure to estimate distance in motor movement

    Answer = B. *Remember you are looking for the exception.* Cerebellar damage is characterized by muscle hypotonicity (*not* **B**), as well as by the other characteristics listed.

78. **Parkinson's disease is characterized by:**
    A. intention tremor
    B. decreased muscle tone
    C. decreased ability to initiate movement
    D. damage to the internal capsule
    E. hypersecretion of dopamine

    Answer = C. Parkinson's disease results from destruction of the pars impacta of the substantia nigra (not **D**), which decreases release of dopamine (not **E**) in the caudate and putamen. The loss of dopamine release causes involuntary tremor, in distinction to intention tremor induced by cerebellar damage (not **A**) and increased muscle tone (not **B**).

79. **The gamma motor neurons:**
    A. innervate the extrafusal muscle fibers
    B. innervate the intrafusal muscle fibers
    C. directly cause muscle shortening
    D. are not activated during alpha-motor neuron stimulation
    E. do not affect the stretch reflex

    Answer = B. The alpha-motor neurons innervate the extrafusal muscle fibers (not **A**), which cause muscle shortening when stimulated (not **C**). The gamma motor neurons are activated in conjunction with alpha-motor neurons (not **D**) to maintain sensitivity of the stretch reflex (not **E**).

80. **The Renshaw cells of the spinal cord:**
    A. inhibit the stretch reflex responses
    B. are excitatory interneurons
    C. connect alpha-motor neurons in adjacent segments of the spinal cord
    D. integrate sensory input with alpha-motor neurons activation
    E. are responsible for recurrent inhibition

    Answer = E. These small, inhibitory (not **B**) interneurons in the ventral horns of the spinal cord receive input from collateral branches of alpha-motor neurons (not **C**). Stimulation of the alpha-motor neurons and subsequent activation of the inhibitory Renshaw cell lead to inhibition of surrounding alpha-motor neurons (not **A** or **D**).

81. **When the receptor portion of a muscle spindle is stretched slowly:**
    A. the impulse frequency in both primary and secondary afferent stretch receptors increases
    B. the impulse frequency in only the primary stretch receptor afferents increases
    C. the impulse frequency in only the secondary stretch receptor afferents increases
    D. the response frequency in the primary afferents decreases after the muscle length stops changing
    E. the continued activation of stretch receptor afferents after the muscle has stopped changing is due to stretch of the nuclear bag intrafusal fibers

    Answer = A. Slowly stretching the receptor portion of the muscle spindle activates both the primary (type Ia) and secondary (type II) muscle afferents (not **B** or **C**). The degree of stimulation is proportional to the amount of stretch in both receptors (not **D**) and is due to stretch of the nuclear chain intrafusal muscle fibers (not **E**), as this fiber has both type Ia and type II stretch receptors, whereas the nuclear bag fibers have only type Ia receptors.

82. **The dynamic portion of the muscle stretch reflex:**
    A. inhibits antagonistic muscles
    B. is polysynaptic
    C. is initiated primarily by activity of the type Ia stretch receptors
    D. inhibits gamma motor neuron activity
    E. is abolished when the muscle is partially contracted

    Answer = C. The muscle stretch reflex is monosynaptic (not **B**), with type Ia stretch receptor afferents synapsing directly on alpha-motor neurons. Activation of these afferents does not directly affect antagonistic muscles (not **A**) or the gamma motor system (not **D**). The stretch reflex is not altered during contraction (not **E**) since alpha-gamma coactivation maintains stretch reflex sensitivity.

83. **Golgi tendon organs:**
    A. are in parallel with intrafusal muscle fibers
    B. are in series with extrafusal muscle fibers
    C. typically excite alpha-motor neurons when stimulated
    D. are rapidly adapting receptors
    E. sense muscle length

    Answer = B. Golgi tendon organs are in series with muscle fibers (not **A**) and are phasic–tonic receptors (not **D**) that sense muscle tension (not **E**); they initiate reflex muscle relaxation by inhibition of alpha-motor neurons (not **C**).

84. **Following decerebration, animals are characterized by:**
    A. spinal shock
    B. peripheral hypotonia
    C. enhanced stretch reflexes
    D. activation of extensor muscles
    E. intention tremor

    Answer = D. Removal of input from higher motor centers disinhibits the lower brain control of extensor tone and produces enhanced tone in antigravity muscles (not **A** or **B**). Stretch reflexes are reduced due to enhanced tone (not **C**), and decerebrate animals do not exhibit voluntary movement (not **E**).

85. **The primary afferent input into the basal ganglia comes from the:**
    A.   associative cortex
    B.   cerebellum
    C.   motor cortex
    D.   muscle spindles
    E.   thalamus

    Answer = A. The associative cortex provides the primary afferent input to the striatum, which receives the majority of all afferent input to the basal ganglia (not **B**, **C**, **D**, or **E**).

86. **Normal movement requires the cerebral cortex to have afferent input from all of the following structures *EXCEPT* the:**
    A.   basal ganglia
    B.   cerebellum
    C.   thalamus
    D.   cortical premotor area
    E.   red nucleus

    Answer = E. *Remember you are looking for the exception.* The red nucleus does not project rostrally (*not* **E**). Input to the motor cortex from the other brain regions is required for initiating and programming movement, for feedback during movement (basal ganglia and cerebellum, cortical premotor area), and for monitoring body position during movement (ventral posterolateral nucleus of the thalamus).

87. **The principal neurotransmitter released at the terminals of nerves originating in the caudate nucleus, globus pallidus, and putamen is:**
    A.   dopamine
    B.   enkephalin
    C.   substance P
    D.   acetylcholine
    E.   gamma aminobutyric acid

    Answer = E. The inhibitory neurotransmitter GABA is the primary substance released from the terminals of basal ganglia. This is consistent with the predominantly inhibitory output characteristic of this brain structure.

88. **The brain structure that controls the "long loop" muscle stretch reflex is the:**
    A.   precentral gyrus
    B.   globus pallidus
    C.   red nucleus
    D.   ventral posterolateral nucleus of the thalamus
    E.   anterior lobe of the cerebellum

    Answer = E. The cerebellum receives extensive input from brain sites receiving information from muscle spindles and Golgi tendon organs (not **A**, **B**, **C**, or **D**).

89. **The "two-point threshold" for cutaneous sensation is least on the:**
    A.   lips
    B.   lower back
    C.   thighs
    D.   palms of the hands
    E.   forehead

    Answer = A. The minimum distance two discrete pressure stimuli must be separated to be sensed as two points of stimulation is smallest on the area surrounding the lips.

90. **A lens brings parallel light rays to focus 50 mm behind the lens. This lens has a refractive power of:**
    A.   1 diopter
    B.   5 diopters
    C.   10 diopters
    D.   20 diopters
    E.   50 diopters

PART 7: CENTRAL NERVOUS SYSTEM PHYSIOLOGY

Answer = D. Refractive power = 1/focal distance in meters. Therefore, the refractive power of this lens = 1/ 0.05 m = 20 diopters.

91. **The second-order afferent nerve cells in the visual system:**
    A. produce action potentials when receptor cells are stimulated with light
    B. exhibit only depolarization during visual stimulation
    C. are primarily responsible for lateral inhibition
    D. can disinhibit ganglion cells during stimulation
    E. project into the brain

Answer = D. Bipolar cells do not exhibit action potentials (not **A**) and are characterized by either hyperpolarization or depolarization (not **B**). Lateral inhibition is primarily mediated by horizontal cells (not **C**). Axons of the third-order ganglion cells form the optic nerve, which projects into the brain (not **E**).

92. **The *Y* of a sinusoidal pressure stimulus is the physical characteristic that produces the psychological perception of *Z*.**

	Y	*Z*
A.	frequency	pitch
B.	phase	loudness
C.	amplitude	pitch
D.	frequency	loudness
E.	phase	pitch

Answer = A. The frequency (cycles per second) of a sound pressure stimulus is the physical representation of the psychological sensation of pitch (not **C** or **E**), whereas the amplitude of the sound pressure stimulus is the physical correlate of the psychological sensation of loudness (not **B** or **D**).

93. **A sound stimulus transmitted by bone conduction:**
    A. initiates a traveling wave at the helicotrema end of the basilar membrane
    B. stimulates the tympanic membrane
    C. initiates a traveling wave at the oval window end of the basilar membrane
    D. is transmitted through the ossicles
    E. directly stimulates the outer hair cells

Answer = C. Sound stimuli transmitted by bone conduction apply the vibratory stimulus to the entire cochlea residing in the skull, whereas stimuli conducted through air stimulate the ossicles and tympanic membrane (not **B** or **D**). However, the traveling waves on the basilar membrane initiated by bone conduction and air conduction are both initiated at the oval window end of the membrane (not **A**) due to the physical characteristics of the membrane, and the mechanisms of hair cell stimulation are similar (not **E**).

94. **The basilar membrane is:**
    A. more flexible at the helicotrema end than at the oval window end
    B. thicker at the helicotrema end than at the oval window end
    C. composed of a series of independent resonators
    D. under constant tension, similar to stretched rubber

Answer = A. The basilar membrane gets thinner (not **B**) and more flexible as one proceeds from the oval window to the helicotrema. The membrane is not under tension (not **D**) and responds as a functional unit (not **C**).

95. **Otoliths:**
    A. are present on the ampular crest
    B. are embedded in the cupula
    C. are located in the semicircular canals
    D. are present in the macula
    E. anchor the cilia of vestibular hair cells

Answer = D. Otoliths are calcium bicarbonate crystals present on the gelatinous layer of the macula in the utriculus and sacculus of the vestibular system; they are not present in the ampular crest (not **A**) or cupula (not **B**), structures located in the semicircular canals (not **C**). The cilia of the hair cells are anchored in the gelatinous layer (not **E**).

96. **The mechanism that makes the greatest contribution to dark adaptation is:**
    A. pupillary dilation
    B. neural facilitation
    C. increased photopigment in cones
    D. increased rhodopsin concentration in rods
    E. accommodation

    Answer = D. Pupillary dilation, cone adaptation, and increased sensitivity of afferent neurons make a minimal contribution to the increase in visual sensitivity during dark adaptation (not A, B, or C). Accommodation does not contribute to dark adaptation (not E).

97. **The receptor cells for audition are contained in the:**
    A. organ of Corti
    B. scala vestibuli
    C. scala tympani
    D. helicotrema
    E. perilymph

    Answer = A. The scalae vestibuli and tympani are the two fluid-filled chambers located above and below the organ of Corti (not B or C), which contain perilymph (not E). The helicotrema is the opening connecting the scala vestibuli and scala tympani (not D).

98. **Endolymph:**
    A. is contained in the scala vestibuli and tympani
    B. surrounds the cell bodies of the auditory receptor cells
    C. has a higher sodium concentration than perilymph
    D. has a higher potassium concentration than perilymph
    E. has a potassium concentration equal to that of extracellular fluid

    Answer = D. Endolymph is contained within the scala media (not A) and has a greater potassium concentration than perilymph (not C) and extracellular fluid (not E). Endolymph bathes the cilia of the auditory hair cells, whereas the cell bodies are surrounded by extracellular fluid (not B).

99. **In a relaxed human adult, at rest with eyes closed, and not concentrating, the most prominent wave pattern of the electroencephalogram would be:**
    A. alpha rhythm
    B. beta rhythm
    C. theta rhythm
    D. delta rhythm
    E. asynchronous, nonrhythmic

    Answer = A. Alpha waves are prominent in resting, nonconcentrating adults. Beta rhythm is associated with attention to an external stimulus or concentration (not B), whereas theta and delta rhythms are found during slow-wave sleep (not C or D). An asynchronous, nonrhythmic EEG is characteristic of mental activity and REM sleep (not E).

100. **During REM (rapid eye movement) sleep, the electroencephalogram is characterized by:**
    A. high-amplitude alpha waves
    B. low-amplitude, high-frequency beta waves
    C. slow-frequency theta waves
    D. slow-frequency delta waves
    E. low-amplitude, high-frequency waves characteristic of the awake state

    Answer = E. During REM, the EEG is similar to that of an awake, alert individual. During this paradoxical sleep state, the EEG does not show alpha waves, characteristic of an awake relaxing subject (not A), beta waves, characteristic of an awake concentrating subject (not B), theta waves, or delta waves, both observed during sleep stages 3–4 (not C or D).

101. **The brain structure that is most responsible for arousal is the:**
   A. neostriatum
   B. cerebellum
   C. motor cortex
   D. sensory cortex
   E. reticular formation

   Answer = E. The neostriatum is part of the basal ganglia (not **A**) and, along with the cerebellum (not **B**) and the motor cortex (not **C**), contributes to motor control. The sensory cortex receives somatosensory information, but is not directly involved with arousal (not **D**).

102. **Periods of dreaming are associated with all of the following *EXCEPT*:**
   A. increased motor tone
   B. rapid eye movement
   C. desynchronization of the EEG
   D. increased brain metabolism
   E. the person is less easily aroused than during nondreaming sleep

   Answer = A. *Remember, you are looking for the exception.* Bouts of dreaming are associated with rapid eye movements (**B**), and the EEG resembles the asynchronous pattern of an awake, alert individual (**C**). In addition, during REM sleep, the brain is active; so metabolism increases by as much as 20% (**D**), and it is more difficult to arouse the individual than during slow-wave sleep (**E**). However, there is strong inhibition of motor systems, resulting in hypotonia (*not* **A**).

103. **Mental concentration is associated with:**
   A. a predominance of alpha rhythms in the EEG
   B. a predominance of theta rhythms in the EEG
   C. an asynchronized EEG
   D. a synchronized EEG
   E. high-amplitude slow waves in the EEG

   Answer = C. Concentration on a mental task results in the conversion of synchronized EEG waves (not **D**) into irregular, low-voltage activity (not **E**) and loss of alpha rhythms (not **A**). Theta rhythms are associated with slow-wave sleep (not **B**).

104. **Sleep induction is associated with decreased release of:**
   A. serotonin
   B. acetylcholine
   C. dopamine
   D. gamma-amino butyric acid
   E. glutamate

   Answer = A. Although there is debate regarding the role of serotonin in sleep, serotonin agonists suppress sleep, whereas serotonin antagonists increase slow-wave sleep. Furthermore, serotonin neurons are very active during wakefulness, less active during sleep, and quiescent during REM sleep.

105. **Axons comprising the corticospinal and corticobulbar motor pathways have cell bodies located in the:**
   A. motor cortex of the precentral gyrus
   B. parietal cortex
   C. premotor cortex
   D. somatic sensory area I on the post-central gyrus
   E. all of the above

   Answer = E. Thirty percent of the fibers of these motor pathways originate in the motor cortex, 30% come from the premotor cortex, and the remaining 40% have cell bodies located in the parietal lobe, especially the somatic sensory areas.

106. Alzheimer's disease is characterized by a loss of CNS neurons that are:
   A. cholinergic
   B. adrenergic
   C. dopaminergic
   D. serotonergic
   E. noradrenergic

   Answer = A. Degeneration of CNS cholinergic nerve terminals and neurons is associated with Alzheimer's disease and senile dementia. Some improvement can be obtained with physostigmine, an acetylcholinesterase inhibitor, and nicotine, a cholinergic agonist.

107. The phenomenon of sensory stimulation perceived to occur at the receptor, regardless of where the stimulus is applied in the afferent circuit, demonstrates:
   A. the law of specific nerve energies
   B. the law of projection
   C. the pattern coding of sensory information
   D. adaptation
   E. feature detection

   Answer = B. The law of specific nerve energies states that sensation is defined by the specific nerve stimulated (not A); pattern coding defines the sensation by the proportional amount of neural activity in a population of neurons (not C). Adaptation is a reduction in response during continued stimulation (not D), and feature detection is the coding of complex stimulus characteristics (not E).

108. Stretch receptors and Golgi tendon organs are examples of:
   A. exteroceptors
   B. interoceptors
   C. proprioceptors
   D. nociceptors
   E. chemoceptors

   Answer = C. Exteroceptors transduce external energy into sensory information (not A); interoceptors transduce information about internal bodily states, e.g., blood pressure, which often are not consciously perceived (not B); nociceptors respond to painful stimuli (not D); and chemoceptors are activated by specific chemicals binding to their receptors (not E). Proprioceptors are mechanoreceptors that transmit information from joints and muscles about body position, tissue and joint sensations, and movement.

109. Most fibers that transmit information about fine touch and to the CNS are classified as:
   A. A-alpha axons
   B. A-beta axons
   C. A-delta axons
   D. A-gamma axons
   E. C-fibers

   Answer = B. Alpha-motor neurons innervating extrafusal muscle fibers consist of A-alpha axons (not A), and A-gamma axons innervate the intrafusal muscle fibers (not D). A-delta fibers and small, unmyelinated C-fibers transmit pain information (not C or E).

110. The anterolateral system of the spinal cord:
   A. transmits information faster than in the dorsal column system
   B. is highly topographically organized
   C. responds to rapidly changing stimulation with great fidelity
   D. can respond to small changes in stimulus intensity
   E. carries crude touch information

   Answer = E. The anterolateral portion of the spinal cord carries information about crude touch, pain, and temperature. This pathway conducts more slowly than the dorsal column system (not A), does not have highly developed topographical organization (not B), and cannot respond to small, discrete changes in stimulus intensity (not C or D).

111. **All of the following mechanisms contribute to referred pain** *EXCEPT*:
   A.   convergence of visceral and cutaneous afferents on second-order pain afferents of the somatic structure
   B.   facilitation of second-order pain afferents originating in the somatic structure by activation of first-order afferents originating in the viscera
   C.   the Law of Specific Nerve Energies
   D.   the Law of Projection
   E.   gating of pain transmission in the substantia gelatinosa

   Answer = E. *Remember, you are looking for the exception.* The perception of somatic pain during stimulation of visceral pain receptors (referred pain) results from innervation of second-order, somatic pain afferents by first-order visceral pain afferents (**A**). Activation of visceral pain receptors facilitates the second-order somatic afferents, which then respond to input from the somatic structure (**B**). Stimulation of these specific afferents signals pain (**C**), which is projected to the site of the somatic receptors (**D**). Visceral pain afferents do not synapse in the substantia gelatinosa (*not* **E**).

112. **The area of the body that has the largest representation in the somatosensory cortex is the:**
   A.   feet
   B.   thighs
   C.   lips
   D.   forehead
   E.   palms

   Answer = C. The volume of cortical tissue devoted to processing information from a body region is not proportional to the size of the region. The areas of the body with the highest cutaneous sensitivity are the lips and finger tips. These two body areas have the highest receptor density, with the smallest receptive fields, and project to the somatosensory cortex with the least amount of convergence (not **A**, **B**, **D**, or **E**).

113. **In the touch-pressure system, sensory units with large receptive fields:**
   A.   have large cortical representation
   B.   permit precise localization of the site of stimulation
   C.   are found in body regions with small two-point thresholds
   D.   are not topographically organized
   E.   innervate areas of low receptor density

   Answer = E. Cutaneous sensory units with large receptive fields have a smaller cortical representation (not **A**) than sensory units with small receptive fields. Large receptive fields decrease the ability to localize the site of stimulation (not **B**) and, therefore, increase the two-point threshold (not **C**). Sensory units of all sizes are incorporated in the topographical representation characteristic of the touch-pressure system (not **D**).

114. **Sensory systems can respond to an exceptionally wide range of stimulus intensities because:**
   A.   the receptor potential represents a log transformation of the stimulus intensity
   B.   the receptor potential increases linearly with stimulus intensity
   C.   lateral inhibition decreases afferent input from adjacent sensory units
   D.   action potential frequency is a log transformation of the receptor potential
   E.   action potential amplitude increases with stimulus intensity

   Answer = A. The receptor potential increases as a log of the stimulus intensity, not as a linear function (not **B**). The action potential frequency increases proportionally with the receptor potential (not **D**), and action potential amplitude is constant (not **E**). Finally, although lateral inhibition can increase detectability and localization of a stimulus, it does not significantly contribute to the wide range of stimulus intensities coded in the sensory systems (not **C**).

115. **The second-order afferent nerve fibers from the touch-pressure (dorsal column) system synapse in the:**
   A.   nucleus gracilis and nucleus cuneatus
   B.   medial lemniscus
   C.   ventral lateral posterior nucleus of the thalamus
   D.   anterior nucleus of the thalamus
   E.   somatosensory cortex

   Answer = C. The first-order afferent nerves of the dorsal column system synapse in the medullary nuclei (gracilis and cuneatus) (not **A**). The axons of the second-order afferent nerves comprise the medial lemniscus (not **B**) and project to the ventral lateral posterior nucleus of the thalamus (not **D**). The third-order neurons project from the thalamus to the sensory cortex (not **E**).

116. **When someone is viewing an object 50 cm from the eye, the:**
    A. parasympathetic innervation of the eye is stimulated
    B. ciliary muscles relax
    C. tension on the suspensory fibers surrounding the lens increases
    D. lens flattens
    E. light refraction decreases

    Answer = A.   The accommodation reflex is activated during near-point vision and involves parasympathetically mediated contraction of the ciliary muscles (not **B**), which decreases tension on the suspensory fibers holding the lens (not **C**), allowing the lens to become more oval (not **D**), and thereby increases light refraction (not **E**).

117. **The heavily pigmented epithelial layer underlying the retina does all of the following *EXCEPT*:**
    A. absorb stray light rays
    B. contain large quantities of vitamin A
    C. phagocytize discarded segments of the receptor cells
    D. produce aqueous humor

    Answer = D.   *Remember you are looking for the exception.* The pigmented layer absorbs light rays that are not absorbed by photopigment, removes the discarded outer layers of the receptor cells, and contains vitamin A, which is exchanged with the receptor cells for photopigment production (**A**, **B**, and **C** are correct). However, the aqueous humor is produced by the ciliary processes in the ciliary body located behind the iris (*not* **D**).

118. **The outer segments of photoreceptors in the vertebrate retina:**
    A. are pointed away from the pupil
    B. produce photopigment
    C. actively extrude sodium ions
    D. contain the cell nucleus
    E. synapse with bipolar cells

    Answer = A.   The outer segments of the receptor cells in the inverted retina of the vertebrate eye are directed away from the source of the stimulus, i.e., the pupil. The inner segment of rods and cones produces photopigment (not **B**) and actively pumps sodium ions into the extracellular space (not **C**). The nucleus is located between the inner segment and the synaptic body (not **D**), which synapses with the bipolar cells (not **E**).

119. **The four photopigments present in the vertebrate retina have the same:**
    A. spectral sensitivity
    B. luminosity function
    C. opsin protein
    D. chromophore, retinal
    E. distribution across the retina

    Answer = D.   The opsin protein, not the chromophore, portion of the photopigments in the rods and three types of cones differs (not **C**). Different opsins account for different spectral sensitivity (not **A**) and luminosity functions (not **B**) between rods and cones. Finally, cones are concentrated in the fovea, whereas rods are more numerous in the perifoveal region and peripheral retina (not **E**).

120. **Maximal dark adaptation in the visual system:**
    A. is greatest in the fovea
    B. occurs more quickly in rods than in cones
    C. is due predominantly to increased sensitivity of the rods
    D. is due predominantly to changes in pupil diameter
    E. is due predominantly to increased sensitivity of the cones

Answer = C. The maximum increase in sensitivity to low levels of ambient light occurs within 10 min in cones, compared to 30–40 min in rods (not **B**). Furthermore, the increase in sensitivity is much greater in rods than in cones (not **E**); hence, the fovea cannot exhibit the greatest increase in sensitivity as it contains only cones (not **A**). Finally, changes in pupil diameter make a small contribution to light sensitivity compared to increased rhodopsin concentration in the rods (not **D**).

121. **Light-induced hyperpolarization of visual receptor cells results from:**
    A. decreased permeability of sodium ions in the outer segment
    B. increased extrusion of sodium ions from the inner segment
    C. decreased concentration of phosphodiesterase in the outer segment
    D. increased concentration of guanosine monophosphate (cGMP) in the outer segment
    E. closing of sodium channels in the inner segment

    Answer = A. Activated rhodopsin increases phosphodiesterase concentration in the outer segment (not **C**), which decreases cGMP (not **D**) and results in the closing of sodium channels in the outer segment (not **E**). This decreases sodium permeability in the outer segment, but does not alter the pumping of sodium outside the cell by the inner segment (not **B**).

122. **Which of the following colors is a principal contributor to the opponent responses characteristic of color-sensitive ganglion cells, but is not a principal stimulus for any population of cones?**
    A. blue
    B. yellow
    C. green
    D. orange
    E. red

    Answer = B. Three types of cones exist in the human retina, maximally stimulated by wavelengths representing blue (not **A**), green (not **C**), and red (not **E**). There are four types of color-sensitive ganglion cells: red-on/green-off, red-off/green on, blue-on/yellow-off, and blue-off/yellow-on. The wavelength representing orange does not maximally stimulate any cones or maximally activate or inhibit color-sensitive ganglion cells (not **D**).

123. **Glaucoma results in blindness because it:**
    A. produces intraocular hemorrhage
    B. decreases intraocular pressure, leading to retinal detachment
    C. destroys the axons of the ganglion cells
    D. induces hypertrophy of the retinal arterioles
    E. induces clouding of the crystalline lens

    Answer = C. Increased intraocular pressure due to glaucoma (not **B**) constricts the axons of the ganglion cell and decreases blood flow in the eye (not **D**). Glaucoma is not associated with intraocular hemorrhage (not **A**) or clouding of the lens, ie, cataracts (not **E**).

124. **In humans, the primary visual cortex is located in the:**
    A. frontal lobe
    B. postcentral gyrus
    C. insular cortex
    D. calcarine fissure area
    E. parietal lobe

    Answer = D. Projections from the lateral geniculate body terminate in the calcarine fissure area of the occipital cortex (not **A**, **B**, **C**, or **E**).

125. **The best visual acuity in the dark-adapted eye, i.e., rod vision only, is in the:**
    A. optic disc
    B. fovea
    C. peripheral retina
    D. macula
    E. parafoveal region

Answer = E.   The macula/fovea region contains only cones, which are not stimulated by low levels of illumination (not **B** or **D**). The optic disc, or blind spot, is the site where the axons of the ganglion cells exit the eye (not **A**), and the peripheral retina contains fewer rods, which exhibit a greater degree of convergence (not **C**) compared to the rods of the parafoveal region.

126. **Efferent nerve fibers from the brain to the cochlea:**
   A.   innervate only the inner hair cells
   B.   innervate the tensor tympani
   C.   depolarize auditory receptor cells
   D.   inhibit hair cells in the cochlea
   E.   increase the amplitude of vibration of the basilar membrane

Answer = D.   Descending nerve fibers from the CNS innervate both inner and outer hair cells (not **A**) and inhibit these cells (not **C**); they do not innervate the muscles of the middle ear (not **B**) or increase the amplitude of vibration of the basilar membrane (not **E**).

127. **All of the following are associated with the utricle and/or saccule *EXCEPT*:**
   A.   ampulla
   B.   otoconia
   C.   calcium carbonate crystals
   D.   striola
   E.   linear acceleration

Answer = A.   *Remember you are looking for the exception.* The otolith organs (utricle and saccule) encode linear acceleration (**E**) and head position with respect to gravity. The cilia of the receptor cells in these structures are oriented toward a central line called the striola (**D**) and are embedded in a gelatinous substance covered with calcium carbonate crystals (**C**) called otoconia (**B**). Ampullae are present in the semicircular canals (*not* **A**).

128. **The semicircular canals:**
   A.   each contain a striola
   B.   are connected to the saccule
   C.   respond to linear acceleration
   D.   each contain a cupula
   E.   are not innervated by efferent nerves

Answer = D.   The cupula is the gelatinous coating covering the cilia of the vestibular hair cells in the semicircular canals, which are innervated by efferent nerve fibers from the CNS (not **E**). The canals are connected to the utricle (not **B**) and are stimulated by rotational acceleration (not **C**). The striola is the line of orientation of hair cells in the saccule and utricle (not **A**).

129. **Auditory receptor cells are different from vestibular hair cells because they:**
   A.   lack kinocilia
   B.   lack efferent innervation
   C.   are not mechanoreceptors
   D.   are depolarized by activation of efferent nerves
   E.   have stereocilia bathed in perilymph

Answer = A.   Vestibular and auditory receptor cells are mechanoreceptors (not **C**) that have inhibitory innervation (not **D**) by efferent nerves (not **B**) from the CNS. The stereocilia of both auditory and vestibular receptor cells are bathed in endolymph (not **E**).

130. **The most important factor correcting the impedance mismatch between sound waves in air and sound waves in the cochlear fluid is:**
   A.   contraction of the tensor tympani to increase tension on the tympanic membrane
   B.   the size difference between the tympanic membrane and the stapes
   C.   the flexibility of the round window
   D.   ossicular amplification of tympanic membrane movement
   E.   contraction of the stapedius muscle

Answer = B. Contraction of the tensor tympani and stapedius muscles reduces the pressure on the oval window (not **A** or **E**). The arrangement of the ossicles decreases the range of movement of the stapes relative to the tympanic membrane (not **D**), but increases the force. This increase in force (1.3 X) is multiplied by the difference in size between the tympanic membrane and the stapes (17 X) to increase the pressure on the fluid of the cochlea 22 X over that on the tympanic membrane. The round window does not contribute to impedance matching (not **C**).

131. **The perilymph contained in the cochlea:**
A.   is in the scala media
B.   has a high potassium concentration
C.   has a low sodium concentration
D.   is in the scala vestibuli
E.   is formed by the stria vascularis

Answer = D. The endolymph is located in the scala media (not **A**), is produced by the stria vascularis (not **E**), and contains high potassium (not **B**) and low sodium concentrations (not **C**). Perilymph is located in the scala vestibuli and scala tympani.

132. **The ionic concentration difference between the endolymph and perilymph is maintained by:**
A.   Reissner's membrane
B.   the tectoral membrane
C.   the basilar membrane
D.   the helicotrema
E.   the organ of Corti

Answer = A. Reissner's membrane is an ionic barrier between the perilymph of the scala tympani and the endolymph of the scala media. The tectoral membrane anchors the cilia of the hair cells (not **B**), whereas the basilar membrane contains the receptor cell bodies (not **C**). All of these structures are contained in the organ of Corti (not **E**). The helicotrema is the opening connecting the scala vestibuli and scala tympani (not **D**).

133. **The cilia of vestibular receptor cells:**
A.   are bathed in endolymph
B.   are oriented parallel to the ampular crest in the semicircular canals
C.   are similar to cochlear hair cells
D.   consist of a single kinocilia circled by stereocilia
E.   always depolarize the receptor cell when bent

Answer = A. The single kinocilia and the aligned stereocilia (not **D**) are oriented perpendicular to the axis of the ampular crest (not **B**) and contain a kinocilium, unlike cochlear hair cells (not **C**). Bending of the cilia toward the kinocilium depolarizes the cell, whereas bending the cilia away from the kinocilium hyperpolarizes the cell (not **E**).

134. **High-frequency stimuli excite hair cells that are located:**
A.   close to the helicotrema
B.   close to the oval window
C.   throughout the length of the basilar membrane
D.   at the distal end of the basilar membrane
E.   far from the oval window

Answer = B. High-frequency sounds maximally stimulate the basilar membrane at a specific location (not **C**) close to the oval window, which is at the same end as the round window (not **E**). Low-frequency sounds stimulate the hair cells at the distal end of the basilar membrane (not **D**), near the helicotrema (not **A**).

135. **The pressure threshold for evoking auditory sensation in young adults is lowest at:**
A.   30 Hz
B.   100 Hz
C.   3,000 Hz
D.   10,000 Hz
E.   30,000 Hz

Answer = C. The human ear is most sensitive to stimuli of approximately 3,000 Hz. The pressure needed to evoke an auditory sensation increases both above and below this optimal frequency (not **A**, **B**, or **D**). The upper frequency limit for human hearing is approximately 20,000 Hz in young humans (not **E**).

136. **Gustatory and olfactory receptor cells:**
    A. adapt completely during continued presentation of a stimulus
    B. have binding sites located on their cell bodies
    C. respond only to chemicals representing single tastes or smells
    D. increase their sensitivity during continued stimulation
    E. are phasic–tonic receptors that maintain depolarization for long periods of stimulation

    Answer = E. These chemoreceptors have chemical binding sites located on cilia projecting from the cell bodies (not **B**). They typically respond to chemicals representing several tastes or smells (not **C**) and only adapt approximately 50% during continued stimulation (not **A** or **D**).

137. **It is postulated that complete adaptation of olfactory sensation involves all of the following *EXCEPT*:**
    A. receptor cell fatigue
    B. stimulation of centrifugal nerve fibers to the olfactory bulb
    C. stimulation of granule cells
    D. inhibition of transmission from olfactory cell to mitral cell
    E. feedback inhibition from the CNS

    Answer = A. *Remember you are looking for the exception.* Olfactory receptor cells are phasic–tonic receptors (*not* **A**). Continued stimulation evokes a gradually developing feedback inhibition from the CNS (**E**), mediated through activation of nerves projecting to the olfactory bulb (**B**) that activate granule cells (**C**) to inhibit the relay of olfactory signals (**D**).

138. **Efferent fibers from the cortex of the cerebellum are composed entirely of:**
    A. climbing fibers
    B. mossy fibers
    C. Betz cells
    D. granule cells
    E. Purkinje cells

    Answer = E. Climbing fibers and mossy fibers comprise the afferent input to the cerebellar cortex (not **A** or **B**); granule cells are interneurons in the cerebellum (not **D**); and Betz cells are the giant pyramidal cells found only in the motor cortex (not **C**).

139. **Stimulation of a Golgi tendon organ (GTO):**
    A. activates alpha-motor neurons of the contralateral antagonistic muscle
    B. activates the alpha-motor neurons of the muscle attached to the tendon innervated by the GTO
    C. results in inhibition of the alpha-motor neuron attached to the tendon innervated by the GTO
    D. results in inhibition of the antagonistic muscle
    E. stimulates excitatory interneurons on the spinal cord

    Answer = C. GTO stimulation activates inhibitory interneurons (not **E**) in the spinal cord that inhibit alpha-motor neurons in the muscle attached to the tendon innervated by the GTO (not **B**). There is no direct effect on the contralateral antagonistic muscles (not **A**); ipsilateral antagonistic muscles may be facilitated (not **D**).

140. **Group II (secondary afferent) nerve fibers from muscle spindles:**
    A. innervate both nuclear bag and nuclear chain nerve fibers
    B. innervate only nuclear bag nerve fibers
    C. respond to both rate of muscle stretch and length of muscle stretch
    D. do not respond directly to rate of stretch
    E. respond to tension on the muscle

    Answer = D. Group II afferent nerve fibers innervate only the nuclear chain intrafusal muscle fibers (not **A** or **B**) and do not respond to rate of change in muscle length (not **C**) as do the group Ia nerve fibers (primary afferents). Muscle tension is signaled by Golgi tendon organs (not **E**).

141. **The patellar tendon reflex (knee jerk) involves all of the following EXCEPT:**
   A.   stretch of nuclear bag intrafusal muscle fibers
   B.   group Ia (primary) afferent receptors from the muscle spindle
   C.   spinal cord interneurons
   D.   alpha-motor neurons
   E.   extrafusal muscle fibers

   Answer = C. *Remember you are looking for the exception.* Rapidly stretching a muscle by tapping the associated tendon stretches the nuclear bag intrafusal muscle fibers (**A**), which stimulates the type Ia afferent receptors (**B**). The type Ia afferents have excitatory synapses directly (*not* **C**) on the alpha-motor neurons (**D**), which contract the extrafusal muscle fibers (**E**) when stimulated.

142. **Stimulation of gamma dynamic efferent nerve fibers:**
   A.   contracts nuclear chain and nuclear bag intrafusal muscle fibers
   B.   can stimulate type Ia (primary) afferent nerve fibers
   C.   increases the response of type II (secondary) nerve fibers to a constant muscle stretch
   D.   results in relaxation of extrafusal muscle fibers
   E.   does not occur during contraction of extrafusal muscle fibers against a load

   Answer = B. Gamma dynamic efferent fibers innervate only nuclear bag intrafusal muscle fibers (not **A**); and stimulation increases the response of muscle spindle afferents (type Ia) to the dynamic portion of muscle stretch (not **C**), which results in greater contraction of extrafusal muscle fibers (not **D**). Alpha-gamma coactivation occurs during extrafusal muscle contraction with or without a load (not **E**).

143. **During contraction of extrafusal muscle fibers against a heavy load**
   A.   gamma-motor neuron stimulation is inhibited
   B.   the stretch reflex is attenuated
   C.   extrafusal muscle fibers shorten more than intrafusal muscle fibers
   D.   there is reflex inhibition of alpha-motor neuron activity
   E.   stretch receptors increase extrafusal muscle fiber excitation

   Answer = E. Both alpha and gamma motor neurons are stimulated during muscle contraction (not **A**). Since only the extrafusal muscle fibers are contracting against a load, they shorten less than the intrafusal fibers (not **C**). This produces a relative stretch on the sensory portion of the intrafusal fibers, which induces the stretch reflex (not **B**) and further stimulates (not **D**) the alpha-motor neurons of the contracting muscle.

144. **The "clasp knife" reflex, i.e., muscle relaxation, which occurs during increases in muscle tension, involves all of the following EXCEPT:**
   A.   stimulation of Golgi tendon organs
   B.   stimulation of type Ia sensory afferents from the muscle spindle
   C.   stimulation of inhibitory interneurons in the spinal cord
   D.   inhibition of alpha-motor neuron activity
   E.   facilitation of antagonistic extrafusal muscle fibers

   Answer = B. *Remember you are looking for the exception.* Increased tension on muscle stimulates the GTO located in the associated tendons (**A**), which activates inhibitory interneurons in the spinal cord (**C**) and reduces activity in the alpha-motor neuron of the muscle associated with the GTO (**D**). There is also facilitation of ipsilateral antagonistic muscles (**E**). Stimulation of type Ia sensory afferents produces reflex contraction of extrafusal muscle fibers (*not* **B**).

145. **Nerve fibers from the cerebellar cortex:**
   A.   have an effect on deep cerebellar nuclei that is opposite to the effect of climbing fibers
   B.   terminate directly on alpha-motor neurons in the spinal cord
   C.   excite the neurons of the deep cerebellar nuclei
   D.   project directly to the motor cortex
   E.   join with fibers from the motor cortex in the pyramidal tracts

   Answer = A. The axons of Purkinje cells in the cerebellar cortex project to the deep cerebellar nuclei and to the lateral vestibular nuclei (not **B**, **D**, or **E**). In the deep cerebellar nuclei, they have an inhibitory effect (not **C**), which is in contrast to the excitatory influences of the climbing fibers and mossy fibers.

146. Degeneration of gamma-amino butyric acid-containing neurons in the caudate nucleus and putamen results in:
    A. Parkinson's disease
    B. paralysis agitans
    C. Huntington's chorea
    D. dementia
    E. Alzheimer's disease

Answer = C. Loss of dopamine from the substantia nigra produces Parkinson's disease (not **A**), also known as paralysis agitans (not **B**). The dementia accompanying Huntington's chorea is probably due to concomitant loss of acetylcholine neurons (not **D**), which also produces Alzheimer's disease (not **E**).

147. All of the following can be characteristic of cerebellar dysfunction *EXCEPT*:
    A. uncoordinated movements
    B. failure of progression
    C. intention tremor
    D. loss of the long loop component of the stretch reflex
    E. increased peripheral muscle tone

Answer = E. *Remember you are looking for the exception.* Cerebellar damage reduces the ability to predict range of movements. Overshoot and conscious dampening result in ataxia (**A**). In addition, the loss of predictive ability prevents the coordinated progression of successive movements (**B**) and increases oscillation of individual movements (**C**). Finally, muscle tone is decreased (*not* **E**), and brain monitoring and modification of stretch reflex-induced responses are lost (**D**).

148. Inability to form new declarative (verbal or symbolic) memories results from damage to the:
    A. hippocampus
    B. medulla
    C. hypothalamus
    D. limbic system
    E. cerebellum

Answer = A. This brain structure is necessary for consolidation of new verbal or symbolic memories. The remainder of the brain structures listed do not play a significant role in consolidation of declarative memories.

149. During sleep in normal adults, the percentage of time in:
    A. REM sleep decreases with age
    B. REM sleep increases with age
    C. stage 4 slow-wave sleep decreases with age
    D. stage 3 slow-wave sleep increases with age
    E. stage 4 sleep increases with age

Answer = C. The percentage of sleep time spent in REM sleep is approximately 25% for all ages (not **A** or **B**), whereas the percentage of time in stages 3 and 4 of slow-wave sleep decreases significantly in the elderly (not **D** or **E**).

150. All of the following structures are part of the basal ganglia *EXCEPT*:
    A. putamen
    B. caudate nucleus
    C. striatum
    D. substantia nigra
    E. reticular formation

Answer = E. *Remember you are looking for the exception.* The basal ganglia is composed of the putamen, caudate nucleus, globus pallidus, subthalamic nucleus, and substantia nigra. The caudate nucleus and putamen are frequently referred to as the striatum.

151. **Decerebration, i.e., transecting the neuroaxis so that the forebrain is isolated from the hindbrain and spinal cord:**
   A. results in spinal shock
   B. decreases alpha-motor neuron excitability
   C. unloads the muscle–spindle stretch receptors
   D. activates the gamma-motor neuron system
   E. inhibits the antigravity muscles

   Answer = D. Decerebration does not produce the muscle flaccidity characteristic of spinal transection (not **A**), but results in decerebrate rigidity characterized by stimulation of the antigravity muscles (not **E**). Decerebration removes inhibitory input to alpha-motor neurons (not **B**) and activates gamma-efferent motor neurons, which sensitize the stretch reflex (not **C**).

152. **The heat transfer mechanism that accounts for the existence of the thermal boundary layer is:**
   A. conduction
   B. convection
   C. evaporation
   D. long-wave radiation
   E. short-wave radiation

   Answer = A. The conduction of heat from the outer layer of the skin to the adjacent air forms the protective thermal boundary. The thickness and, hence, the effectiveness of this thermal boundary layer are greatly affected by air currents (convection). Evaporation takes place from the surface of the skin, not from the thermal boundary layer.

153. **The major heat source for a febrile reaction in a nude, 65-kg person in an environment of 29 C is the:**
   A. brain
   B. brown adipose tissue
   C. liver
   D. skeletal muscle
   E. white adipose tissue

   Answer = D. At the onset of a febrile reaction, the shivering response generates the additional heat needed to elevate body temperature. Adults have no brown adipose tissue (not **B**); and heat production by the brain, liver, or adipose tissue is minimal (not **C**, **D**, or **E**).

154. **A thermoregulatory response of man controlled by cholinergic sympathetics is:**
   A. brown adipose tissue thermogenesis
   B. hand vasomotion
   C. shivering thermogenesis
   D. sweat secretion
   E. thermoregulatory behavior

   Answer = D. The sweat glands are controlled by cholinergic sympathetic nerves.

155. **Which of the following most faithfully reflects changes in human core temperature caused by immersion in a warm water bath?**
   A. oral temperature
   B. rectal temperature
   C. axillary temperature
   D. esophageal temperature at the cardia
   E. tympanic temperature

   Answer = D. The most accurate core temperature would be taken near the heart because the heart receives blood from all parts of the body. A thermistor placed down the esophagus will be in thermal equilibrium with neighboring tissue, i.e., the heart. All of the other sites approximate core temperature, but may be influenced by local circulatory or metabolic events.

156. **Which of the following structures is likely to have the highest skin temperature in a comfortably dressed individual standing upright, at rest in the shade, in a still (windless) environment at 20 C?**
   A. forehead
   B. trunk
   C. finger
   D. toe
   E. all will be equal

Answer = A. The skin on the forehead lacks vasoconstrictor activity and hence receives blood that is independent of the temperature-regulating needs of the body. Therefore, feeling the forehead of a patient is a logical and simple method for detecting an elevated body temperature.

157. **All of the following are correct for human neonates *EXCEPT*:**
   A. cold-exposed neonates never shiver
   B. the mean skin temperature of neonates is lower than that of adults
   C. the cutaneous circulation of humans is not well organized at birth
   D. they possess relatively little subcutaneous fat at birth
   E. the thermal conductivity of neonatal skin is higher than that of adult skin

Answer = B. *Remember you are looking for the exception.* Skin temperature tends to be high in neonates (*not* **B**) because they have little subcutaneous fat (**D**), which gives their skin a very high thermal conductivity (**E**), and because they have a large surface area to volume ratio. The cutaneous circulation is not well organized at birth (**C**). If nonshivering thermogenesis fails or is inadequate, neonates can shiver when cooled sufficiently (**A**).

158. **In a man passively warmed such that his mean skin temperature reaches 40.5 C, which of the following circulatory responses will occur?**
   A. increased cardiac output, decreased splanchnic blood flow
   B. increased cardiac output, increased muscle blood flow
   C. unchanged cardiac output, decreased right atrial pressure
   D. unchanged cardiac output, decreased renal blood flow
   E. decreased stroke volume, increased finger blood flow

Answer = A. When skin temperature reaches 40.5 C, there will have been a large increase in cutaneous blood flow and sweating will have been stimulated. This leads to an increase in cardiac output, which is often associated with a reflex decrease in splanchnic blood flow.

159. **At the beginning of the rising phase of fever:**
   A. sweat secretion is stimulated
   B. mean skin temperature is below normal
   C. muscle blood flow is decreased
   D. behavioral thermoregulatory responses are inhibited
   E. warm-sensitive neurons in the preoptic–anterior hypothalamus are excited

Answer = B. The two processes that are induced at the beginning of a febrile response are increased heat production (shivering), leading to an increase in muscle blood flow (not **C**), and decreased heat loss (cutaneous vasoconstriction), leading to a lowering of skin temperature. Febrile patients tend to seek a warm environment (not **D**) to ''warm up'' and do not sweat (not **A**) until the febrile response is over. The activity of the warm-sensitive neurons in the hypothalamus is depressed and, hence, does not cause the activation of heat-losing processes (not **E**).

160. **The most characteristic endocrinological feature of cold acclimatization is an increased responsiveness to the metabolic effects of:**
   A. growth hormone
   B. thyroglobulin
   C. norepinephrine
   D. cortisol
   E. insulin

Answer = C. An enhancement of chemical thermogenesis is induced by the elevated level of catecholamines induced by exposure to a cold environment. This increase in responsiveness to catecholamines may be caused by the concurrent increase in thyroid hormone secretion.

161. **Which of the following is currently believed to ultimately account for the febrile response that is the hallmark of infection?**
A. the invading pathogenic organisms per se
B. products released by the pathogenic organisms during their encounter with the host's immune system
C. mediators released by the host's immune cells during their encounter with the invading microorganisms
D. prostaglandins released in the host's brain
E. none of the above

Answer = D. The invading lipopolysaccharides of the wall (**B**) of invading gram-negative bacteria (**A**) are thought to react with monocytes and macrophages (**C**), inducing the release of endogenous pyrogens. These in turn cause the release of prostaglandins (and other agents) in the brain that are the ultimate cause of the fever.

162. **A feature that essentially differentiates a febrile from a hyperthermic patient is that a febrile patient:**
A. typically has a core temperature in excess of 39.5 C
B. generally seeks a cool environment
C. generally has warm, wet skin
D. is often thirsty
E. generally has dry, cool skin over most of the body

Answer = E. Although both patients have an elevated body temperature (not **A**), the nonfebrile hyperthermic patient will physiologically and behaviorally attempt to lower body temperature. In contrast, the febrile patient will attempt to raise or at least maintain the elevated body temperature (not **B** or **C**). Hence, a hyperthermic patient will sweat, whereas a febrile patient will have peripheral vasoconstriction to help conserve heat. A febrile patient, therefore, does not tend to lose fluid per se, and, thus, is less likely to become thirsty.

163. **The principal physical mechanism that accounts for the transfer of heat within the body is:**
A. conduction
B. convection
C. radiation
D. evaporation
E. none of the above

Answer = B. Blood flow (forced convection) is the primary mechanism of transferring heat from one section of the body to another.

164. **When a euhydrated 70-kg man at rest is exposed for 30 min to a dry 30 C environment, the expected order of his thermoregulatory responses will normally be:**
A. behavioral changes, sweating, cutaneous vasodilation
B. behavioral changes, cutaneous vasodilation, sweating
C. cutaneous vasodilation, sweating, behavioral changes
D. sweating, behavioral changes, cutaneous vasodilation
E. none of the above; these responses generally occur simultaneously

Answer = B. The first thing that will occur is some type of behavioral change (e.g., seeking shade, removing clothing, and fanning). Then there will be a cutaneous vasodilation that increases conductive heat loss; and, finally, sweating will be initiated.

165. **All of the following are characteristics of our shell or insulating layer EXCEPT:**
A. in the cold, the subcutaneous fat layer contributes significantly to the insulation of the shell
B. in the heat, the subcutaneous fat layer contributes significantly to the insulation of the shell
C. in the cold, most of the heat transfer through the shell occurs by conduction
D. in the heat, most of the heat transfer through the shell occurs by circulatory convection
E. the insulation value of the shell is determined by its thickness, which varies with the environmental temperature

Answer = B. *Remember you are looking for the exception.* When the subdermal capillary network is receiving a large amount of blood per minute, as it does in a warm environment, the deeper subcutaneous fat layer is shunted out of its insulating role.

166. **Naked human neonates exposed for 1 h to a dry environment of 26 C do not adequately maintain their body temperature because:**
   A.   they are unable to produce heat in an amount and duration sufficient to compensate for their body heat loss
   B.   they possess insufficient subcutaneous fat to adequately insulate them
   C.   their surface area-to-body mass ratio is unfavorable for heat conservation
   D.   their cutaneous circulation is poorly organized and poorly innervated
   E.   all of the above

Answer = E. All of the statements are true for the human neonate.

167. **Long-term adaptation to tropical climates involves:**
   A.   increased thyroxine production
   B.   decreased maximal sweating rate
   C.   increased catecholamine release
   D.   increased aldosterone release
   E.   all of the above

Answer = D. Adaptation to a warm environment is accompanied by an increase in the maximal rate of sweating (not **B**) and an increase in the release of aldosterone to retain sodium. Catecholamine and thyroxine release are not stimulated by a warm environment (not **A** or **C**) but by a cold environment.

168. **When environmental temperature increases, blood flow to the skin:**
   A.   decreases to stop the transport of heat from the skin surface to deeper tissues
   B.   decreases because the local thermoreceptors in the skin sense an increase in body temperature
   C.   decreases because the sweat glands release vasoconstrictor kinins, which increases skin blood flow resistance
   D.   increases as part of the body temperature regulatory mechanism
   E.   increases as the metabolic needs of the skin tissue increase

Answer = D. As the environmental temperature increases, warm receptors sense the increase in temperature and induce a cutaneous vasodilation (not **A** or **B**) to increase heat loss as part of the body temperature regulatory mechanism. Sweat glands, like salivary glands, may release vasodilatory (not **C**) substances like kinins, which induce an increase in blood flow to the sweat glands. The increase in blood flow is a reflex dependent on the thermoregulatory needs of the body (not **E**).

Hemorrhage
    kidney function in, 47, 190
    renal blood flow and, 46, 187, 190
Henderson-Hasselbach equation, 47, 188
Histamine
    actions, 37, 55, 164, 209, 210
    blockers, 55, 210
    ECL cell release, 56, 214
    as paracrine, 56, 214
Human chorionic gonadotropin (hCG), in pregnancy, 61, 225
Human menopausal gonadotropin (hMG), actions, 69, 243
Hypertension
    adrenergic antagonist in, 16, 116–117
    pulmonary, 41, 174
Hyperventilation, effects of, 47, 190
11 β-hydroxylase, deficiency effects, 65, 66, 234, 235
Hypokalemia, vomiting induced, 16, 117
Hypophysectomy, infertility and, 66, 235
Hypopituitarism, diagnosis, 68, 239
Hypothalmus, hormones of, 62, 72, 226, 250
Hypoxemia
    causes, 43, 179
    diffusion capacity and, 40, 171
    reversal, 37, 163
Hypoxia
    chemoreceptors in, 44, 182
    effects of, 38, 166
    hypercapnia and, 43, 180
    pulmonary hypertension and, 41, 174
    pulmonary vasoconstriction, 44, 182

I

Inihibin, actions, 63, 228
Inhibitory postsynaptic potential (IPSP), properties of, 6, 10, 93, 103, 104, 105
Innervation, reciprocal, 9, 100
Insecticide poisioning, treatment, 11, 106
Insulin
    actions of, 62, 66, 227, 236
    glucogon and, 64, 231
    hypersecretion, 67, 237
    hypophysectomy and, 65, 233
    in meal absorption, 64, 231
Internal capsule, lesions, 79, 267
Interstitial fluid, (ISF)
    factors influencing, 5, 24, 91, 133
    protein concentration, 24, 25, 133, 136
    volume, 4, 5, 89, 91
Intracellular (IC) volume
    factors influencing, 5, 91–92
    measurement, 4, 90
Ion channels, *see also* specific ion channel
    inactivation, 10
    neurotransmitter effects on, 10, 11, 104, 105
    voltage-dependent activation, 12, 107
Ion flux, electrochemical driving force and, 6, 95

K

Kidney
    arterial blood pressure, 46, 186
    ATP-proton pump of, 46, 187
    Bowman's capsule, 50, 199

Ca^{2+} excretion, 50, 198–199
carbonic anhydrate, 49, 194
clearence rates, 53, 206
cortical collecting duct, 46, 183–186
distal tubule, 50, 198–199
efferent arteriole, 50, 197–198, 199
free filtration, 49, 193–194
free water clearence, 48, 192
glomerulus, 52, 204
glucose reabsorption, 47, 189–190, 196
HCO_3^- reabsorption, 46, 186
Henle's loop, ascending, 45, 47, 49, 50, 52, 185, 188, 195, 199, 203
H^+ secretion, 48, 49, 50, 191, 194, 196
hypotonic solution ingestion effects, 52, 202
inulin excretion, 52, 202
K^+ excretion, 46, 53, 186, 204
Na^+ reabsorption, 52, 53, 203, 206
osomolar clearance, 48, 192
PAH secretion, 47, 190
papillary collecting duct, 50, 53, 199, 206
parathyroid hormone and, 46, 187
phosphate reabsorption, 46, 187
proximal tubule, 45, 49, 51, 53, 185, 194, 195, 200, 206
sympathetic activity and, 46, 50, 187, 196–197
T_{max} for, 49, 53, 196, 206
tubuloglomerular feedback hypothesis, 52, 202
in water deprivation, 53, 206
water reabsorption, 53, 206

L

Lactation, regulation, 69, 243
Lactic acid
    exercise and, 42, 178
    metabolic acidosis and, 50, 198
Laplace's Law, 32, 154
Lipids, partition coefficient and, 11, 107
Lipophilic substances, properties of, 6, 94
Liver cirrhosis, edema of, 53, 205
Lung, *see also* Pulmonary
    airway pressure, 38, 40, 168, 172
    alveolar pressure, 44, 181
    alveoli volume, 36, 163
    bacterial infection of, 39, 169
    capacity, 38, 42, 168, 176
    compliance, 41, 175
    compliance curve, 36, 162
    dead space, 40, 43, 169, 173, 179
    diffusing capacity, 39, 41, 171, 174, 175
    expiration and, 36, 39, 42, 44, 162, 170, 178, 181
    FRC, 38, 39, 166, 168
    functional residual capacity, 37, 41, 42, 164, 176, 177–178
    inspiration and, 44, 181
    liquid ventilated, 40, 171
    minute volume, 40, 43, 172, 179
    obstructive disease, 42, 177–178
    pleural pressure and, 42, 44, 178, 181
    tidal volume, 36, 43, 162, 169, 179
    tuberculosis growth in, 41, 174
    zone II flow in, 41, 175
Lung perfusion rate (Q), at lung base, 36, 162

INDEX   291